672 - H69   45878

Holbrook

Iron brew

IRON BREW

THE MACMILLAN COMPANY
NEW YORK · BOSTON · CHICAGO
DALLAS · ATLANTA · SAN FRANCISCO

MACMILLAN AND CO., LIMITED
LONDON · BOMBAY · CALCUTTA
MADRAS · MELBOURNE

THE MACMILLAN COMPANY
OF CANADA, LIMITED
TORONTO

IRON BREW

A Century of
American Ore *and* Steel

BY STEWART H. HOLBROOK

New York · THE MACMILLAN COMPANY · *1939*

For
My Brother
ROLAND C. HOLBROOK

CONTENTS

CONTENTS

IRON BREW

1 *A Bessemer Blows at Aliquippa*

IT WAS dusk, and we stood looking down into a valley that often knew the night but never day. Smoke poured from a few of the scores of stacks below us, and when the wind rose a bit a mild warm shower of cinders fell where we stood. They were light cinders, falling silently like so much tarnished snow.

One was conscious of more smoke than could be seen coming from the stacks. I actually felt that smoke was everywhere in the valley, and on the hills, too—an all-prevailing smoke, not black, not white, simply a haze that clouded everything from a fly to a building and left nothing in true perspective.

There it was below us, Aliquippa in western Pennsylvania, at work under a smoky moon.

Aliquippa is a mighty enough steel town in a region that knows Steel and little else. I looked down at it through the enveloping haze and knew that the place held secrets that neither the sun nor the moon ever discovered. Even its vast noises seemed muted, here on the hill. Only a dull rumbling, rising and falling on the breeze, remained of the accumulated sound of ten thousand men working and sweating in a madhouse that thundered until it shook the walls around them.

But the eye told better of doings in the valley. Now the haze was streaked with bursts of flame, with billows of smoke, and again with small volcanoes of orange and yellow sparks. I thought of Aliquippa as an old man sitting there in the gloom of the valley, sullenly smoking his pipe in the evening: a moody old man, given to expressing visibly his fits of silent temper. When he thought of something long past that made him seethe, he puffed furiously, and the sparks came.

Suddenly, as if the smoke and sparks and streaks of fire had been but a mere kindling of it, the whole valley blazed with a lurid glow—not lightning, not heavy artillery, nor yet a flame thrower, but all three together. One saw the stacks plainly now, stark black silhouettes against a background of red and yellow. . . . The old man and his pipe had gone wholly mad.

That, said my friend, is a Bessemer in blow.

We went down into the murky lowland and into the steel plant, a place that took in more acres within its high fence than do most farms. Cinders were thicker here, and heavier. The noise was such as to discourage talk. Men spoke with their fingers, their hands, their arms.

On and on we walked, past the glittering coke ovens that winked with eight hundred eyes, past the furnaces muttering over their nightly fare of Mesabi ore, and on to the hulking Bessemer shed. Its outside was lost in gloom. Inside was a scene to stop the late Dante Alighieri dead in his tracks.

Here were three tall Bessemer converters in a row. How a Bessemer looks to a veteran steelworker's eye I don't know. To a layman it looks like the egg of a roc, that fabulous bird which was said to have borne off the biggest elephant in its flight. A roc's egg with one end cut off and gaping. It is a container of brick and riveted steel, twice as tall as the tallest man and supported near its middle on axles. It is set high up on a groundwork of brick. Into this caldron goes molten ore, fifty thousand pounds at a time. Through the iron is blown cold air— oxygen forced through the hot metal with the power of a giant's breath. Out of the egg, in good time, comes steel. It is little short of pure magic.

One of the converters was in blow as we entered the shed. Tilted almost but not quite straight up, the mouth of it belched flame like a cannon built for the gods. It was a terrifying sight, and hypnotic. I didn't want to look elsewhere, to turn my eyes from that leaping flame which towered thirty, perhaps forty, feet above the converter.

The roar was literally deafening; and little wonder, for here was a cyclone attacking a furnace in a brief but titanic struggle, a meeting in battle of carbon and oxygen, cleverly arranged by the sweating gnomes whose red faces appeared white in the Bessemer's glow. Both carbon and oxygen would lose, each consuming the other, and men would be the winners by twenty-five tons of bright new steel.

The roaring continued. The red fire changed to violet, indescribably beautiful, then to orange, to yellow and finally to white, when it soon faded. "Drop," the boys call it. I saw the great vessel rock uneasily on its rack, moved with unseen levers by an unseen workman. A locomotive pushed a car close under. On the car was a big ladle. The hellish brew was done.

Slowly the converter tilted over, and from its maw came a flow of seething liquid metal—Bessemer steel. A Niagara of fire spilled out, pouring into the waiting ladle, and sixty feet away the heat was too much for comfort. A cascade of sparks rolled out and over, a sort of spray for this cataract, and it seemed everything in the shed danced with light.

Steel was being born in a light so blinding that one must wear dark glasses to look on it long. It was a dreadful birth. The pygmy men who ran about on the floor seemed entirely too puny to cope with such a thing. One preferred subconsciously to trust in the tall shadows on the walls, for the weird towering shapes looked more in character for this business.

In perhaps five minutes the ladle was filled with the running fire. The bell on the locomotive rang. The ladle was pulled away, out into the darkness of the yard, and a sudden deep gloom settled down in the Bessemer shed. The devil's pouring was over.

It is the most gorgeous, the most startling show that any industry can muster, a spectacle to make old Vulcan's heart beat faster, enough to awe a mortal. No camera has ever caught a Bessemer's full grim majesty, and no poet has yet sung its splendor.

What was behind those ten minutes of hell-blowing and pouring of fire? What was back of it? What and who made them possible, these great moments of Steel?

It is a thundering story, the Saga of Iron and Steel in America.

Eight hundred and twenty miles northwest of Aliquippa, as the roc flies, is the town of Hibbing, Minnesota. Nine-tenths of a mile north of Hibbing is one edge of the biggest man-made hole on earth. Out of this hole comes much of the ore that has kept Bessemers roaring and belching for the past forty years.

Officially, this ungodly hole-in-the-ground is known

as the Mahoning Hull Rust open-pit mine, and it is a churlish name for such a chasm. To stand anywhere along its miles and miles of rim is to view something really great. If the Pyramids are Great, then so is the hole at Hibbing. As an arresting scene it ranks with the Rockies and the Grand Canyon.

There is no way of setting down figures or making comparisons to give much of an idea of what you see at Hibbing. It is lame to say that more earth has come out of this hole than was removed in digging the canal across Panama. Engineers tell that two hundred and thirty-two million cubic yards of earth were dug up to make the canal. Miners at Hibbing passed that volume years ago. But all figures are meaningless and fail dismally to describe this crater of the Mesabi Range.

Cold measurements reveal the Hibbing pit to be more than four miles long. Much of it is a mile wide, from rim to rim. It is three hundred and fifty feet deep. Not very long ago a city of fifteen thousand people, together with their habitations, had to be moved to a new site to let the hole grow larger. New Yorkers like to brag of their Polo Grounds. Thrown into the middle of this Hibbing pit, the Giants' baseball park would look like a doll house. If California's much-touted Rose Bowl were added, Hibbing miners might work a day or two before they noticed either.

Deep down in the bottom of the pit are what appear to be toy steam shovels, swinging their arms. They are hardly toys, for one of them picks up thirteen tons of ore at a scoopful. Locomotives pulling long trains move about. In the pit are seventy-five miles of standard track. As Calvin Coolidge, President of the United States, so

aptly remarked when he stood on the Hibbing pit rim
one day in 1928: "That's a pretty big hole."

It is not only the immensity of the pit that strikes one.
It has sheer beauty, this amphitheater carved out of
solid iron by countless Finns and Slovenes, with a
Cornish mine captain bossing. In the bright sun of a
Minnesota morning the terraces mount one above another like crimson-lined benches. Men of Gath would
have room to hold forum here.

The crimson deepens as the day wears on, and when
the Mesabi's brief twilight falls over the range, the red
dissolves into rich browns and blues, and brooding pur-
ples. To stand on the rim and look as night comes down
is to know a mood akin to that cast by the sea. A man
who says he has seen America but has never gazed on
the Hibbing pit is deluding himself.

An open-pit mine and a snorting Bessemer are fit symbols for an industry that is both immense and dramatic.
Making steel can also be grim, and it has been ruthless
from the first. No other modern industry can match the
savage drive of Steel, the cruelty and size of its machines, the ferocious tempo that seems to go with it. Its
indifference to flesh and blood has been as remarkable
as the speed and magnitude of its growth. From the bottom of the deepest mine to the sheered edge of the finest
rail Steel is a brutal business.

This is not to say that Steel is malevolent. It is not. The
men of the mines, the furnaces and mills are no different from other men; nor are their bosses, from a mine's
shift captain to the corporation lawyers who are paid a
quarter of a million dollars a year for posing as presidents of steel companies.

It is the very process of mining and manufacturing its product that makes Steel a savage industry. Its raw materials are heavy. They are hidden in dark caverns or remote places, sometimes both. Mother Earth may be a good earth, but she often treats those who dig in her belly in a truly diabolical manner. And when the materials are safely above ground the cruelty of Steel continues.

For a thousand years men have been devising new and bigger ways to make more and better and quicker steel. The machines that were born of their imaginations improved slowly until about seventy years ago. Since then the pace has been very swift, and with almost every improvement the machines became bigger, and far more cruel and ruthless.

It was in the very nature of the things they worked with. Fire hotter than the Devil himself could make had to be devised, for ore had to be boiled at astounding temperatures before it was iron. Iron had to be boiled again to make it steel. Tons of white-hot running metal had to be poured, and more tons of red-hot metal had to be kneaded and squeezed and lifted and set down. The steel had to be forged and pounded and rolled and drawn.

This was grave business, with every man's life in the hand of him who tapped the heat or moved the lever that rolled the rail. But the work did not make grave men. It did not make them cruel. It did make them overly strong, and it made them ruthless. Come what might in a steel plant, the ore was to be smelted as hurriedly as possible and rolled into steel even quicker.

The mass production of steel in the United States began less than seventy years ago. Iron was made from the times of the first colonists. As far back as 1619 the Virginia Company sent John Berkeley and a group of twenty-two ironworkers out of England to erect a forge on Falling Creek, not far from Jamestown. The venture did well for three years. It was a noisy business, what with the din of the hammering and the roar of the thunder-gust bellows, and the men at the forge did not hear the beating of war drums in the surrounding forest. Screaming "Indeans" came out of the woods and butchered all but one of the workers. It was to be a dangerous industry from the first.

More successful, and also more typical of the later iron industry, was the business set up at Saugus, Massachusetts, in 1643 by English and Colonial capitalists. For building a forge the company was granted a monopoly for twenty-one years, no taxes for twenty years, and free land for every new furnace put into blast. After a while, because of what must have been pretty terrible conditions, the imported ironworkers revolted. They sulked, did poor work, and ran away when they got a chance. To this the company replied in characteristic fashion by bringing over a gang of chained Scottish convicts and putting them to work under guard.

At the Saugus Works was made the first casting in America, a kettle of one-quart size. One Joseph Jenks, who seems to have been the genius of the enterprise, invented and patented an improved scythe which was made in considerable numbers at the forge. Jenks also built a fire engine and made the dies from which the famous Pine Tree shillings were cast. The Saugus company lasted ten years. It apparently went on the rocks because of the desertion of its convict workers and the sullen temper of those who were unable to escape.

From these two early beginnings, ironmaking spread rapidly to all inhabited parts of the Colonies. New Jersey was making good iron at Hanover in 1710, toting its bars of metal on pack horses over the mountains into Newark. At about the same period a forge was built on Manatawny Creek, three miles above Pottstown in Pennsylvania, by Thomas Rutter, an English Quaker whose "Pool Forge" iron soon became known as the best in America. Rutter's crew was attacked by Indians in 1728, but Quaker or no, the ironworkers fought like demons and sent the red men a-packing. In Delaware Sir William Keith established a forge on Christiana Creek, with skilled Scandinavian help.

The father of the Father of His Country was something of an ironmaster. From his Virginia estate Augustine Washington supplied ore for smelting in a near-by furnace. By 1734 "fine edge tools of steel" were being manufactured in Trenton, New Jersey.

Up in the Litchfield Hills of Connecticut, young Ethan Allen, a busy and profane man, had a hand in building a blast furnace and forge which he swore, by the Great Jehovah, should turn out the best goddamned cannon-metal in those parts. A little later, when he was looking for tough adventurers to help drive the scurvy Yorkers out of the New Hampshire Grants, Allen returned to the Litchfield Hills and recruited from the ranks of the many ironworkers there. He considered them, correctly enough as matters turned out, to be savage fighters who fairly reveled in violence.

These Connecticut hills were the ironmaking center of New England of late Colonial days. On Mount Riga was built a great forge whose smoke could be seen for fifty miles. It was the wonder of its day. Swiss and Russian charcoal burners went there to work as soon as they got off the boat from Europe. The ore had to be carted uphill, but there were plenty of oxen. Hardwood grew on every side. On the outbreak of the Revolution the town of Salisbury enjoyed the first munitions boom the country had ever known. Two thousand men worked day and night making shot and cannon, to say nothing of the big anchor for the frigate *Constitution*, which was forged here and hauled away down the mountain by six yoke of cattle.

Fully as famous as Mount Riga was the Durham Furnace in Bucks County, Pennsylvania. This supplied pig iron to a dozen or more near-by forges which cast large quantities of shot and shell for use of the Continental Army. Negro slaves were employed at the Durham Furnace for sixty years.

Perhaps the most stupendous ironmaking job of the period was turned out at the Sterling Forge of Peter Townsend, some twenty-five miles from West Point, New York. This was the famous West Point Chain. For six weeks Townsend drove a large crew of men at seventeen forges, night and day, to fashion a barrier to keep British ships from passing the fortress on the Hudson at West Point.

The completed chain was nearly one mile long and weighed one hundred and eighty tons. Its links were of iron bars two and one-half inches square and weighed one hundred pounds each. Supported on logs and stretched across the river, the gargantuan job of Peter Townsend's men did the trick. The British Navy never passed the Point.

The making of iron played a part in the movement of Colonial populations. After the Revolution came a big demand for nails. These had been supplied in the past by the countless little forges which New England farmers set up in one corner of their kitchens. Here, on long winter evenings, the entire family, young girls included, worked at making the blunt square iron nails then in use.

Invention of various nail-making machines came close on the heels of the increased demand. Factories sprang up in New York, New Jersey, and Pennsylvania. There was a shortage of help. Agents from the nail factories came to New England on the hunt for experienced nailers. They found them on the farms and in the smaller villages. It is the chief reason why so many descendants of Yankees are found today in nearly every town where there are ironworks and nail factories.

Spreading up into New York State, New Englanders developed the then important ore fields of the Champlain district. They improved the old hand-driven Catalan forges—the thunder-gusts—by driving them by water-powered machinery, and engaged in making anchors, farm tools, and horseshoes. On the eastern side of Lake Champlain Vermonters mined iron and smelted it to make the huge kettles demanded by the thriving potash industry.

In spite of its fairly rapid expansion, the American iron industry lagged in technological improvement. Even in those days Americans called the English pigheaded. The American ironmasters were as pigheaded as anyone—more than most. In 1812 Colonel George Shoemaker hauled nine wagons of his Centreville hard coal into Philadelphia. He managed to sell two loads for the bare cost of transportation, but he had to give away the remainder. The ironmasters and other people said he was an impostor attempting to peddle stones as coal.

The Americans had begun making iron with charcoal, and they clung so tightly to the method that none would give it up until the receding forest forced them to it. Not until 1819, or eighty-six years after the introduction of coke in England, was the first coke iron made in this country. The brave experimenters were the proprietors of the Bear Furnace in Armstrong County, Pennsylvania.

The use of coke spread slowly, and in America it was hardly successful until 1835, when the Mary Anne Furnace in Pennsylvania turned out a superior grade of pig iron by using soft coal that had been previously baked in an oven. Ironmasters from all parts of the state journeyed to see the Mary Anne at work.

The Mary Anne was something of a revolution. All at once, in the manner of Americans, everybody wanted to use coke. In a few years Connellsville started the smudge of its thousands of beehive coke ovens which have fumed ever since. From this point on the supremacy of Pennsylvania in the American world of iron was never in doubt.

From Germany, which then vied with England as ironmaker to all the world, had come thousands of experienced workers to settle in Pennsylvania, and to work alongside the able iron men from Sweden, Scotland, and England. One of the Germans, Peter Schoenberger, founded an illustrious firm in Huntingdon County, and his son, "Doctor" Peter, carried on nobly, becoming one of the earliest of the true iron barons who carried a cane and wore a plug hat fourteen inches tall.

Another, John Roebling, set up in Saxonburg to make the first wire rope in this country. Pittsburgh began building the first iron boats, small affairs for use on the many canals. John Fritz of Johnstown started his mechanical experiments which were to make American rolling mills the best in the world.

A furnace for welding pipe was built in Philadelphia. Matthias Baldwin built his first locomotive and named it Old Ironsides. Short railroads were being laid in a dozen states. And in 1841, Congress took cognizance of the rising industry by passing a tariff act that carried a duty on rails and other important iron commodities.

Smoke and cinders were filling the air. By the time this first duty on iron was imposed, American iron manufacture was of no importance to the world at large, yet close to a thousand blast furnaces were at work. A year or so later the production of iron rose to more than one million tons, for a twelve-months period. This was considered a wonderful expansion of an important industry whose first two hundred years had been slow and discouraging. The figure of the ironmaster had come into being. In many a town of New York, New Jersey, and parts west as far as the Ohio or a little beyond, he was already a personage. These industrialists had done very well for themselves. But now they looked at the slim beds of ore which were handy to their furnaces and wondered if they would last another ten years.

Maybe so. But there wasn't a great deal of ore in any one of the industrial states of the time. It was in widely scattered places, and much of the known deposits was of low quality. Thoughtful men could vision a day not long ahead when the end would be in sight.

America had plenty of capital, the ironmasters told

one another; it had the machinery, and it was fast getting the skill. What was sorely needed was a supply of ore such as the English had in Cornwall, the Germans in the Harz Mountains, and the Swedes at Dannemora.

There would seem to be a distinct pattern to the history of discoveries. At exactly the right time a party of roaming men made one that eased the minds of ironmasters and supplied the stuff for America's ribs and backbone.

The big drama of ore and steel was about to begin.

Part I

ORE

2 *Great Cold Lake in an Iron Collar*

LATE in the afternoon of September 19, 1844, the region
just south of Lake Superior ceased to be a howling wilderness. At that hour the needle of a magnetic compass held
by William A. Burt dipped and jittered furiously. Then,
it quivered with uncertainty a moment and, like a man
lost in the woods and gone wholly mad, it darted west
and east and south, describing wild arcs, pointing nowhere for long.

Burt was amazed. By comparing the magnetic needle
with his solar compass, which continued to point soberly
to the poles, he could tell exactly how wildly the needle
was performing. Burt and the rest of his survey party
had seen needles dip and dodge before, but never anything like this. When the arrow registered a variation of
87 degrees, or almost a quarter of a circle, old Burt
could contain himself no longer.

"Boys," he said, "look around and see what you can
find."

The boys looked around, and without any trouble
they found a score of outcroppings of ore that appeared
to be almost pure iron. There it was, hard, black ore in
abundance, seemingly an entire hill, almost a mountain
of it.

Old Burt didn't give a whoop for iron, but he was
immensely proud and pleased. "Look where you'd be if

it wasn't for my solar compass," he shouted over and
over like a parrot. "Look where you'd be. Why, you
wouldn't know where in thunder you were!" The solar
compass was his own invention,[1] and now the old gentleman stalked around on the hill, whacking at stones with
the blunt end of his ax, cackling his triumph.

The surveyors judged from the wild needle that magnetite ore must be present in large quantities, but none
of them was interested in ore. None carried away a sample. They were making a survey of Michigan's Upper
Peninsula for the United States Government, and they
were tending to business. At the moment their compass
started jumping so weirdly, they were running the east
line of Township 47 N, Range 27 W, which was to become a part of Marquette County.

Such was the time and the place. What had been until
then a howling wilderness indeed, was about to enter its
time as a howling region of wild-eyed men seeking copper and iron.

But nothing happened immediately. Burt and his
party completed their survey and made the usual accurate and quite dull report, merely noting the "existence
of large iron bodies."

Before Burt's party there had been others. Farther
east and some two hundred years before, the explorer
Champlain had been amazed at the gift of a friendly
Indian. It was a piece of copper "a foot long, very handsome and quite pure." This metal had come, so the red
man said, from some vague country to the west, a land
near Gitche Gumee, the Big-Sea-Water that awaited a
New England poet to make its name famous.

---

[1] Patented in 1836 and still used. Burt also invented "The Typog-
rapher," father of the typewriter.

French voyageurs ranged across and upward through the Great Lakes to the last and greatest of them, trading for furs. Père Marquette came to found a mission near the wondrous rapids that tumbled so hurriedly out of Gitche Gumee. Other great men came to do this or that and to leave their names secure—LaSalle, Hennepin, Joliet. Some of them heard tales of mysterious lands where stood mountains of mysterious metals—mysterious, and quite useless to the red men. But the early palefaces seemed not interested; they wanted to wish a new and wholly unsuitable kind of God onto the red men and to get the red men's furs. John Jacob Astor didn't worry much about God, but he got a good many of the furs.

For two hundred years this Michigan was a very bloody ground. French and English fought for it, while the Indians fought both. Then the Colonials fought the British. When the smoke of 1812 had blown away Michigan was discovered to be a part of the new Republic.

The new Republic had considerable trouble in setting the boundaries of Michigan. When the Territory was forming a government in preparation to being admitted to the Union, Michigan wanted within its borders a strip of land around the southwestern bend of Lake Erie. Ohio claimed, and got it. To appease Michigan, Congress with a grand gesture handed it a large hunk of uninhabited and unknown land above the Straits of Mackinac— away, as one local statesman put it, to hell and gone.

Michigan wanted none of this so-called Upper Peninsula. Its officials fought its being saddled on them. Not even deer and bear could live there, they said. They shouted to Congress that this was barren land. It had not a great deal of timber. Grain would not grow there. The place was too close to the Great Cold Lake.

Like it or no, Michigan got the peninsula.

For the next few years the busy new state paid no attention to its upper portion. Then, by some marvel of persuasion, young Douglass Houghton, a geologist who had been giving lectures to a culture-hungry Detroit, got the Michigan legislature of farmers and lumbermen to grant him a little money. He proposed to investigate this upper and well damned peninsula and see what was there. The money soon petered out. Houghton went to Washington, talked Congress into starting a geological survey of all wild lands in the United States, and returned to Michigan to begin the work.

Sometimes with an Indian or two, often alone, Houghton cruised the south shore of the Great Cold Lake, a vast inland sea, lying so remote from all else. He followed the rivers to their sources. He chipped rocks. He observed temperatures and elevations. He even noted the flora and fauna. Everywhere he went in this silent country he mapped and charted. It was well he did. One bitter October night the sinister brooding of Superior whipped to sudden fury and wrecked Douglass Houghton's small Mackinac boat. His notes were saved on the spot, but the lake kept his body for seven months more.

Houghton had written his reports in guarded language. He had foreseen what might happen and had tried to minimize his findings. He wanted no rush of madmen to this northern solitude. But he was an honest man and he had to set down what he had found: an almost incalculable wealth of copper.

What Houghton feared happened soon after his reports were made public. It was a stampede of prospectors seeking copper on the tiny Keweenaw finger that thrusts out into Lake Superior. The rush was sudden and frantic. Men stormed up through the Soo rapids from Lake Huron, pushing small steamboats ahead of them on rollers. Others came by canoe and in bateaux. Hundreds of them came, swinging their picks wildly at every rock, assured that somewhere was a mountain of purest copper. Nobody thought of iron nor looked for it.

The stampede ebbed as quickly as it had flowed. Thousands of men staked their claims to copper, and many of them starved or froze in the climate of the Great Cold Lake's winter. Some went mad in the clouds of the brief summer's gnats and wandered off into the woods, gibbering of copper mountains, to be eaten at their leisure by billions of flies and mosquitoes.

And some, true enough, found copper. There was plenty of copper. The prospectors had not stopped to realize that finding copper and mining it are two different things. Nearly all of them, who survived at all, went back down through the Soo with their boots and clothes in tatters and nothing in their clothes. The great copper rush was over. Companies formed in Boston would come in good season to do the mining and make the money.

It was at this copper-rush period that William Burt's compass pointed four ways at once and started what was to be the rush for iron.

Surveyor Burt's reports made note of the probability of large bodies of iron ore. Philo M. Everett of Jackson, in lower Michigan, who thought he wanted to own a copper mine and had gone looking for one, heard of Burt's findings. Everett also came in contact with an Indian chief who claimed to know where there was an entire mountain of strange rock.

This Indian labored under the name of Madjigijig, or sometimes Marji Gesick, in paleface spelling. He told Everett that the queer mountain was of black and blue and red and many colors. Everett asked to see it. The chief replied that the mountain was strictly Bad Medicine, filled with countless devils and spirits of one kind and another.

Whether or not Marji Gesick, the Chippewa, had any inkling of the value of this mountain to the palefaces isn't known. In any case, he grunted and muttered—which was hemming and hawing—until Everett offered to give the chief a part of the value of the find, if find it were.

Old Marji Gesick led Everett and his party to a spot on high land near the present city of Negaunee. It was rough, broken ground, with outcroppings of rock all over its surface. The chief, doubtless sweating from fear of Bad Medicine, directed Everett to a huge pine tree lying flat on the ground. He wouldn't approach the windfall himself.

"Catch um there," said Marji Gesick, pointing.

Everett went over to look. Exposed under the big roots was a broad expanse of black ore—heavy magnetic stuff that caused Everett's pocket compass to dip and flutter. It was a June day in 1845, six months after Burt had surveyed along this very hill.

One may be sure that Marji Gesick got none of the money that came from the heavy rock. Nor did Everett. Millions of dollars were dug out of the rough hill, and years later Charlotte, Marji Gesick's daughter, sued for

a share.[2] More years passed while Charlotte's case wound
its interminable way through the maze of paleface chi-
canery called courts. She got less than her father did; *he*
got his name put on a pretty marker,[3] but by that time
he was dead and didn't care.

Whether it is gold or copper or lowly iron ore, there
would seem to be little use in trying to keep secret the
news of its finding. The news escapes like quicksilver.
Everett and his party managed to hold their tongues
until they obtained possession of the land on Jackson
Mountain, as the property was called; and then the word
got out that the whole of Michigan's unwanted Upper
Peninsula was one range of solid iron hills.

There were no telegraph lines, but news of the find
spread through the wilderness as though the birds had
carried it. By the time it had emerged from the wild
lands, the iron hills were said to be mountains, each at
least a mile high and all of purest iron. The Great Cold
Lake, lying there so vast and silent, was rimmed with a
collar of iron—iron a mile high, a mile deep and nobody knew how wide. . . . It was a picture to stir the
minds of restless men in far places.

---

[2] Charlotte's claim was in a paper she possessed, the authenticity of
which was never in doubt:

"River du Mort, May 30, 1846

"This may certify that in consideration of the services rendered by
Madjigijig, A Chippeway Indian, in hunting ores of location No. 593 of
the Jackson Mining Co., that he is entitled to twelve undivided one-
hundredths part of said mining company in said location Number.

"A. V. BERRY, *Superintendent*
"F. W. KIRTLAND, *Secretary*"

[3] The marker is near Negaunee, Mich., and says in part: "The ore was
found . . . by Marji Gesick, a chief of the Chippewa Tribe of Indians."
It was erected in 1904 to "mark the first discovery of Iron Ore in the
Lake Superior Region."

Presently there was another traffic jam at the Soo rapids, as men of Buffalo and New York and Cleveland and Boston worked their boats up through the boiling white water or carried them around in a costly portage. It was tough going, this Soo that connected Lake Huron with the Great Cold One.

The young state of Michigan already had looked at the rapids of the St. Mary's River and had asked the Federal Government for permission to build a ship canal through the military reservation there. Congress laughed at the idea and no less than Henry Clay, a very great man, stood up to damn it. "It is," he said, referring to the need for a canal, "it is a work beyond the remotest settlement of the United States, if not the moon." Clay liked the city of Washington, and he didn't get around much.

Charles T. Harvey got around a lot more than Clay did. He was a traveling salesman for the Fairbankses, who made scales in far-away St. Johnsbury, Vermont, and he had been sent West to establish agencies for the Fairbanks products in the new state. While recovering from an attack of typhoid at Sault Ste. Marie, young Harvey spent several weeks in the newly discovered iron district. The wealth being uncovered there, at Jackson Mountain and elsewhere, fascinated him. Here was ore without end, he thought. But how would it be taken to the furnaces of Ohio and Pennsylvania? They were a thousand miles off. There were no railroads, nor likely to be. There was water, sailing water as far as the Soo —and water beyond the Soo. The Soo had only rapids.

Harvey's lively imagination conjured up a canal around the dangerous rapids, with locks, big locks that could raise and lower the largest boat to sail the Lakes.

In spite of Henry Clay, Congress finally granted permission to build the canal, and Harvey, with the sponsorship of the Fairbankses and others, undertook the job of organizing a group to build the canal for Michigan.

Harvey was not quite twenty-five years old. He had the rare qualities of engineering skill and what is called promotional ability. He also had the powerful backing of the Fairbanks family and other men of substance. In a surprisingly short time he had formed a contracting company. He himself took charge of the digging and construction.

It was a titanic job in its day. Harvey's capitalist backers were in New York or even farther east; it required six weeks for an exchange of letters. Nearest telegraph station was at Detroit, 450 miles away. Nearest machine shop was on Saginaw Bay, half as far. Every stick of blasting powder had to come from Delaware, a good thousand miles.

There was not sufficient labor at Sault Ste. Marie to dig a well, to say nothing of a canal 5,700 feet long. Harvey sent agents to board ships before they docked in Boston and New York and grab off what immigrant labor they could, paying fare to the Soo, and doubtless telling whoppers of lies about the opportunities to get rich [4] by digging the Soo Canal.

Harvey's agents managed to get the labor. Starting with a crew of four hundred, he soon had two thousand men on the job. All drilling was by hand, and there was a pile of it to be done, done through rock that was flinty long before history began.

---

[4] Nevertheless, many a wealthy family of Michigan's Upper Peninsula had its beginnings in drill and shovel work performed during construction of the Soo Canal and locks.

During the short days of winter, which was five months of the year, there was a bare eight hours of sunlight. The temperature hovered around zero much of the time, with sudden drops to as low as 35 degrees below zero. At the head of every runway for wheelbarrows, Harvey stationed a man to watch the workmen and to rub with snow the faces of any who gave sign of frostbite.

January winds roared down off the Great Cold Lake, bringing blizzards that piled snow higher than the bunkhouses and sleet that stung like birdshot. They had winters up there on the Soo. Refrigeration was assured, and every cook in the outfit was furnished with an ax; when he wanted more meat he went out into the shed and hacked it off the sides of beeves that were frozen hard as plank.

Young Harvey was no desk engineer. He faced the winds and the cold and drove his men to the limit. Then, during the last few months of the work, an epidemic of cholera broke out. Men died like flies and were buried as discreetly as possible and late at night in an effort to keep the gang from knowing the dread disease was upon them. Although more than two hundred died within a few weeks and were buried furtively here and there in the woods, not a day was lost by the main crew.

It was a hard and cruel two years of labor and pain and death. Only one strike marked it. The grumbling of hard-driven workmen flared up one day, and a thousand of them paraded the camp, demanding more pay. Harvey met them head on. He shut down the cookhouses at once and placed armed guards at the doors. No work, no grub. The strikers lost two meals and suddenly decided to return to their drilling. There was to be no monkey business on this job. Harvey's driving frenzy continued until the day he opened a sluice gate to let water from the Great Cold Lake flow into the completed locks, and thence into Huron.

Meanwhile, in the rough hills along Superior's south shore, one hundred and fifty miles west of Harvey's new locks, an army of miners, many of them out of Cornwall by way of Pennsylvania, were digging a big hole in Jackson Mountain. Scores of other men were roaming the hills, looking for outcroppings to tell them where to dig for iron that would match the wealth coming out of Jackson. They found it, too, at places soon to be known as the Cleveland, the Winthrop, the Humboldt, the Argyle, and a hundred others.

The Jackson and Cleveland mines were the first. Both were eight miles from Gitche Gumee water, so the Cornish miners loaded the ore into sleighs and Canuck-Frenchmen drove and cursed double teams down dangerous grades to the shore. A little later, over an elegant plank road, the ore went by mule team the twelve long miles to Marquette, destined to be the first great ore shipping port in the United States.

On the 14th of August, 1855, the brig *Columbia,* Judson Wells, master, stood out from Marquette with a hundred tons of rich black ore on her deck. On the 17th she passed without trouble through the new Soo locks and canal, while a blacksmith fired an anvil-cannon and half the men at the Soo were reported to be drunker than so many fiddlers' bitches. If they weren't, they should have been, for the *Columbia* was the first ship to pass down the locks with ore. The Great Cold Lake had ceased to be remote and the Marquette Range had come into being.

Incidentally, a traveling salesman for weighing scales had built what was to be the most important commercial canal in the world, not excepting the Suez and the Panama.

3 *The Marquette Comes to Life*

LONG before the Soo Canal was done, men who doubtless had vision but lacked certain qualities of judgment felt positive that Michigan's Upper Peninsula was about to become not simply the iron-mining center of the United States but the ironmaking center as well.

One of these men was Robert Graveraet. Having secured what he thought to be a solid interest in one of the newly discovered mines, he set about to develop it. First thing he needed was money. Alone and on snowshoes he plodded the four hundred untracked miles to Saginaw, then made his way to Worcester, Massachusetts, where he had little trouble in raising capital.

Graveraet's idea was to make iron at what he thought was the logical place—the very mines. Plenty of good hard maple to make charcoal grew everywhere around the iron deposits. Charcoal and labor were all he needed —dig the black stuff, puddle it with charcoal on the spot, forge it into pretty blooms and ship it to Cleveland and Pittsburgh. It looked simple enough.

Graveraet selected a spot for his furnace and forge operations. Near by, on an easy slope of ground that rose to handsome bluffs overlooking a quiet bay, would be his headquarters and his port. He named it "Worcester" in honor of the home town of his backers, the Messrs. Clark, Harlow, and Fisher. In June of 1849, when much of eastern United States was rushing to California, Graveraet landed his pioneer gang of mechanics and laborers and started to clear ground for the "Iron Metropolis." First to fell a tree was young Peter White, who was soon to be a very important man.

The forge was set up in the wilderness. Swarms of French-Canadians soon arrived. They were noted axmen and were easily seduced from logging camps of lower Michigan by promise of an extra two dollars a month. Graveraet sent them into the forest to whale into the hardwood for his charcoal.

Back in the mines, in which Graveraet still fancied he had a large interest, Cornish and Irish miners were piling up tons of ore, some of it the black magnetic stuff that the miners called hard ore, some of it the pretty and softer blue-brown hematite. They had to pile it up all summer, for there was no road; but come winter, the Canucks drove teams with sleighs over rocks and stumps that were well covered with snow.

For six or seven months there was little but snow everywhere. Snow or not, Graveraet was everywhere, too. He scurried away through a blizzard to Milwaukee and shipped back on the *Fur Trader* a large number of Germans to help the Cornish and Irish at the mines. Fever broke out on the little schooner, and when it arrived at "Worcester" most of the arrivals had to be lugged to a log cabin hurriedly turned into a hospital. The fever was believed to be cholera. The white people were frightened and some talked of leaving, and inside of two hours not one of the many Indians who had been attracted to the bay by paleface doings was to be seen. They melted into the woods or disappeared in canoes around the point, in great fear of the dread disease of the white man. It was weeks before they returned.

The ore was now coming down from the hills in larger quantities. The forge was making iron. Graveraet, never still, set his men to building a dock for the new town which, for reasons now unknown but happily, was changed to Marquette, in honor of the great explorer and missionary. The harbor was christened Iron Bay.

The townfolk were pretty proud of their new dock when it was finished. It was built of timber and stone, stanch as could be. But they didn't yet know what the Great Cold Lake could do. On the morning after the dock's completion, people were amazed to find the beach as clear and as uncluttered as it had been before the white man came. Not a timber, not a trace of the dock remained. One of Superior's sudden storms had whipped it away and licked the shore clean.

A new dock was built. Even then the ships did not come often enough. Food was the big problem. One had to have something on hand to face seven months of winter. The coming of new gangs to work the mines and the forge added to the difficulty. Late one fall it became known that the supplies of food at Marquette were wholly inadequate. Muttering went on, and threats. Graveraet had armed guards placed at the storehouse. Fearing famine, a gang of German laborers struck out on foot, doubtless heading for Milwaukee and thinking of pigs' knuckles. But a supply ship arrived in time.

Marquette suffered shortages of this or that, but it never had a real famine. A cook in the Harlow family, however, never ceased to fear. She was a huge Indian woman, Angelique by name, and a noted character.[1] When there was talk of a shortage of food, Angelique

---

[1] Angelique once bet a teamster she could pack a full barrel of pork up a Marquette hill. She did it without half trying.

often would wake up in the night, screaming enough to wake the household. It was little wonder, when you knew Angelique's story.

A few years before, Angelique and her husband Charlie had been put on small Isle Royale in Lake Superior by white men who wanted them to remain to guard a large deposit of mass copper that had been discovered there. The two Indians were given a half-barrel of flour and told to remain on the island. A stock of provisions was promised before winter set in.

Winter came, but not the provisions. A great storm swept the lake, taking their canoe with it and destroying their one fish net. There was no game on the island. They couldn't eat the valuable copper that shone so red in the sun. So the two savages dug for roots and chewed bark, getting weaker all the time.

Charlie died after long fits of madness during which he threatened his Angelique with a knife. "Charlie, he was so tired of being hungry," is the way Angelique put it.

The woman kept the fire going in their hut, and there she lived for five weeks with the corpse of her man for company. Worst of it was, as she afterward told, the half-frozen corpse put an idea into her head . . . But no, she couldn't do that. She stuck it out somehow, living until white men came in May and rescued her. She was very happy that her Charlie could have a Christian funeral. . . . No, it was little wonder that Angelique sometimes awoke the Harlow family with screams that she was "going to eat my Charlie."

Keeping Marquette in food was only an item in Graveraet's frantic efforts to build the Metropolis of Iron.

He shipped in still more Irish and Germans. He drove in a troop of horses, bringing them through the thick woods overland from Escanaba. Often he had to threaten and promise and wheedle to quell incipient bread riots among his workmen. But the forge was turning out a fine grade of charcoal iron. Marquette was elated when it learned that a test made by the United States Navy of a chain forged of Marquette iron did not break a link until the strain registered 169,120 pounds. "Pittsburgh's day is done," said Robert Graveraet, "and so is Johnstown's."

Meanwhile, however, certain economic factors were quietly at work. A team of mules or horses, delivered at the mine, cost on an average of $1,400 a pair. Hay was $50 a ton, hard to get at any price. The haul from mine to forge was long and hard. In a short time it was apparent that a ton of iron made in Marquette could not be laid down at the mills in Cleveland, New Castle and Pittsburgh for less than $200. It cost not quite $80 to make iron at the mills.

It was a possibility that seems not to have entered his mind, and Graveraet's dream of a Pittsburgh on Lake Superior was done. So was Graveraet. The ore continued to come down from the hills and to be shipped from Marquette—as ore, not iron—but Graveraet, the great dreamer, owned none of it. While he was bringing in men and machinery and horses and mules and capital, and was founding the Iron Port, he had failed to watch the cards being dealt him in the ever shifting poker game of mine ownership. He had fully believed he owned large interests in the Cleveland and Lake Superior mine locations. He learned suddenly that he owned not a pound of ore. It was one of the earliest personal tragedies of a business that was as hard as its product. Graveraet and his name faded quickly. Only the most ancient of old-timers can recall either.

It was different with young Peter White of Graveraet's party of pioneers. Peter was a husky young man, versed in the ways of the woods, who also had the faculty of getting along well with the Indians. It was a valuable thing to have in one's knapsack, those days. In an amazingly short time he had mastered all the dialects of the various Michigan tribes. He served as interpreter in the new settlement, and when the Marquette Iron Company was formed Peter went to work in its store. His first bid for fame came in connection with the Jackson company which operated the mines.

There was trouble brewing at the Jackson, and President Jones of the company wanted to get away from there quickly and to go a long way off. The trouble was money, or lack of it. The Jackson concern had been running on a shoestring. The string broke in the spring of 1850. The miners had not had a pay day all winter, and they weren't going to have one now. Cornish mutterings rose to a shout that sounded like, " 'Ang 'im! We'll 'ang the bloody bleeding bounder!" It referred to President Jones.

On some sort of pretext Jones managed to evade the workmen who planned to hang him and got away from the mine. Knowing of Peter White's ability to go anywhere through the woods of the wild country, Jones sought him out. "I have some pressing business down below," he told White, by which he meant anywhere south of the Peninsula. "I want you to guide me to Escanaba, where I can get a boat."

It was a sixty-five-mile trip overland. Peter agreed to

do the guiding at three dollars a day. He led the thoroughly scared mine official to Escanaba, but it took seven days to do it. Peter returned to Marquette in three. A little later he founded the tradition by which he still is remembered. It was the good old American tradition of Getting the Mail Through. Melodramas have been founded on it.

Letters and other mail from down below were important things in the lives of two thousand pioneers beached on the bleak shores of Superior. Letters were literally read to pieces, while newspapers were wrapped in cloth and circulated from family to family until they were many months old and quite dog-eared in spite of the wrapper.

The winter of 1850 was long, and no mail whatever had come in from Green Bay, down in Wisconsin, the nearest depot. Marquette citizens called a meeting to raise pledges to pay someone to go to bring the mail. Young Peter White's eyes fairly bulged when he heard the pledges run up to twelve hundred dollars. He applied for the job and got it.

With two Indians to help with packing, Peter made nine trips that winter between Marquette and Green Bay, bringing in huge loads of mail, first on their backs, then by dog team. It was common for the entire town of Marquette to turn out in a body and plod through the drifts to Carp River, to meet Peter and the mail.

Peter and his Indian bucks did a right good job, fighting through blizzards and cedar swamps, over streams frozen so thick that no gurgle could be heard, and often completing the trip to the dancing fire of the Northern Lights which blazed high in January and made a weird day of Marquette nights.

But in the spring, when the sun shone and mail started coming in regularly by boat, the big-hearted citizens, the important grand-gestured fellows who had pledged the twelve hundred dollars, forgot all about it. Only one remembered his pledge. His name was Silas G. Smith. He had promised three dollars and he went to Peter to pay it. "Keep your money," Peter told him, pretty well disillusioned by now. "I don't want you to pay for the mail for the whole town."

But the mail-carrying job cut Peter's eyeteeth, and it also started him on his way to fabulous fame on the Upper Peninsula. He added to his growing reputation when he set out to get a winter mail service to Marquette.

Having been appointed postmaster, Peter harassed the Post Office Department until they agreed to send an official to meet him and to discuss the matter of a regular mail service. The meeting was held at Green Bay, Wisconsin. Peter got there first. While hanging around the Green Bay post office he noticed some two hundred empty mailbags. With the connivance of the local postmaster, Peter stuffed half the empties into the others, packing in hay and any old thing that would take up space. Then, into the top of each bag he put genuine mail, leaving the tops slightly open, arranging everything so that a casual glance at any of the one hundred bags would indicate a good two bushels of post-office matter for nowhere but Marquette, Michigan.

It all made a stupendous pile, large enough, had it been genuine mail, for the thundering city of Chicago, down at the other end of the lake. The post-office official was impressed. "Those iron mines around Marquette must be powerful busy," he remarked. "Yes, sir, they are busy," agreed Peter, "and every one of those miners can read and write."

The official immediately wired Washington that a state of emergency existed and that regular all-year mail service should be started at once to the Upper Peninsula. It was done.

Meanwhile the strap-iron railroad from Marquette back to the mines was having trouble. A mule team, pulling a small cart of ore, could make but one trip a day. Sometimes they started out but never completed a trip. The grades were very bad, steep and long, often with sharp curves. Runaways became too common. Down the iron hills they'd come, the mules striving to keep ahead of the heavy carts that gained speed with every yard, and the Canuck drivers yelling like demons. It was too much, even for mulish stubbornness. The animals were broken and mangled in increasing numbers, which was not only cruel but very costly. As for the French drivers, they crossed themselves every time they started a trip down the mountain. It was well they did, for they were often mangled along with the mules.

A steam railway to the mines had started building at the same time with the strap-iron affair. It was having even more trouble. The Ely brothers, Sam and Heman, who were building the road, had not been able to get a State land grant to aid them in financing the operation. So they helped elect Peter White to the legislature.

Peter took to his snowshoes again. He strapped a pack of provisions on his back and tramped down to Escanaba, a mere sixty-five miles, thence by stage to Fond du Lac, and again by snowshoes to Lansing. Word of this

How did he cross Lake Michigan?

stanch legislator's progress was flashed ahead to Lansing.

In that day Marquette was positively the end of the world, and Peter White's monumental journey to the capital created quite a stir. The boys in the legislature gave the husky bearded lad in the red woolen shirt a big hand when he took his seat. Here was a man from the real backwoods, the country that was two hundred miles beyond yonder, up there where winter was all night and little children were rocked to sleep to the howling of timber wolves.

Peter was backwoodsy enough, but he knew exactly what he had come to Lansing to do: It was to get a land grant for the struggling railroad. First thing he ran into was the usual crowd of hangers-on and steerers with which even then our legislative halls abounded. Peter paid his respects to them in his maiden speech, a remarkable oration which is talked about ninety years after. In it he referred to "lobbyists as thick as autumnal leaves which strew the brooks of Vallombrosa." It was classical and sonorous enough to hold the house enthralled, and it stamped the gentleman from Marquette as a statesman of the first rank. You didn't get Vallombrosa every day in Lansing.

Representative White lived for the next few weeks in rooms reeking with the fumes of tobacco and hard liquor and decorated with massive cuspidors—things necessary to the making of laws, either state or national, then as now. He treated the right men to brandy and canned oysters, rarer than hummingbirds' tongues. He mixed well with all. He horse-traded and logrolled. He got the land grant. Then he put on his snowshoes and walked back to Marquette.

The steam railroad began operation in 1857 with a

fine twenty-five-ton locomotive that was rigged out with plenty of brass and named "The Sebastopol." It tooted and teetered over the rough twelve miles of light rail into Marquette with what the local paper termed "an avalanche of ore." It amounted to a thousand tons daily. A new dock with ten ore pockets was built for the ships that were now coming regularly through the new Soo Canal from the lower Lakes.

During this period the idea of making iron near the mines was revived. But this time it was to be pig iron, smelted in a blast furnace, and not the puddled charcoal iron that Graveraet had hoped would make his fortune. The first furnace to go into blast was the Pioneer, at Negaunee, not far from Jackson Mountain. And at about the same time the operating company put into blast a prospectus as gaudy and glittering as anything seen since. It sounded like one of those egg-and-chicken-farm deals, where one thing leads to another and all lead to success.

The prospectus pointed out that the concern owned over four thousand acres of timberland which "at the usual estimate that a cord of wood will produce 40 bushels of charcoal of which 125 bushels will furnish fuel to melt one ton of iron, and assuming that each acre will yield sixty cords of wood, the company's lands will furnish fuel for nearly 80,000 tons of iron ore, sufficient to supply two stacks [blast furnaces] for ten years," and so on and so on until the pretty pig iron had been sold at a fantastic profit in Chicago or Pittsburgh.

It was quite an elegant prospectus, and so were the stock certificates—which were soon being used for shelf paper by the wives of men who had listened and bought. In its first year the Pioneer Company had spent all of its

$125,000 of original capital and had somehow accumulated a debt of $95,000.

Other concerns built blast furnaces. The woods were dotted with them. A few of the companies actually made some pig iron. They also lost money on every ton they produced. No, Marquette on Iron Bay wasn't to be a Pittsburgh, not even a Lorain.

But things went better with the companies that kept strictly to the business of producing ore. Hard times came when the Civil War broke out. Nobody wanted any ore. The slump, however, was brief. Before the war was over iron and steel were in such demand that manufacturing plants in the East were sending out buyers to seek more ore and scrap and pig iron, with which to make cannon and rails.

Peter White always read the newspapers, and he closely followed the doings of General Grant. "Grant's an able man," he said. "He is going to win." In 1863 Peter casually bought what iron he could find lying around the quiet blast furnaces at Marquette. He packed his grip and went down the Lakes, stopping everywhere along the line to buy every stray pound of pig he could locate on wharves and in warehouses. Then he went on to Cleveland. He was exactly in time. Iron prices had made a sudden and dizzy advance. Peter sold all he had bought at a large increase in price and cleaned up thirty thousand dollars. It was the foundation of the White fortune.

Overnight, it seemed, the iron mills of Ohio and Pennsylvania were crying for pig at any price. So were the new mills at Chicago. And the blast furnaces at Pittsburgh and Johnstown wanted ore, all the ore they could get.

There was plenty of ore in the hills back of Marquette. Men to work the mines were coming in to Iron Bay on every boat. The snorting Sebastopol couldn't begin to bring the ore down fast enough, and new locomotives were added to the Iron Mountain Railway. What had been Jackson Mountain became Negaunee, a town with plank sidewalks, a school, and a church. What had been Cleveland Mine Location became Ishpeming, with a dozen shafts going down into the iron hills. In three years the annual shipments of ore out of Iron Bay rose to the unthought-of total of 240,000 tons.

In spite of this new activity there seemed always to be a shortage of United States money on the Marquette Range. Off and on for several years the mining companies had issued scrip. This was paid as wages to the mines and circulated freely throughout all the mine towns, and in Marquette. In time this scrip led to the locally famous Negaunee counterfeiting scandal.

When the Panic of 1873 hit the iron range, all hard money disappeared at once. The mine company scrip, which was known as Iron Money, was the only form of exchange. Presently, at the bank in Marquette, officials looked hard at certain pieces of scrip they had accepted. The signatures were faked. On close scrutiny, even the printing of the scrip appeared to be a counterfeiting job. The bank sent to Chicago for a Pinkerton detective, who then had a great name in the land. The sleuth soon traced the work to a police official of Negaunee. He was arrested.

The defendant's attorney readily admitted his client had printed and signed the counterfeit scrip. It was a wrong thing to do, he said. "But, gentlemen," the attorney went on, "it has always been my belief that the

United States Government and only the United States
Government has a right to issue paper money or any sort
of currency. Thus, if you prosecute my client, I must, as
a patriotic and law-abiding citizen, ask for an indictment against these mine companies and their officials
who also have been guilty of counterfeiting."

The indictment of counterfeiting against the Negaunee policeman was quashed.

But now the Federal Government wanted to know
more about this mine-company scrip. Colonel William
Gavett, a special agent for the Treasury Department, appeared in Marquette. His face was very grave. He had
come, he said, to collect a retroactive tax of 10 per cent
on each piece of scrip for each time it had been paid out.

The budding mine barons slept very poorly that night.
Their companies, they well knew, had issued millions
of dollars in the paper scrip. In the morning they came
to face Colonel Gavett, who was gracious enough but
very sober.

"Gentlemen," he said, "my figures indicate that you
have issued approximately one hundred million dollars
worth of scrip in the past fifteen years. The tax due to
the Federal Government is therefore ten million dollars. You will please remit directly to the Treasury in
Washington." Then he put on his silk hat and went
away.

Marquette had been through fires, strikes, and blizzards, but never anything like this. When it became public, as presently it did, the miners and other common
folk had a long laugh. The sweating mine-company officials chewed untold numbers of fine cigars to tatters, and
they cursed government in all its forms. Anarchy would
have been better than this.

Once again it was up to Peter White, now called "The Honorable," to Get the Mail Through. Peter was now a banker who could wear a plug hat and carry a gold-headed cane with any of them.[2] He packed his flowered carpetbag and took a boat down the Lakes. Exactly how he managed it is lost to history. He saw the right people in Washington, and before the end of the current session of Congress the lawmakers had hurriedly passed a special relief bill that did away with the tax on scrip.

When the new magnetic telegraph lines brought the news to Marquette, more than one mine baron took an extra snort of old sherry and went to sleep like a baby, for the first time in many months.

---

[2] Peter White lived to a ripe old age in the next century and became the Upper Peninsula's greatest legend. A good rugged punch was named for him. Poets sang his great deeds while he lived. He lived so long and had been seen in so many places that many Indians and French-Canadians actually believed him to be at least two hundred years old. Some of them were sure he was an ancient voyageur left over from Père Marquette's time.

4 *They Dug Deep at Ishpeming*

THE mine barons visited Ishpeming once in a while, but they never stayed long. It was no place for a man, once he had become a baron. It was a place of many deep holes in the ground and of men who went down into the holes.

So far as ore was concerned—and ore was what counted in iron country—Ishpeming was the fairest flower on the Marquette Range. The town was quickly cut and sawed out of green timber that grew in a swampy depression high up in the queer broken hills of magnetite and soft ore. It took its name from its position in the world. It was fair on top of the height of land between the two lakes. One way, the Carp flowed into Superior; down the other side, the rippling Escanaba hurried into Michigan.

In Ojibway jargon, "Ishpeming" meant "highest ground," or even "heaven." Perhaps "High Ground" was a fit name, but "deep hole" would have fitted as well or better, for, long before the town got its name, Cornish and Irish miners were well on their way at digging down to China, living in dark places ten hours of every day.

Ishpeming founded the classic pattern of iron-range cities everywhere. It budded and grew out of a hodgepodge of mine "locations." Every hole in the ground was a mine, and every group of shacks around a mine was a location. First, there was the Cleveland Location, then the Superior Location, and then they came without end —the New York, the Barnum, the Salisbury, the Lake Angeline, the Winthrop, the Saginaw, the Lowthian, the New England, and many more. One, even, was called the Baron.

Each location was originally a town by itself, simple and self-sufficient. You could mark one by the shaft house, which rose high above the hole; and long rambling stock piles of ore. Then, there was always a "dry" —the dryhouse where the miners changed clothes when coming on or going off shift; and a cluster of shacks where the miners lived, most of them with their families. The Cornish and Irish were seldom bachelors for long.

Some of Ishpeming's early locations were as much as five miles apart, with wilderness between. In a little, however, so rich were the hills, that Ishpeming became a veritable land of locations. They sprouted everywhere, on every hand, putting down their roots, which were shafts, so close together that a man might go down into a hole on one side of town and not come up until he was two miles away.

For fifty miles the Marquette Range bound the Great Cold Lake with an iron collar. These were old hills, ancient hills of an age so great that the first professors to see them—geologists to whom a thousand years is a fraction of a moment—these first learned men afterward told how they felt when confronted by the evidence of Time reaching back almost to infinity. They viewed these old rocks in awed silence and went away to write in their books that here was a part of the original Laurentian Nucleus around which the North American continent was formed. Little wonder they were awed by so vast a birth.

The miners knew nothing of this Laurentian Nucleus and cared less. What they wanted was a whopping big pile of ore; and once the original finds had been made at Negaunee and Ishpeming, they were away over the fifty miles of hills, looking for likely places.

They found them, one after another, and quickly. Run a line generally west from Negaunee and you will mark their trail—Ishpeming, Humboldt, Republic, Champion, Michigamme, Beaufort, almost to L'Anse. All of these were great names once, some of them are today. Many more petered out, soon or late, and the children of miners who worked in them don't know where they are. One would have to leave the highway and dig deep in underbrush and timber to find many a hole that was once a shaft. When a mine is done, the forest quickly takes over.

For almost forty years this range of hills was the biggest producer of iron in the country. A few of the early mines were merely pits, but mostly they were underground. The miners were lowered into them in skips that were little more than big buckets. Down they went, as many as could hang aboard the huge pail, two hundred and more feet, to get beneath the glacial drift that had no good ore in it, down to the black magnetic rock that would catch and hold a wire nail thrown against its face.

The miners wore leather boots. These were important, and so was the proper kind of hat. Through the front of the hat, where a piece of leather was stitched, the miner ran a sharp iron pin, much in the manner of a woman and her hat. Attached to the pin was a Cornish sconce, a candlestick. Before he went down-shaft a miner was given four long candles for the ten-hour shift below.

It was a poor light at best, flickering, dropping hot wax on a man's nose. But the Cornishmen, as well as those Irish who had worked in the salt mines of their native Bear Haven, needed but little light. They could go anywhere in a hole in the ground.

From the main shaft, the miners hacked and drilled their way into tunnels called drifts. Away from the shaft at different levels, but always—or nearly always—leaving plenty of "roof" to support each level, the miners gouged immense rooms, far bigger and vastly more murky than any mine baron could boast of in his Boston or Cleveland mansion.

Some of these great chambers were large enough to hold all the people in Ishpeming, with space left over. They were dim, dark chambers, yet handsome in a hard sort of way when the light shone on them and brought out the black brilliance of the lustrous magnetite ore. Many an Irish miner said he never worked but in black marble halls. But then, the Irish must be poetic, even when they were miners.

This stuff had to be drilled and blasted,[1] to break it up for removal to the surface. In the early days all the drilling was done by hand. It was hard work and quite precise, and the young Irish and Cornish developed arms that were almost as hard as the drills. The preciseness came from hitting the drill fair and at the right time, for two men wielded hammers while a third held the drill.

---

[1] Today, in 1939, housewives of Ishpeming know when it is four o'clock in the afternoon by the shake and rumble that comes from some mine level, perhaps fifteen hundred feet under their kitchens.

The fellow holding the drill had to have confidence in
his hammer men, because a slip might and sometimes
did break an arm into bits. He must also know how and
when to turn the drill to make it bite into the ore. Every
turn of the drill, every blow of the hammers meant just
so much money to men who worked on tonnage, as most
of them did. They got paid for a specific amount of produce, not for putting in time.

It was the same with blasting, once the drilling was
done. The cap had to be bitten firmly to the fuse. The
powder man did this with his jaws, and it was said of
iron miners that they had *copper* teeth, from chewing
down on the caps. Exactly the right amount of powder
must go into a hole. It had to be tamped just so. When a
man was working by the ton, he wanted the stuff cracked
up the right size for easy handling.

The tunnels ran out from the main shaft, and on and
on, following the vein of ore until it played out or a
miner struck his pick plumb through the wall and found
himself looking at another surprised miner working in
another hole.

They didn't stop at the two-hundred-foot level on the
Marquette Range. On they went down to four hundred
feet, five hundred feet, and old-time Cornishmen snorted
that this was no mining at all, this ramming around at a
mere five hundred feet. They said that a man shouldn't
be satisfied until he had dug down to the exact center of
the world; and many hoped to keep on from there and
come out at a spot somewhere on the Rand, near Johan-
nesburg, in South Africa. "I 'ave 'eard they 'ad fine beer
down there," they told one another.

So they kept going deeper on the Marquette. It was
thought something pretty fine when the famous Cliffs

mine got down to one thousand feet; but this was hardly
in a good cool shade. Other and later mines on the Marquette went down three thousand feet.

But even a thousand feet was quite a hole to work in,
in the days before mine ventilation and other improvements came in. The air got pretty heavy down there.
There were no coal gases to contend with, but blasting
made a gas of its own. They called it whitedamp. It
didn't explode. First thing a miner knew, he began to
get sleepy. His head ached. Then, if his candle flickered
out and refused to be relighted, he knew it was time to
get away from there. If he didn't, the whitedamp might
fell him in his tracks like an ox under the hammer.

There were dangers all around in the old days. Little
attention was paid to timbering; a roof might fall any
time without warning. And there was always the menace
of water—water from any of the small lakes, some of
them underground and mysterious, that could pour
water into a chamber and drown a man before he knew
what was happening.

That was why the Irish and Cornish always wanted rats
in a mine. Not all of them would admit it, but all of them
privately believed that rats possessed some extra sense—
something magical, beyond the ken of man—which told
them when any sort of disaster was due in a mine. The
superstition likely stemmed from the ancient belief of
seafaring men that rats will leave a ship which they
"know" is about to start on its last cruise. In any case,
the miners told one another that no rat ever was found
dead in a flooded mine; no rat ever was caught by a
cave-in; no rat's whiskers were ever singed in a mine
fire.

Small boys of Negaunee and Ishpeming and Michi-

gamme used to haunt the barns of the few farmers on
the range to catch rats alive and sell them to men who
worked in a new and ratless mine. The miners, trying to
put a more logical face on it, claimed they liked to have
rats around to clean up the few morsels of food thrown
away at lunchtime; but down in their hearts they believed the rats would somehow warn them of impending
danger. It was a cheap enough charm at ten cents a
head.[2]

Improvements came very slowly at first. If a mine, by
some means or other, did not kill one man a week—in
spite of the rats—it was considered very strange indeed.
The cemetery on Deer Lake road at Ishpeming grew
rapidly, steadily.

It wasn't the underground men alone who got it.
Things could happen up in the open air, in sunlight.
There was that bloody second day of January in 1877,
at the Jackson mine. A crew was unloading cans of nitro-
glycerin near the mine shaft. The locomotive of the
powder train had just been uncoupled and had gone
some two hundred yards down the track when a mighty
plume of flame and smoke belched higher than the
course of birds. All Jackson Mountain rocked as it had
never rocked since man first went there to live. The
blast made small shreds of the three workmen who had
been unloading. It blew the big locomotive off the rails

---

[2] Rats played a big part in mine life on the Marquette. Jim Murphy,
born 1862 in Ishpeming and living there in 1939, recalls how one Perry
Bergen could charm rats. Bergen worked on the fourteenth level of the
old Burt mine. When lunch was over, Bergen would gather the few remnants and whistle in a queer manner. Instantly the rats came flocking in
droves. Other miners might whistle and be damned: the rats paid no
attention, remaining hidden until Bergen—who may have been born in
Hameln—gave his magic call.

and it blew the engineer into Kingdom Come—they never found enough to bury, and they looked hard.

It killed the fireman and switchman. Dan Foley was the switchman. "I saw what had been poor Foley, dead there," recalls John Kelly of Ishpeming. "They had all the pieces in a blanket."

The blast shook windows out of houses at Saginaw Location, six miles away. It brought dishes down with a crash in Ishpeming cupboards. Men on the streets of Marquette, twelve miles off, heard it and wondered what sort of business was afoot back there in the iron hills. A small boy found a big Canada jay dead on the ground, without a mark on him.

That was the kind of stuff miners handled every day. Not even rats could know when it was going to get out of hand.

A majority of the early miners on the Marquette were Cornishmen. Many came direct from the mines in England, although some had stopped awhile in Pennsylvania and Ohio, to work in the coal mines. All of these Cornish were born miners. For generations they had lived much of their lives underground. They were tough and wiry and almost as clannish as the Irish who quickly followed. Cornish worked best when bossed by a Cornish mine captain.

Other than for his ability as a miner, which was so good it was taken for granted, the Cornishman's greatest contribution to life on the range was the pasty. This was a mixture of diced meat and vegetables that was wrapped in a sort of piecrust and baked. It looked like an overgrown apple turnover. A pasty or two and a tin dipper of tea was the Cornishman's invariable midday meal.

When you saw a Cornishman, down in a mine and eating, you could be sure he was eating a pasty.

It was a logical meal, both as to content and as to utility. Here, although nobody had heard of it then, was a balanced ration, proper food for a hard-working man. Warmed on a "miner's stove"—which was a common shovel held over two candles—a thousand feet down in the earth, it came forth hot and appetizing as though direct from the oven. The pasty was quickly adopted by all races who followed the Cornish to the iron ranges.[3]

Everyone called the Cornishmen "Cousin Jacks." In time they applied the name to themselves until it became one word, "cousinjacks," like "damnyankee" in other parts, although with different connotations. "Jack"

---

[3] Because recipes for the genuine Cornish pasty are seldom if ever seen in print, the following is offered. It was supplied to the author by the Rev. Reginald Hicks, now of Milwaukie, Oregon. Mr. Hicks was born in Cornwall of a mining family, and later spent many years in mining towns of the Marquette and Gogebic ranges in Michigan. His recipe:

"Mix 3 heaping cups flour, 2 teaspoons baking powder, one teaspoon salt. Sift into bowl. Add shortening to make a fairly rich paste. Mix with knife or mixer, add water to hold it together. Turn out onto kneading board and roll into lengths of about 12 inches. Cut off a small piece and roll it to thickness of ⅛ inch. Trim to size and shape of a pie plate. Fold over to get the center, then lay flat on board. Now, for the ingredients. Cut 1½ lbs. round or flank steak. Lay beef strips along center and edges of the pasty dough. Slice raw potato thin and lay inside of meat; 2 layers of potato are enough. Add as much sliced onion as desired. (Some use other vegetables.) Then, lay more beef and pork strips crossways of the onion. Salt and pepper. Place 3 small lumps butter on top. Wet edges and seal by crimping. (Care should be taken not to have pasty too full.) Place on cookie sheet or in cake tins and bake in hot oven, 350 to 375 degrees. Lessen heat when pasties start to brown. Bake 50 min. to one hour. If leak occurs, place a little dough on leak."

Warning: Mr. Hicks has often gagged at the very thought of "Cornish pasty" recipes printed by alleged homemakers in the daily press. About everything except whipped cream has been suggested in these ghastly columns.

was a favorite Cornish name, and all Cornishmen had cousins by the score. Cornish mine captains were often charged with gross nepotism, probably justly so.

Germans came to Ishpeming on the heels of the cousinjacks and the Irish. Some of them worked in the mines, but more set up in business. And in the 1880's came a large and sudden influx of Swedes and Norwegians—excellent miners, too, but looked down upon in the early years, as damned furriners, by the Originals, most of whom had been born in Ireland or Cornwall.

Frenchmen from Canada were in the vanguard, at Ishpeming and everywhere else. They weren't natives, yet they weren't damned furriners, either. They were just Canucks, in a class by themselves. And no Jean Baptiste ever was a miner. No hole in the ground for him. The Canucks stayed on the surface and did anything there was to do in the open air—cutting down the forest, making mine timbers, driving horses, everything; and they added much to the color of life with their gaudy mackinaws and fringed sashes and bright toques. They chattered like blue jays as they worked. As for those deep shafts into the ground—well, one old man from three-hours-on-top-Ottawa summed it up. "Man have plaintee tam en de groun' after w'ile," he said.

All these races did not melt so rapidly in the pot as did Ishpeming's iron ore. They worked together in the mines, but socially they lived as far apart as possible, in the early years. The Cornish formed a lodge of the Sons of St. George and had a curling club. The Irish had their Ancient Order of Hibernians, and those in Ishpeming also formed what they were pleased to call St. Patrick's Literary Society, which the local priest frowned upon because he thought it tended to promote alcohol rather

than literature. The Germans, of course, had a singing
society; and in Ishpeming Scandinavians organized in
1886 what possibly was the first ski club in the United
States. There was plenty of ski weather in Ishpeming.

On the feast days of their assorted saints, the clubs
and societies would stage a parade, sometimes winding
up in battle with those who favored other saints. On
every Fourth of July there was sure to be a hand-drilling
contest. This was more important than fireworks or ora-
tions. Negaunee sent its best team of drillers, while other
muscle-bound men came to Ishpeming from the big
mines at Republic and Michigamme.

Three men made a team. While four or five thousand
persons watched and yelled, a team would attack a big
boulder with drill and hammers. There was never a
shortage of boulders to work upon, nor lack of strong
men to drill.

The teams competed at a drilling contest by various
techniques—downward, upward, sideways—and those
who made the deepest hole in a given time were declared
the winners. It was a postman's holiday; but the cheers
of the crowd were sweet, and the prize that bitterness
Cornishmen love so well—a barrel of beer.

Always there was Cornish wrestling. This was no
grunt-and-groan work such as today's professional wrestlers put on. Cornish wrestlers wore short canvas coats,
or jackets, with the edges piped with strong rope. You
couldn't grasp an opponent except at the rope edges.
Rules were strict, and contestants were closely watched
by the "stickler" (referee).

The quick, wiry wrestlers seized each other by the
rope edges of their jackets, then they wrenched, twisted,

tripped. When three points of a man's body touched the ground, he was declared "down."

The Irish sniffed a bit at this kind of sport. They preferred knock-down-and-drag-out fighting; and when they could not get the cousinjacks to fight with them, or when they failed to rouse the steady Scandinavians to battle, they fought joyfully among themselves. One of their fights resulted in murder and riot, going into local history as one of the finest evenings imaginable.

It started at the Iron Puddlers' Ball. At the time, Ishpeming thought it was going to become a metal-making city, and a gang of Irish puddlers had been brought in from Ohio.

Now, iron puddlers considered themselves a race apart, far removed from and far above the lowly miners. They staged their ball at Ishpeming and were chary of invitations, except to the prettiest daughters of miners. But a wild miner named Cummings crashed the gate. He picked the belle of the ball and started in to have a lovely time. A few of the large and very strong puddlers left their partners, escorted Cummings outside the hall, and killed him as quietly as possible. Then the puddlers returned to the dance.

Even a quiet murder becomes known. Before the dance was over, Ishpeming police had learned about Cummings. They raided the dance hall and arrested four puddlers who were said to have had a hand in the killing. By this time the streets were alive with Irish and Cornish miners, bent on revenge. They shouted so loud for puddlers' blood that the cops were alarmed. They hustled the four men into a freight car and hooked on a locomotive, with the idea of taking their prisoners to Marquette City for safekeeping.

The mob swarmed down to the railroad track and all over the police and puddlers. The cops fought bravely, but the miners managed to get one of the suspects into their hands. Somebody said to tie the so-and-so to the track and run over him once with the locomotive—just to give puddlers an idea.

Strong hands held the struggling, screaming puddler while others bound him to the rails. Still others of the mob chased the engineer and fireman from their cab. It was to be a revenge in the manner of melodrama of the day.

But the Ishpeming cops were Irish, too. Battered, bleeding, and outnumbered ten to one, they fought and clubbed like demons, whacking heads right and left and finally getting their prisoner loose from the track. The four puddlers were taken to Marquette, and Ishpeming has never had a lynching.

The town got wild once in a while, but there was always excellent discipline in the mines themselves. The mine captains saw to that. A captain who was worth his ore was a fabulous fellow. Under him were the various shift bosses, and over him was the general mine superintendent. But in reality the captain ran the job. He was the Works, a little less than God but far above man.

Many of the mine captains were cousinjacks. They were always addressed as "captain." To call a mine captain "mister" were like saying "Hey, you!" to a king or a President. Miners touched their hats when they passed them on the street, and many captains grew into legendary characters while they were still alive.

There were Captain Johnson and Captain Duncan, and Captain Collick who designed the famous Cleveland Cliffs Sheet-Iron Sconce, for protecting the flame of candles. One of the very great was Captain Tom Walters, so much revered that his title was applied to his first name. Captain Tom grew to a stature as high as the iron hills into which he sent his hundreds of men. Like all good captains a driver of slaves, Captain Tom never sent a man to work where he would not go himself. In a day when human life was regarded almost not at all, he took safety measures that were years ahead of his time. Captain Tom always used plenty of timbers in his tunnels, too.

Captain Tom was a sort of heretic. He thought that eight hours was long enough for a man to work in a hole. In 1892 he inaugurated an eight-hour experiment at the Lake Angeline mine. Within two months it had proved a success.

Another fabulous character at Ishpeming was Big Dan Donovan. Big Dan was probably the biggest, strongest man ever to drive pick into the Marquette Range. Mike Nevins, still living on the range in 1939, remembers Big Dan. He estimates Dan to have been close to seven feet tall and to have weighed three hundred pounds, none of it fat. But Big Dan wasn't very bright in the head. They didn't want him underground, for a fool in a mine can readily kill an entire crew without half trying.

They set Big Dan to breaking ore on the surface, at the Burt mine, and to loading it into railroad cars. Now, Dan could strike a terrific blow with pick or hammer, a giant's blow, but he didn't know how to strike the ore to break it easily; and Captain John McEncroe had made the rule that no piece of ore that two men could not lift should go into a car. That is, three or more men were prohibited from ganging-up on a tough piece of ore and loading it unbroken. Big hunks would not go through the hoppers at the Marquette docks.

Not long after Big Dan went to work, however, cars that should have been wholly empty were being returned with huge boulders in them—refused at the docks. Captain John stalked up and down the line of ore loaders, pouring his best invective onto them. The men protested that they had not loaded any large chunks. Suspicion fell on Big Dan, who often worked alone.

Captain John set a man to watch. That afternoon he saw Big Dan pound away on a huge hunk of magnetite. Dan struck mighty blows, grunting loud enough to be heard at the dryhouse, a hundred yards away; but the ore remained intact. Big Dan let go an oath as big as the boulder of ore. He threw down his pick. He leaned over and embraced the ore. Calling down all manner of imprecations from St. Patrick, St. Michael, and the Holy Mother of God, he picked up the small mountain of ore and tossed it into the car, which all but bounded from the rails at the impact.

The mystery was solved, and Captain John put Big Dan at other work. Ever a curious man, Captain John had the Dan Donovan Boulder weighed before it was broken up. It tipped the scales, so honest men tell, at four hundred and twenty pounds.

The miners of all races were likely to be very superstitious. Maybe it was because they knew they worked with death all around them and never far off. They were sure that a crying dog meant a sudden death somewhere near. They would never pick up food which dropped from a table, saying that some departed soul wanted it. They firmly believed that the last person to be buried in a cemetery had to carry water for all the other dead to drink until the next corpse arrived.

Until nearly all of the original Irish were dead, they continued the old custom of the three-day wake.[4] Ofttimes they had to shovel themselves out of their own shacks and make a path through the mountainous snow to get to some remote cabin where a wake was to be held; but go they did.

By 1890, however, both the Irish and Cornish were becoming minority groups on the Marquette Range. Of seven hundred miners who applied for naturalization in Ishpeming that year, more than five hundred were Swedes and Norwegians, and one hundred and seventy-five were from Finland. And long before 1890 many of the pioneer Irish and Cornish had packed up and left the Marquette, lured away by tales of newly discovered mines in a range of hills called the Menominee. It was told that the Menominee ore was soft blue stuff that worked easily. A man could make big wages, so the stories went, a-taking of it out on tonnage.

---

[4] Patrick J. Lyons, who was born in Ishpeming of old-country parents, recalls once ribbing his father about the absurdity of wakes. "The old gentleman told me," says Mr. Lyons, "that I had better look up the origin of wakes before passing judgment. He said that many years ago, and before embalming became common, many folks were buried alive. Purpose of the wake was to have someone on watch in the room with the corpse, so that any sign of life could be detected. The old-timers figured that if a body showed no sign of life within three days, it really was a corpse."

5 *Backwoods Gangster*

SOME fifty miles south of the Marquette Range, the Menominee follows much the same contour, forging a second collar of solid iron around Lake Superior. It extends northwest from Vulcan, Michigan, runs through Norway, Quinnesec, and famous Iron Mountain, then into Wisconsin to Florence, and on to Crystal Falls and Iron River, in Michigan again.

The tales the Marquette miners had heard of the new range were only part of the story. It was true there was much fine soft hematite to be dug out of shallow pits; but there was a heap more of it that wasn't soft at all, and it was a long way down. It was just as difficult to get rich swinging a pick on the Menominee as it was on the Marquette.

However, the Menominee had plenty of good soft ore in its early years, and it also had Old Man Mudge.

Old Mudge mined neither in pit nor underground, but he got along famously for years. Mudge mined the miners. His was doubtless the first organized gang to operate in the Great Lakes district, Chicago included, and as for Mudge himself, he was top hellion of all the iron ranges for more than a decade.

Mudge was ahead of his time. Long before Al Capone was born, he had introduced kidnaping and one-way rides into his racket. He bought up or terrorized district attorneys and county sheriffs. He dynamited newspapers and "independent" houses of sin. He built and stocked a central warehouse in which he kept prostitutes for distribution to the various cribs and joints in which he had an interest. His collectors and muscle men roamed everywhere in Mudge "territory," which roughly covered the four hundred miles between the Michigan Soo and Duluth, Minnesota. There was a distinctly modern flavor about Old Man Mudge's mob.

Mudge was attracted to the Upper Peninsula of Michigan in the seventies by the big doings that were then going forward on the Menominee iron range. Iron ore had been discovered there as early as 1867 by the Breen brothers, Thomas and Martley, but nothing much was done about mining until Nelson P. Hulst, young man out of Yale, became engineer for the Milwaukee Iron Company.

Hulst was a genius at picking rich mines out of the ground and developing them. Short, slight, and quiet but tough and wiry as they came, he set out to find ore that would make good iron rails. At Vulcan, Michigan, he discovered outcroppings of an extremely high-grade blue hematite. In the meantime, however, steel rails had come into use through the so-called Bessemer process, and the Milwaukee Iron Company, which had been rolling iron rails, gave up the ghost.

Young Hulst, though, knew he had something. He interested capital in forming the Menominee Mining Company and went back to the new range with men and machinery. The Vulcan panned out big, and so in quick succession did the Cyclops, the Norway, the Quinnesec, the Chapin, and the Florence. With such mountains of ore in sight, a railroad came quickly on the heels of the miners. It was a short haul to Escanaba on Lake Michigan. The Menominee had waited a long time for development, and it came with a bang.

Old Man Mudge heard the bang.

Mudge had another name, doubtless several of them, but he never used them. When he appeared first on the Menominee he was Old Man Mudge, and Old Man Mudge he remained until things caught up with him and he became the late Old Man Mudge.

Of rugged build, Mudge carried his two hundred pounds well; but he somehow had the scandalous appearance of a cross between a tinhorn gambler and a parson. "He tried to look like Henry Ward Beecher," as one ancient who knew Mudge puts it, "but his get-up soured on him. He reminded me more of Cold-Deck John Barrows, who used to ride the Chicago & North Western smoking cars and trim suckers."

Mudge's get-up was rather impressive. He wore a boiled hard shirt, with gates-ajar collar and string tie, a Prince Albert coat with satin lapels, and a high plug hat. He wore these clothes everywhere, night and day, and many thought he slept in them.

His command of language was remarkable and often classic. He could not proffer a cigar without an allusion to Sir Walter Raleigh or Queen Elizabeth; and when he dealt a stud-game every card he laid down was accompanied by a dissertation from the Greek philosophers. His least small-talk was garnished with biblical quotations, some of them rather lewd.

It got around, probably from someone who had known him in the past, that Mudge actually had been a preacher in Indiana and Ohio—that is, a traveling preacher. He never stopped long in a place. He had to travel on account of the women; he was always getting into messes with them, breaking up married couples, seducing young girls, and one thing and another. Somewhere along the line he had paused long enough to marry and to beget a daughter, Mina.

When Mudge first appeared on the Menominee he had Mina with him. Mina was charming. Chase Osborn, an ex-governor of Michigan who now lives at Sault Ste. Marie, remembers her well. "She was a stunning woman," he recalls. "Her concentrated depravity was glossed over by a fine animal figure, a rubescent complexion, semi-pug nose, and lurking gray eyes and sensual lip. Her eyes and a sharpish chin were cruel. She was nothing less than a she-hyena."

Mudge arrived on Michigan's Upper Peninsula some time around 1875. One of his first ventures appears to have been a small fancy house at Manistique, a lumber town, and another at Escanaba. By the time he got to Escanaba, ore was coming down by railroad to that port from the new mines on the Menominee. The railroad also was extending its line westward, to reach still newer mines. Mudge, with daughter Mina, a few other women and his plug-uglies, went out at once along the right-of-way, following close to the end-of-steel, carrying on business in a large tent.

The place fairly teemed with potential customers— five hundred men building a railroad, a couple thousand more digging iron, and perhaps another thousand wild lumberjacks, whacking into the surrounding pine forest. It all stirred the pioneer in Old Mudge.

"Here they were, opening up new country," Mudge later liked to tell in his best platform voice. "Opening up God's great new country. I resolved to help."

The old satyr got around a lot. He was everywhere, talking to everybody, reading all the papers, tracking down every new rumor. He learned that some miles ahead of the railroad builders, across the Wisconsin line, a new town was about to be born. A huge new mine, said shortly to become the biggest producer on the range, was operating a crew, and the town, which was to be called Florence, was building up fast.

Wanting to "help" with all this pioneering, Mudge upped stakes. With Mina and a part of his hellish crew he forged ahead overland, arriving in the new town a few months ahead of the rails.

Mudge surveyed the new layout. It looked pretty good. "Promised land, sir, that's what it was," he afterward liked to relate. Great stock piles of red-blue ore already were waiting for the railroad. The miners were living in bunkhouses; few or none had their families along. Nearby logging camps were going full blast.

First thing Mudge did was to hire a crew of Canuck axmen and boss them himself in putting up what was perhaps the vastest log building ever seen in Upper Michigan. It was on the edge of a cedar swamp, a short mile from town. "I am always," said Old Man Mudge, "discreet."

Experts do not agree on how large the structure was, but all say it was big enough to hold a long bar and goodly dance hall on the ground floor. The upstairs, of course, was cut up into small rooms. The house had framed gables, front and rear. It was pretty swell, but Old Mudge was modest about it. "I regret," he said, "that it wholly lacks a Greek influence. I should have liked at least a portico with Doric columns."

Around this immense den of sin Mudge and his merry

men built a high-peaked stockade such as was used
against Indians in the old days. There were two gates
large enough for teams to enter, a stable for the Mudge
horses, and a hitching shed where the carriage (and
sleigh) trade might blanket their animals.

When construction was about finished, Mudge went
away for a few days, returning with half a dozen more
women and closely followed by several teamloads of
hard liquor. With the booze unpacked and the girls in
their war paint, Mudge let it be known that his place of
"entertainment and refreshment" was ready. As a final
touch he arranged one of the best advertisements of all
time, a ballyhoo that has come down the years and is still
talked about by miners too old to dig iron and much,
much too old to dance with partners such as Mudge
supplied.

Old Mudge got four of the largest timber wolves ever
beheld—hulking, great gray fellows, big as Newfound-
lands and shaggy as Shetland ponies. He staked these
animals just inside the main gate, where they might howl
and rattle their chains but could harm no one.

The entire Mudge layout was stupendous and elegant,
for the time and place. The chained wolves were a stroke
of pure genius. A hungry wolf will howl, and Old
Mudge, who fed the animals in person, wearing his
Prince Albert and plug hat the while, gave them just
enough to keep them in a howling mood. They made an
advertisement that soon was talked of all over the Menominee and even up north in the copper country. Old
men vow it was a sight to see—Old Mudge stalking across
the glistening white yard, great hunks of raw venison in
his hands, his silk hat tilted back, in the eerie light of a
full and cold Wisconsin moon, while the chains clanked

and frost crackled like gunfire all along the peaked stockade.

The legend grew up—and it will not down—that Mudge kept the wolves to frighten his girls from making any attempt to escape, and that the stockade had been erected for the same purpose; viz., to prevent the poor little white slaves from getting away from that nasty, heartless Old Mudge.

It is a nice fairy story, and thus will always be believed, despite the fact that old-timers, who knew the joint, have pointed out that the wolves were so chained that they could get at nobody; and that the stockade was merely a businesslike method by which Mudge could keep track of the number of visitors (all entered through the main gate) and make sure that none of his gang was holding out on him.

Once Mudge had set up his place and the railroad had come to town, Florence,[1] went into its brief lurid heyday. Mina, the beautiful she-hyena, was in charge of the girls. One Pat McHugh, an ugly customer, acted as Mudge's lieutenant. The Old Man had to be away a part of the time, opening new brothels here and there along the new range railroad, collecting from established houses, and "seeing" officials who might cause trouble if not properly handled.

It was Mudge's order that in none of the places operated by his mob was a district attorney, high sheriff, or any judge or police chief to be permitted to *pay* for liquor or for enjoying the company of the Mudge houris. It was all free, to "reasonable" officials. And to those of-

---

[1] Named, ironically enough, for a very lovely pioneer woman. She was Mrs. Florence Terry Hulst, wife of Nelson P. Hulst who is credited with doing most to bring the Menominee Range into being.

ficials, if there were any, who did not drink and did not care for dancing, the Old Man made substantial and continuous gifts in cash. He had little trouble with the law. It was the newspapers that harassed him most.

At Manistique, Michigan, the editor of the *Pioneer* was Major Clarke, Civil War veteran and a tough old rooster. He attacked the Mudge gang in print and called for their suppression. One day in 1883 Mudge made a special trip to Manistique. The *Pioneer's* office exploded with sudden flame that night and was destroyed by the fire.

By now the Mudge Administration, as it was cynically known, was a real power. Murders were fairly frequent. When any official was so careless as to allow a complaint to turn into an indictment, witnesses disappeared overnight and were never seen again. The box stoves in fancy houses running in opposition to Mudge took to blowing up without warning. Sheriffs left town without bothering to turn in their badges. Then came the Dickinson affair.

Captain William E. Dickinson, in charge of the Commonwealth mine two miles out of Florence, was a brave man who had come from the comparatively orderly Marquette Range. He was disgusted with the Mudge regime and resolved to clean it up and out. He sent word to the Old Man to move on.

A few days later the mine captain's small son Willie disappeared. The captain received an anonymous message to the effect that if he did not behave, he would never see his Willie again.

Captain Dickinson employed spies inside the Mudge gang. He hired detectives and spent a small fortune running down any clue. All the clues led nowhere. Young

Willie was never found. It is the Charlie Ross case of the
Upper Peninsula. The oldest miners still speak of little
Willie Dickinson and wonder what was his end.

The Dickinson affair proved to be the undoing of Old
Mudge and his organization. The kidnaping aroused a
small but determined group of Florence citizens to action. Among them were Charley Noyes of the sheriff's
office and his brother Bill, an able man anywhere; the
Rev. Harlan P. Cory of the local Presbyterian church;
Chase Osborn, who had started a paper in Florence and
was attacking Mudge in print; and one Rolbstell, a little
chap who ran a hardware store and was tough enough to
chew the nails he sold. These men and a few more held
a secret meeting in Florence one night and organized the
Citizen Regulators.

After perfecting their plans, the Regulators served notice on the district attorney and sheriff of Florence that
they had better clean up the Mudge gang—or else. This
brought on an argument between the two men, each
seeking to blame the other for "lax enforcement," which
wound up in a real old Western gunfight. They shot it
out in the street, and the sheriff got a bullet through his
lungs.

Next, the Regulators sent young Osborn, the newspaper editor, to see Governor Rusk at Madison. Held up
by Mudge men at the point of a gun, Osborn was taken
to Iron Mountain and thrown into jail. No charges were
placed against him; it was simply strong-arm work. A
lawyer friend got Osborn released, and the young man
finally got to the Wisconsin capital. The governor was
helpful. He promised to send troops if necessary, and he
appointed a new district attorney, an honest man, to fill

the place of the Mudge tool who had fled town after shooting the sheriff.

But the Regulators were now strong, and spoiling for battle. They couldn't wait for the Law. They held a special meeting, and when they came out of the hall it was seen that all of them were armed, some with rifles, others with blacksnake whips. It was to be a great day in Florence.

The Regulators went to the attack promptly and with what must have been considerable gusto. They first drove all the Mudge pimps off the streets, making them step lively from stings of the long whips. One of the Mudge lads started to draw, but thought better of it when a .45 slug turned his hat halfway around on his head.

With the streets cleared, the Regulators proceeded to the Mudge stronghold. The Old Man had been warned of the coming hurricane and had done everything he could to batten down his hatches—bolting the gates, piling furniture against the doors, and arming his crew. The wolves rattled their chains and whimpered miserably.

The Regulators went to the assault in force, knocking in the gates and breaching the stockade. They yelled bloody murder and shot out every pane of glass in the fine gable windows. They piled on, into the big house, whipping the startled women, who were reported to have cursed most horribly, and taking shots at the bartenders and bouncers.

For the moment, Old Mudge disappeared. The men and women, with Mina lugging a sack of money, ran screaming into the swamp. Even Pat McHugh, the boss bully, took it on the lam, with Bill Noyes of the Regulators close at his heels, both men shooting wildly. Noyes ran him down and brought him in a captive, ready for a trip to the state pen (for "carrying concealed weapons"). The rest of the mob, both men and women, left town without further hint.

What became of Old Man Mudge is a mystery to this day. He disappeared that day and has never since been seen, not even a plug hat or Prince Albert coat remaining. There are rumors that he escaped and made his way to Alaska; that he went to Nevada; that he was killed in some sort of scrape in Chicago.

But certain old-timers vow that an inner circle of the Regulators led the old hellion out into the cedar swamp, that day, shot him full of holes, and buried him so deep that not even his great gray wolves could have found him. What became of the wolves isn't known either. It was the end of organized gangsterism on the Menominee Range.

6 *The Wild Ore Trimmers*

OLD MUDGE might come and Old Mudge might go, but the millions of tons of the Menominee's red-blue ore continued to roll their way down to water at Escanaba. Here, on a flinty flat spit of ground at the mouth of Little Bay de Noc, a few huddled shacks and a sawmill grew suddenly into Lake Michigan's biggest ore-shipping port.

Before the Menominee Range was opened, considerable ore from the Jackson and other mines of the Marquette came to Escanaba by way of the Peninsula Railroad. For several years, in fact, Escanaba liked to call itself the Iron Port of the World, and local journalists wrote reams of copy to compare their city most favorably with the ancient iron cities of Spain. Local bards put their town into verse that was as purple as the ore that went over Escanaba's docks. It is passing strange that none of them ever paid homage to Escanaba's men of iron—the ore trimmers.

Ore trimmers considered themselves a race apart; they were an aristocratic clan of working stiffs who looked down upon miners, mechanics, locomotive engineers, and such riffraff. They had their own tight little union that amounted almost to a guild. A man just didn't step out onto the dock at Skin-ah-by, as they called it, and say he wanted to be an ore trimmer and proceed to work. Hardly. No candidate for admission to a secret order was ever more thoroughly investigated, and tried, as he who would become a trimmer.

Ore trimming, they said at Skin-ah-by, was a science, the science of loading a ship to an even keel. Trimmers were jealous of their jobs and took as much pride in their work as any handcraftsman.

Ore cars from the mines ran out onto the long docks and dumped the stuff into pockets, hoppers. When a ship came alongside, pockets were opened and the ore tumbled down a chute into the hold. It was the work of the trimmers to pack and level the stream of ore as it poured through the hatches of the ship.

Stripped to the waist and wearing a cap and leather boots, the trimmers went down into the hatches, armed with pick and shovel. Here they performed like clock-work. That is, clockwork to the accompaniment of some of the most elegant profanity ever heard. It was said that uptown, a mile away, folks could hear the lewd cries of the trimmers above the pounding of the ore as it rum-bled out of the dock pockets.

With plumb bob and measuring tape in hand, the boss trimmer stood above the hatch, gauging the height of the ore, yelling bloody hell for more here, more there, keeping all points in the hold evenly packed and filled. When a job was finished it had to appear as smooth and level as a dance floor, with no loose or open spots be-neath. Ancient ex-trimmers today, forty years afterward, point to the record with pride. They brag that in the days of wooden ore carriers, nary a ship was ever lost, or even in trouble, because of a shifted cargo. Pure sci-ence, m'lad.

It may have been science, and it surely was work.

Shoveling ore isn't like shoveling earth, as many a man has learned. Picture a spadeful of lead and you have an idea. Yes, trimming was likely as hard a job as any in the mines whence the ore came or in the blast furnaces whither it went. A few years spent as a trimmer developed men until all had physical traits in common. They looked to be mostly arms and shoulders, with heads set fair on shoulders without any neck between—something of a cross between a gorilla and a professional wrestler.

Trimmers never worked for wages, and none of them ever knew or talked about a "workday." They had no workday. They were paid by the ton, and they worked constantly so long as a ship in the harbor waited for ore. It was the same, morning, noon, midnight. Working a twenty-four-hour spell was a common thing, and no trimmer was considered to be of full stature until he had put in a forty-eight-hour shift in the hatches, stopping only to gobble a quick bite of cold bread and a dipper of tea.

Every last thing the trimmers wore or possessed, at home or at work, was stained deep red from the ore. Just a common hot-water bath, with much soap, made no inroads on the skin of a man who had trimmed a ship. Clothing, bedding, tablecloths, furniture, carpets and even pipes and tobacco were dyed the Menominee color. Men quickly gave up the idea of getting free of iron during the season, and housewives hung out lines of wash that seemed not to have been washed at all.

The ore trimmers' season was the same as that of shipping on the Great Lakes. Average was seven months; but, one glorious year that was long remembered, the ice broke up on March 6 and the Lakes remained open until January 5.

Trimmers earned astonishingly high pay for the eighties and nineties. Fifteen hundred dollars was considered a fair but not a top income for seven months. Many made two thousand in an average season. Some raised the total to twenty-five hundred, which was probably a record.

The pay, as said, was by the ton, and the pay-off came immediately a ship had been loaded. This was called a "reckoning," and the money was paid out to the men, all at the same rate, by the boss trimmer. The boss not only supervised the actual loading of a boat; he also solicited business from the ship captains. In the old days of individualism, a hundred different shipping lines, with no interlocking directorates, called at Escanaba for ore. Some of the lines might consist of a single ship—an old tub at that. It was up to the boss trimmers to be on good terms with as many ship captains as possible, for the captains were empowered to hire trimmer crews and to pay off the boss trimmer, on the spot, in gold. Thus, a boss trimmer who not only could produce a gang of trimmers when needed but was genial and well liked by captains was assured of his share of the work. It was rumored, too, but never proved, that certain boss trimmers, in a rush season, received a furtive bonus for favoring some captain in the matter of speedy work. One judges from the reputation of the trimmers that no boss was ever caught at such skulduggery. He would have been killed.

The waiting ships took their turn at the docks in the order of their arrival in the harbor. This rule proved workable most of the time; but on occasion, when two and sometimes three ships hove in close together, there was dispute and battle, the rival crews of trimmers taking sides with the vessels they hoped to load. On the whole, though, what fighting the trimmers did was as individuals, not gangs. Much of it occurred after a big reckoning. The gold and silver was paid out at the saloons favored as headquarters by the various gangs. The sight of the hard metal often called for whisky, which often called for a fight.

Pete Walsh's saloon near the docks was headquarters for one crew. Another used John Cahill's place; still another held forth at Gannon's joint. These are Irish names, and most but not quite all the trimmers had been born in Ireland. In time they allowed perhaps half a dozen Swedes to join their union, and a few French-Canadians. The Swedes they called Roundheads; [1] the French were Canucks, or Frogs.

The Irish trimmers were great for nicknames. Hardly a man was without one. There was the Rabbit, whose real name is not remembered, if ever it was known. The Rabbit in cold weather, when not actually working, would stand and stamp his foot, stiff-legged, in the manner of a wild hare. In time he developed notable leg muscles which could deliver powerful kicks when there was trouble at Walsh's place. But kicking wasn't much thought of. Only "Frogs" stooped to it.

Paddy the Rip was another wild tarrier. It was said he lived wholly on iron ore and alcohol, but some old-timers think this is an understatement. "Paddy the Rip didn't need no ore to eat, so long as he had whisky," they say.

And there was Yank Sullivan. No Yankee, he got his name when he yanked a fellow trimmer out of the bay and saved his life.

---

[1] Lumberjacks always have termed Swedes Squareheads.

A noted fight, still told of in Escanaba saloons when a March wind drives old-timers to cover, was that between Mike Gannon and one Bonner. No animosity entered it. It occurred right after the world's championship fight at Carson City, when Bob Fitzsimmons beat Gentleman Jim Corbett. Neither Gannon nor Bonner had seen the fight, but Bonner had read an account of it in the paper and was trying to show Gannon, who couldn't read, the high lights of the scrap.

"It wint like this," said Bonner, and he made a mighty pass at Gannon. It broke four of Gannon's ribs.

Stories differ as to what happened next, but the results were beyond question. All the windows and furniture in the place were broken, the stovepipe crashed, the stove was overturned and started a fire that required a call by the Escanaba department. The stove went over when Bonner, in fine form by then, made another pass at Gannon but hit the stove, suffering a compound fracture of his left forearm. . . . Ore trimmers didn't need movies or golf; they composed their own entertainment as they went along.

They had a lot to talk about, too. There was the time one of the long docks burned and put men out of work for months. No trimmer was to blame; it took worthless sailors to wreck a man's living. The fire started in an old wooden ore schooner, the *Nahant*, when two drunken members of the crew came back late from a wild evening on Escanaba's Thomas Street. They got into a fight, tipped over a lantern, and the ship went up in flames, burning the two sailors and much of the docks.

Once only, and late in their career, did the trimmers really have serious trouble. It had an up-to-date flavor about it. One O'Brien, president of the Escanaba ore trimmers' union, was sent to Cleveland to negotiate a scale of pay for the coming season. Instead, O'Brien is said to have made a deal to start a brand-new union, one that would trim ore for less than the established group was demanding.

O'Brien returned to Escanaba, announced the rates to be paid, and started to sign up trimmers in a union of his own devising. O'Brien must have suffered from a lapse of memory. He surely knew that his old union was composed of the Gallaghers, the Sullivans, the Reillys, and similar Celts. The new union didn't get very far.

The rumpus began promptly with clashes between the dual unions. There was a lot of clubbing and some shooting. And then, one afternoon, a gang of the Originals caught sight of O'Brien as he was leaving Vasso's barber shop. Escanaba's police got the riot call too late. When they arrived O'Brien was ready for ten months in a hospital and nobody on the street seemed to know who had prepared him.

Although trimmers never sailed the Lakes and didn't think highly of the men who did, they liked to discuss the merits and defects of the ships they loaded and trimmed. The old wooden schooners, with their sails, made a pretty picture in Escanaba harbor, thirty, forty of them at a time; but most trimmers preferred working the steamboats. There was the famous "Iron" series of carriers—the *Iron Duke*, the *Iron Age*, the *Iron Cliff* —which could take 2,000 tons aboard and were considered the last word in size and efficiency in the eighties.

Then came the Red Bellies, as the first of the larger steam carriers were known, great steel arks in which you could trim no less than 6,000 tons of ore: ships like the

Andrew Carnegie, 400 feet long and with 21 hatches, and the *Sir Henry Bessemer,* which took 7,000 tons in its belly, and was away down the Lakes with black smoke pouring out over her wake. "Like Dewey a-headin' into Manila Bay," said the admiring trimmers.

These giants were a long way from the old *Inter-Ocean,* the vessel that went to the bottom of Escanaba harbor when an extra large hunk of ore went through her hatch and on through her wooden bottom.

The big new boats had many wide hatches that made for nice easy trimming, and even larger boats were on the way—but the ore trimmers would not load them. Their huge size and the steel industry's continuous mania for speed did away with the ore trimmers.

Back there in Pittsburgh and Youngstown, even in comparatively near Chicago, the steel workers were howling for more ore, and faster. The Red Belly fleet grew in size and capacity. Then, it had to happen: Inventive mechanics who had no respect for the ore trimmers' short-bladed shovel and pick got busy. They devised a bumper beam to deflect a stream of ore to the exact place it was needed to keep the cargo on even keel. Ships were made with more hatches, closer together; the bumper beam was operated by steam and could work forever without tiring, while a trimmer had to stop once in a while for a bite and a snifter. The red-blue Menominee ore couldn't tumble out of the dock pockets fast enough to make the bumper beam sweat.

So, the mighty men of the ore-trimming gangs, the nearest thing to a guild in the iron industry, passed out of existence. They didn't disappear all at once, but by the century's turn the washings hung out over Escanaba's back yards showed little trace of raw iron.

7 *Old Stuntz Cruises the Hills*

AT ABOUT the same time Old Man Mudge and his gang were going great guns in Florence and along the Menominee, a mining captain turned prospector discovered still another segment in the iron collar around the Great Cold Lake. Near what is now Bessemer, Michigan, Captain N. D. Moore put down a test pit and came up with some pretty fine ore. A few months later J. Landseer Norrie sunk a shaft not far off that became the Ashland mine, a big producer. And then, seemingly an integral part of any picture with ore in it, John M. Longyear of Marquette showed up in the new country.

Miners could be sure that whenever John Longyear was seen tramping the hills with his compass, a new iron range was about to be uncovered in a big way. Longyear never was a pioneer, nor was he ever very late; he always got there when things were ripe. After exploring the Marquette in the early seventies, he had moved over to the Menominee. He struck rich ore on both ranges. By the time the Menominee got into its full stride in 1880, Longyear struck out again, this time farther west, locating mines and getting land options in the range of hills Norrie and Captain Moore were finding good. Six months later these hills were recognized as a new iron range, the Gogebic.

The Gogebic wasn't to be a very extensive range, but

there was a lot of ore in it. It runs today some twenty miles from Wakefield in Michigan to the Atlantic mine, just west of Hurley, Wisconsin.

Ironwood, Michigan, immediately became the metropolis of the new range, growing up, as other range towns before it, in the center of many shafts. The Gogebic ore was rather deep. The great Newport mine, opened in 1886, was soon down to the 2,300-foot level and producing a million tons of ore annually. The East Norrie mine was taking out half as much. At Wakefield, pioneer town of the range, the strangely named Sunday Lake mine, and the Mikado and the Castille shafts, became heavy producers late in the century. Across the Montreal River from Ironwood, the lovely town of Hurley, Wisconsin, soon grew into its dual importance—as a mining town in its own right, and as a Mecca for miners seeking entertainment.

Both the Cornish and the Irish came to the Gogebic to dig, just as they had done on the other two ranges; but now, in the mid-eighties, they were far outnumbered by the Scandinavians, the Finns and a conglomeration of races even then on the way from Eastern Europe.

Other new things were happening, or were about to happen. Hand drilling became an exception. Drills operated by compressed air sent through miles of pipe and hose were common in the underground mines on the three ranges.

Electricity was coming in. As early as 1879 one of Mr. Edison's new incandescent lamps had been tried out in the Lake Superior mine at Ishpeming and was "giving the best of satisfaction." Now, in the eighties, the magic juice was being used to light the shafts and the main levels, and a bit later to operate the underground ore railroads, thus moving thousands of mules up into fresh air to get their first look at sunlight in many years.

The old candle and sconce disappeared, to be replaced by neat carbide lamps attached to the front of miners' hats. . . . They liked to have blinded the owlish old micks and cousinjacks who had done all their work to the flickering wax or tallow.

Mine cages by which men were lowered to work ceased to be haywire death traps. The new cages were large, substantially built, and for the most part safely operated. The old "system" of mine signals—the yanking of ropes, or mere yelling—was supplanted by an elaborate system of electric bells, plus a standard and printed code.

In earlier days there was little organization in a mine crew; it was a hodgepodge of labor who did this, did that and the other thing. In a shift of ten hours a man might work at three or four quite different jobs.

The new machinery brought about what experts term "technological organization"; men had specific jobs to tend to. There were the general superintendent and the master mechanic, who had a hand in nearly everything; then, the mine captain, still great but of not quite the godlike stature he once possessed, and his shift bosses; the miners, both drillers and powder men; the muckers; the track layers and cleaners; the pumpmen and the plumbers; the skip tenders; the samplers; and a miscellaneous crew of timber hoisters. On the surface were the timber framers, the carpenters, machinists, blacksmiths, electricians and engine-room men. In time, even, there was a safety man. Not all these occupations came into being at once, but they all followed close on the heels of the new mine machinery.

Huge ore crushers hulked high near every shaft. Into these the mechanical skips hoisted the ore to be crushed and dropped into railroad cars, ready to roll to the docks. . . . No place for Big Dan Donovan who broke ore with pick and hammer and, if he couldn't break it that way, picked up the entire hunk and heaved it into the car.

The Machine Age, indeed, arrived on schedule, ready to handle the really *big* strikes of ore just ahead.

The first of these new finds had been made twenty years before; but finders on the iron ranges have seldom been keepers, and in the case of poor old George Stuntz it was almost two decades before he could find anybody even to *look* at what he had discovered, and then to take and keep it. Few prospectors have had to wait so long.

George Stuntz was never to make any money out of mining or out of anything else, but he was the recognized Nestor of the Head of the Lakes—the Old Man of the Mountain, the man who was there before the Indians, the hills, before even the lake itself—a frost-nipped, fly-bitten yet genial soul who figured a January as unseasonably warm if the thermometer went up to thirty degrees below zero.

Stuntz liked wild country. He had probably surveyed more of it than any man living. When he had finished running lines in the new Wisconsin, he noted that half a dozen settlers had moved into the northern part of the state and built cabins. This was becoming altogether too populous for Stuntz. He threw his few belongings into a canoe and struck out as far west as he could go, which turned out to be Minnesota Point on Lake Superior, where Duluth would be in good time.

With his headquarters on the lake shore, Stuntz, still surveying for the Government, started blocking out the township lines of Minnesota. When he wasn't actually surveying, he spent his time simply ranging through the virgin timber. He got to know the country better than the red men did. When he wasn't cruising, he half-heartedly operated a small trading post on the Point.

Along in the mid-sixties a State geologist, who had been ranging around in northeastern Minnesota, came out of the woods to report indications of gold in the Lake Vermilion district. A rush started, with Stuntz in the vanguard. He didn't stay long. He knew something about minerals, and he soon came to the conclusion that there wasn't any gold around Vermilion; but he discovered a lot of ground that he thought was composed chiefly of iron ore. He put fifty pounds of it into his turkey and packed it out to Duluth.

After thinking the matter over several months, Stuntz took his sack of ore and went on to Astoria, Long Island, where he showed his find to General Sargent, who had been in charge of the Wisconsin survey on which Stuntz had worked. The general thought it was iron, too. He gave Stuntz a letter of introduction to the eminent Jay Cooke of Philadelphia and New York, by all odds the greatest financier of the day.

Cooke listened while the lean-bellied man from the back country told of mountains of iron ore up there north of Lake Superior. "All it needs," Stuntz said, "is a short railroad—not more'n seventy miles of it."

Mr. Cooke was interested enough to promise Stuntz he would make a trip to Duluth to consider the matter. He did so, appearing there in good time and in a tall plug hat and the general atmosphere of vast wealth, passing out two-bit pieces to small boys and gaping red men. It was a wonderful day for Duluth. The great man from the halls of gold said without qualification that he would at once start construction of a railroad from Lake Superior to the new iron range at Lake Vermilion. Then he went away, and Duluth went on a stupendous drunk.

By the time Duluth had recovered somewhat from its celebration, the house of Jay Cooke & Company had blown sky-high and the Panic of 1873 was in full swing. Banks all over the country closed their doors, and so did most of the country's iron and steel mills. The population of Duluth dropped in a few weeks from 6,000 to less than half that number.

It was a terrific blow to Duluth and no less a blow to George Stuntz. Stuntz had no money to spend on eastern trips in a try to interest other capital. He had, however, interested George Stone, Duluth business man, in the project. With a sack of ore toted out from Vermilion by Stuntz, Stone went East and to Pottsville, Pennsylvania, where lived the very remarkable Charlemagne Tower, already a millionaire. Stone showed Mr. Tower the ore and told him the simple need for a railroad to make everybody rich.

Mr. Tower was a man of parts, and a gambler, too, but he called in Professor A. H. Chester, geologist of Hamilton College, to look closely at the cards. Mr. Tower asked the professor to go West with Stone and look over the iron mountains. He had a lot of faith in Chester. "If they look good to you," he said, "go ahead and buy them, and we'll see about a railroad."

At Duluth Stone turned the professor over to Stuntz, who took him to a place just south of Vermilion Lake. Stuntz revealed the ore, a whole mountain of it, just as he had said, and after spending some weeks on the new range, Professor Chester went East to report to Mr. Tower. The report was very favorable, and Tower immediately formed a company and sent his son, Charlemagne, Jr., to oversee the operations. Tower Junior retained Stuntz to buy land for the company, paying him eight dollars a day.

George Stuntz did his work faithfully, grabbing off 17,000 acres of what turned out to be the best mineral land on the range for the modest price of but $40,000. Then, the aging surveyor—still a mighty hard man to follow in rough country—whacked a trail through the wilderness and took in provisions for a crew of test-pit men, along with buckets, windlasses, and plenty of powder. Still working for his eight dollars a day, Stuntz next located the misnamed Duluth & Iron Range Railroad which didn't touch Duluth at all but started into the forest at the port of Two Harbors, some twenty-five miles east of Duluth.

It was a heartbreaking job, building that seventy miles of road to the new range. It was as tough country as railroaders ever found east of the Rockies, anywhere, and every mile of it cost a fortune. George Stone had sunk what money he had into it. The senior Tower put three million dollars of ready cash into it, then mortgaged himself to raise another million. The old man was game, although by the time the road was ready for use in 1884, he wasn't just sure but that it had ruined him.

The first mine opened on the Vermilion was the Soudan, and there were big doings on June 30 when the first train of Minnesota ore ever loaded was put into the cars. A hundred Chippewa braves, decked out in paint and feathers, put on a dance. Charlemagne Tower, Jr., spoke a few well chosen words, and Captain Elisha Morcum, the Cornish mine boss who dropped his *h*'s fearfully enough to be heard two rods away, wheeled the first barrow of ore from dump to car. That afternoon the first trainload of ore [1] rocked and rumbled down over the seventy miles of new railroad to Lake Superior. Two weeks later the steamer *Hecla*, with barge, left Two Harbors for Cleveland. Henceforth, Minnesota would compete with Michigan and Wisconsin.

The Messrs. Tower and Stone had gambled well. The Vermilion Range extended only fifteen miles, but its mines paid out enormously. They paid the gamblers back their four million dollars in almost no time at all, with another four million dollars for good interest.

As for fly-bitten, frost-nipped old George Stuntz, he got his eight dollars a day while he worked, and that was all. If ever he complained of being entirely left out of the huge fortunes he had made possible, it seems not to be of record. Old-timers say Stuntz wasn't much interested in money, anyway, or in ore. Once the railroad was completed, he turned his attention to certain prehistoric mounds he had discovered in his roaming, the work of some unrecorded race of men long dead. Stuntz himself died broke, but not before he had prepared a paper about his beloved mounds for the Minnesota Academy of Natural Sciences. He was that kind of man. Anyhow, they named a town in Minnesota for Stuntz, and he had his eight dollars a day while he made fortunes for others. It was enough for a Nestor at the Head of the Lakes.

---

[1] Thomas Owens, who was still living at Two Harbors, Minn., in 1938, was engineer of the train that brought the first load of ore from the Vermilion Range. He reports the Duluth & Iron Range R.R. to have been rough riding in its early years.

Mining the Vermilion wasn't easy work. Geologically, it is the oldest of the ranges, dating from a period almost beyond the conception of man. Much of the ore from the western end of the range was the hardest ever taken out of the ground. Working with a high-powered drilling machine, it took miners one hour to drill eighteen inches into the Soudan ore. At Ely, a bare fifteen miles away, they could drill eighteen inches in a minute.

On the Vermilion as on the other ranges, mine locations soon grew into small cities—Tower, Soudan, and Ely. Soudan had the most ore, it turned out, but Ely was the liveliest town.

Even before the railroad was finished, a rush of all sorts of people had come to the new range, and the first trains came in loaded with millionaires and bums and working stiffs and tinhorn gamblers. At Ely the late and beauteous Daisy Redfield came to open one of the swellest honky-tonks of the iron country. It was really very elegant for the back country, with plush furniture and crimson bedspreads, and a large dance hall with mirrors. Just before she held her formal opening, Daisy sent neat printed invitations to every male in town, married or not, describing in delicate but quite understandable language the delights she and her rare charmers had to offer. It created a mild scandal that doubtless helped business.

In a little while Ely's reputation for open sin became such that an ex-ballplayer down in Chicago heard of it. Billy Sunday came to hold one of his first great revivals in Ely, using for a ballyhoo his great desire to "save" Daisy Redfield and her poor little white slaves. When the Reverend Billy had departed, Daisy, who of course continued in business at the old stand, was heard to make a remark that became classic on the range. It was to the effect that Sunday had done her work more good "than a whole free barrel of sloe gin woulda."

In its first twenty-five years of existence, the little Vermilion Range produced better than thirty million tons of high-grade ore. More important to the iron and steel industry of the United States, however, was the fact that the Vermilion excitement brought about discovery of a newer range that was to produce more iron than all the other ranges put together; in fact, what was to be the greatest body of ore in the world, anywhere and at any time, before or since.

8 *Saga of the Merritt Boys*

IN THE no-good gold rush to Vermilion Lake in 1865, nobody brought back any gold; but one of the rushers named Lewis Merritt scooped up a handful of dull red dust he found there and took it to his homestead on the edge of the forest at Oneota, near what was about to be the city of Duluth.

Merritt was a timber cruiser and landlooker, and all his seven rugged sons were taught the science of running lines and estimating timber on the hoof, where it stood. The small package of red ore was kept in the Merritt cabin for many years, and every once in a while old Lewis would get it out. He'd sift the heavy grains through his fingers and tell his boys that some day iron would be a great thing in Minnesota. "Somebody will find it," he said, "and it will open up the country." He advised his boys always to keep a sharp eye on the ground as well as on the trees. All the Merritts had keen eyes—at least in the woods they knew so well.

The elder Merritt must have expected great things of his seven sons, for he gave them names of splendid and ancient glory. There were Leonidas and Napoleon, Jerome and Cassius, Alfred and Lucien, and Lewis the younger—names fit for king or consul, names to please either a Gibbon or a Bonaparte. Jerome went to teaching school and died young, while Lucien became a preacher who could sweat the brimstone out of any backwoods sinner. As for the rest of the boys, they were known as able men in the woods anywhere, lads who could walk into a timbered "forty" and tell almost to an inch how many board feet of lumber it contained.

The boys had a chance to do plenty of cruising. The big woods of Michigan were thinning out. Daylight was getting into the swamp, back there on the Tittabawassee, the Flint, and the Muskegon. Timber barons of Saginaw and Detroit were looking for new stands to buy, or, better still, to hornswoggle out of easily corrupted legislatures. Or, they might hire a pack of "homesteaders" to file on land, then turn it over for a few dollars. Such doings kept the five Merritt brothers, and three or four sons and nephews of Merritts, busy ranging through the vast forests of pine in northeastern Minnesota.

The elder Merritt died in 1880, but the boys did not forget the package of iron dust the old man had brought back from the Vermilion fifteen years before. They continued to cruise white pine, and to cruise it well, and wherever they went they looked hard at rocks.

Then came the railroad and the opening of the Vermilion iron range; this was the very country where the elder Merritt had found the red stuff. The Duluth region went crazy about ore. Every train to the new boom town of Tower brought hundreds of prospectors.

In their years of running lines and looking at timber, the Merritt boys had often talked about the queer range of rocky hills that stretched for some fifty miles across northeastern Minnesota. Whenever they camped there, they pawed around, digging earth from beneath the pine needles which covered everything a foot thick. Indians

called these hills the Mesabi,[1] the "height of land," and
the Merritts came to the conclusion that here was the
place to look for more of the same stuff that was making
the Vermilion country, farther north and east, rich—or,
at least was making somebody rich; trains piled high
with ore were rolling down to Two Harbors every day
in the week.

Once the boys had made up their minds about the
Mesabi, they gave all their spare time to investigating it.
Here and there they dug into heavy soil they thought
contained iron—but not quite what they thought good
ore looked like. Getting warm, though. They hacked a
trail through from Tower, at the end of the Vermilion
railroad, and brought in wagons, tools, and a test-pit
crew—men to dig holes where the ground looked likely
and take samples of the soil.

The heavy wagons rumbled slowly, for it was tough
going and the wheels sunk deep into the forest floor;
they sunk deep enough in one place to bring the caravan
to a full stop. The churning wheels threw up leaves and
pine needles and roots, and finally some soft powdery
stuff of a dull red color.

The Merritts liked the look of this soil. It hefted well,
too; heavy as lead. But they thought it too fine, too
dusty, too loose to be iron. Iron was something *hard,*
something you had to drill and to blast out with dynamite, the way they were doing on the Vermilion and the
other ranges. But this soft red stuff might be a good sign
—an "indication," prospectors called it.

The Merritts were wise enough, at this stage, to realize they were timber cruisers and not experts on ore.

[1] Also spelled Mesaba, Missabi, etc.

After they had dug around a good deal, they brought in an experienced mining man, Captain J. A. Nichols, and put him in charge of the test-pit crew. On November 16, 1890, the captain struck the first body of soft hematite ore to be discovered in Minnesota. Without further ado the honest captain put fifty pounds of it into his knapsack and struck out for Duluth, to show his employers what they had back there in the Mesabi hills. The sample tested 64 per cent pure iron, which is about as pure as iron ever is found.

It was a real strike, no doubt of it. Captain Nichols warned the Merritts against those he termed the Down-Lakes Slickers—the promoters, the easy-money boys from the cities. He urged that the rich find be covered up and everything kept as quiet as possible until the Merritts were ready to mine the property and to take the ore to market. He pointed out that the market was one thousand miles distant.

The Merritts told Nichols never to mind about secrecy —let the world know. They wanted ore, lots of it, and ordered the captain to return to the hill and to dig like hell before winter set in. With a grandeur that would have pleased their father they named the new mine "Mountain Iron."

It had taken a good deal of money to bring in tools and provisions and to operate test pits. The Merritts sold what pine timber they had acquired over the years. They put all their pine money and their savings, too, into Mountain Iron. They mortgaged everything they owned for the same purpose. Long before the first load of ore was to leave the mine, the boys had sunk $20,000 into the hill. It was a lot of money for timber cruisers to put into a business they knew nothing about.

There seemed to be enough ore at Mountain Iron to serve old Vulcan himself—a big mound of red and purple stuff you could kick out of the ground with your shoes. News of the find spread quickly, and Cornish miners—all cagey, conservative fellows who had worked the Marquette, the Menominee, the Gogebic—came to look. They told the Merritts flatly that this was iron, all right, but it couldn't be mined. "Look," said the cousin-jacks, "there's no slates, no granite, no greenstone, no diorite. Why, man alive, you couldn't even sink a shaft down ten feet into such stuff! Too soft. All would cave in at once." No Cornishman, nor anyone else for that matter, had ever seen a flat deposit of iron in America. Hence, there couldn't be such a thing.

All this didn't trouble the Merritts much; their troubles were a lack of money. When Leonidas started out to raise capital to build a railroad to Mountain Iron, he found the big men of the mining world as skeptical about flat deposits of ore as the Cornish mine captains had been. There had been open-pit mining, of course, on the other ranges, but none of the ore had been soft and loose like this. One after another the moneyed men turned Leonidas down. When he protested that he could mine this soft ore with steam shovels, they had the office boy show Leonidas the door. It didn't do to have crazy persons around. . . .

"Lon" Merritt came and went, looking everywhere for an "angel." Meanwhile, the other Merritts and their crews were uncovering acre upon acre of rich soft ore, scooping it up with homemade steam shovels. And they had struck another deposit, maybe as large as Mountain Iron: One of their friends, John McCaskill, trapper and woodsman who knew ore when he saw it but wasn't interested, had told the Merritts to look under a certain tree he described to them. They looked and found more red and purple ore. This became Biwabik, one of the greatest mines on the new range. Like Mountain Iron, it too could be mined with steam shovel and in no other way.

But things were getting desperate. Here they were, with more ore than most men ever dreamed about, and no money to build a few miles of railroad to get it to water. Lon packed his extension suitcase again, put on a necktie as a concession, and went to one of the greatest names in the steel industry, to Mr. Henry C. Frick of Pittsburgh. Mr. Frick permitted Lon Merritt to see him, and that was about all. "Frick did not treat me like a gentleman," Lon told afterward. "He cut me off short, and bulldozed me." Which, although Lon didn't know it, was rather much like Mr. Frick.

Well, it looked as though the boys might as well have a gold mine on the planet of Mars. Lon returned to Duluth, disappointed but far from discouraged. It is of record that the first thing he did after getting home was to sit down and compose a long poem about building a railroad to the new mines from Duluth, which he liked to call Zenith City.[2]

---

[2] Leonidas Merritt was fond of Longfellow. One strophe of his poem:

> We are going to build a railway,
> With easy grades for transportation,
> From the mines of the Mis-sa-be
> To the smokestacks of the Zenith,
> To the furnaces for smelting,
> To the mills where cunning fingers
> Fashion articles for commerce,
> Structural steel and heavy castings,
> Tools and rails and nails and what not.

The smart-alecs of Duluth had made fun of the crazy Merritt boys for years; and even now, with a world of iron in sight at Biwabik and Mountain Iron, Lon could not interest Duluth capital in his proposed railroad. But Duluth business men wanted to get in on the Mesabi strike; they sent and grubstaked scores of prospectors. None were so good at it as the Merritts. While at least five thousand ore seekers ranged along the fifty miles of hills the Merritt clan made still another strike, a huge one this time. They discovered what became Mesabi Mountain, richer and wider and more of it than either of their first two mines.

Duluth went mad into the biggest iron-mine boom of the century. The city at the head of the Lakes was packed and overflowing with people who slept in tents, in barns, on barroom floors, anywhere at all. Men were incorporating alleged mining companies to a paper value of five million dollars a day, for weeks on end. Honky-tonks ran day and night. Everybody was going to be rich from the wonderfully soft purple ore back there in the hills. The Merritt boys, apparently, were the only ones who realized that iron ore is worthless until you have a way to get it to the furnaces.

Among the thousands attracted to Duluth by the excitement was Henry W. Oliver, who made plows and shovels at Pittsburgh. He spent his first night in Duluth sleeping on a billiard table, and next day he started for the Mesabi mines.

Oliver wasn't interested in mining stock, but he knew that the ore of Michigan wouldn't last forever. More, he knew that the Michigan ore was coming from deeper and deeper in the ground every day; cost more to get out. Once Oliver saw the acres of soft ore that lay fair on the surface of the ground on the Mesabi, he sent for Captain Edward Florada.

Captain Florada had earned his title on the Menominee at Crystal Falls and Iron Mountain, deep mines all, but he had more imagination than most underground miners. The moment he saw how the stuff lay so wide and shallow on the Mesabi, he advised Henry Oliver to lease a property at once, if he could, and buy steam shovels. "It will be the cheapest ore ever laid down in Pittsburgh," he said.

Oliver leased the Mesabi Mountain property from the Merritts, with the understanding that the Merritts would provide a railroad to Lake Superior. Lon had written the poem; he was sure they could do it, somehow. He continued to look for capital.

The tempo of life on the Mesabi increased daily. Now came Peter Kimberly, the big iron and steel man of Sharon, Pennsylvania, wanting to lease the Biwabik mine. The Merritts leased it, and every day Lon thought he had found the needed capital for the railroad. He'd have to get it pretty soon, for the Charlemagne Tower railroad to the Vermilion Range was building a branch to Biwabik and if it got there first, it would endanger the traffic contracts the Merritts signed with Kimberly when they leased him the mine.

At last Lon got the capital, not in Pittsburgh, nor even in New York, but in small Faribault, Minnesota. The Duluth, Missabe & Northern became an incorporated fact, even though the Merritts and their new partners were not sure of the "Duluth" in the title, nor of the "Northern" part of it, either. At least, they were fairly positive of the "Missabe." Incorporators with the Merritts were K. D. Chase and Donald Grant of Faribault, and the Messrs. Guthrie and Foley.

Cassius Merritt, with his young nephew Wilbur, and old Tom Sunderlands, an able woodsman when not drunk, made the preliminary survey for the road in record time. They ran a straight pretty line from Mountain Iron for twenty-five miles across the muskegs, then slanted her on an easy grade down to Lake Superior. It was a good right of way, what railroaders call a down-hill haul.

Everything seemed ready. It was, except for one thing, and that was the terminal. When the Duluth, Missabe & Northern applied to the Duluth city council for a right to run its tracks through the town, it was refused rather coldly.

It was quite a blow. Whether or not Lon Merritt wrote a poem about it isn't known; but Lon went ahead and contracted to link the new road with that of the Duluth & Winnipeg, at Stony Brook. The D. & W. had a terminal at Superior, Wisconsin, just across the bay from Duluth.

In mid-October of 1892 they had a big celebration at Mountain Iron. It was the formal opening of the mine, and that afternoon the first trainload of Mesabi ore rolled down over the new railroad. It was also a great day for the Merritt clan. They owned Mountain Iron; they had leased two other big mines; and they owned control in the railroad that would move all the ore. For the first time their names began to appear in the financial pages of Eastern newspapers. Some of the boys bought fancy vests and took to wearing derby hats. Small wonder. The Minnesota Iron Company, controlled by Charlemagne Tower, offered the Merritts eight mil-

lion dollars for their interests in the Mesabi mines and
the railroad from Mountain Iron to Stony Brook. That
was in 1892, and the Merritt boys laughed good-naturedly
at the piddling offer.

The Merritts must have wondered later, with hindsight, why they had not taken the eight million dollars
cash. Some people, even in 1892, wondered why they
didn't. But then, the boys had something more than
their own money in those hills: They had been chewed
to bleeding by flies and mosquitoes, for more than a
decade. On snowshoes and in 50-below weather they
had plodded into those hills, packing supplies that
would have tired a truck horse. When ore finally was
found, they brought in equipment overland that cost
them more per pound from Duluth to Mountain Iron
than it would have cost to ship from Duluth to Liver-
pool, England. They had spent twenty thousand dollars
before ever they located a ton of ore. They had been
laughed at as crazy for close to two decades. And Lon
had roamed the country over before he found capital
enough to build a few miles of railroad. They had put
more than their money into the Mesabi; their very lives
were in it. . . . Sell out for eight million dollars? The
Merritt boys knew they were sitting pretty on top of the
Mesabi. They thought they were sitting pretty on top
of the world.

When Henry Oliver, the Pittsburgh plow and shovel
man, had taken a lease on the Merritts' Mesabi Mountain
property, he went directly to the Steel City to see Mr.
Frick. That was in the late summer of 1892 and Mr.
Frick wasn't feeling very well. For one thing, his workmen had suddenly gone berserk at the Homestead mill,

on strike, prohibiting anyone from entering the plant, and fighting a bloody battle with imported Pinkertons.

For another thing, Mr. Frick himself had just been shot and wounded by an anarchist named Berkman. But Mr. Frick was too tough for mere bullets. He sat up in bed and was pleased to see Mr. Oliver, his glance as cool as ever it had been, which was pretty cool.

Oliver told Frick of the huge deposits of shallow ore he had seen on the Mesabi, what fine ore it was, how cheaply it could be mined with steam shovels. Lon Merritt had told Frick all this years before, and Frick wouldn't listen. But Oliver was a steelmaster, a brother manufacturer. He offered Frick half an interest in his lease on Mesabi Mountain in return for a loan of five hundred thousand dollars.

Frick knew more about steel and iron than ever his boss, Mr. Carnegie, did; but Little Andy must be consulted. The Scotsman was at his castle in Scotland that summer, having gone abroad, as many thought, to permit Mr. Frick a free hand in crushing the steel workers' union at Homestead. Frick sent a cable about Oliver's proposition. Carnegie replied, "No." The imperturbable Frick went ahead anyway, putting through the deal. It was one of the most important moves the Carnegie company ever made; it gave the world's greatest steelmakers an interest in the world's greatest iron range.

That put Andy Carnegie into the iron-ore business. It might have given the Merritts warning that lowly ore, as well as steel and oil and railroads, could have an attraction for the industrial Titans who were soon to be known as the Robber Barons.

At this period the Merritts were shocked and surprised to learn that they had nowhere near the number of ore cars needed to handle the tonnage from the Mesabi mines. The Duluth & Winnipeg road, with which the Merritts had linked the D., M. & N. in order to reach Lake Superior, had fallen down on a previous agreement to provide the cars. Oliver at Mesabi Mountain was howling for cars, and so was Kimberly at Biwabik. Again they threatened to switch their ore-hauling business to the approaching Vermilion Range railroad.

The Merritts and their partners in the D., M. & N. held a meeting that was little short of a knockdown and drag-out. Some wanted to do one thing, some another. Just what happened is not clear, but it is known that Lon Merritt stood up and said by God he'd build ore cars and, what was more, he would extend the Merritt line from Stony Brook to Duluth and let the Duluth & Winnipeg road go hang.

Lon had reason to talk that way, it appeared. By Charles W. Wetmore, the well known promoter of Wall Street, Lon had been given assurance of a big loan from the American Steel Barge Company, if Lon would agree to ship his Mesabi ore in the company's barges. With the loan, the Merritts could build all the ore cars they needed; they could also build ore docks at Duluth, which was now ready to receive the Merritts with open arms; and they could do away with the doubtful privilege of paying the Duluth & Winnipeg for using its rails.

Lon bulled it through. There was an immediate shuffle in the directorship of the Merritt railroad. The old partners were out. Lon and his brothers, with the cash the exuberant Mr. Wetmore stood ready to furnish them from the barge company, would build the railroad clean through to Duluth. Yes, sir, Merritt locomotives would whistle all the way from Mountain Iron to the lake shore at Duluth. It would be a Garrison finish.

The calendars that year were marked "1893"—a year that has often since been compared to 1929. It was a panic year, a quick panic, even more sudden than that of 1929, and it seemed to freeze hard cash as a July frost freezes spring wheat. Banks and mills were closed. Bread lines formed and lengthened. Brokers jumped out windows which, while not so high above the pavement as they were by 1929, were high enough.

The Merritt boys were soon in the tightest fix of their lives. They had let contracts to build the connecting link they needed. They couldn't pay the contractors, the contractors could not pay the men. The mines were idle. Men came into the Merritt offices in Duluth, pulled wicked-looking guns from their pockets and demanded their wages. There were near riots at the mines.

Lon looked around hurriedly for a loan, even for credit that would feed the thousands of men at work on Merritt enterprises. He couldn't even get credit for a carload of potatoes. Word had seeped back that this new kind of soft loose ore was raising all kinds of trouble at the blast furnaces. It was too powdery; when a furnace was put into blast, the fine particles of ore stopped up the flues, which had been made for coarser stuff. Hundreds of stories, no one of them such as to help the credit of the Merritts, were going the rounds. One had it that a trainload of Mesabi ore, being hauled from Ashtabula Harbor to Pittsburgh, had been blown out of the cars by the wind and scattered over three counties; that the cars were empty when they reached the furnaces. Things like that, no matter how untrue, didn't help any.

Times rapidly became so bad that Mr. Wetmore said he could not swing the big loan he had promised; but through him the Merritts were permitted to borrow $350,000 from Mr. John D. Rockefeller, who had his hand in the American Steel Barge Company and a number of other affairs.

And that, of course, was the beginning of the end of the Merritt saga.

No one can say today just how it happened, for there are many versions. But the results were quite clear, even pathetically so. In a few months it suddenly appeared that neither Lon nor any of the other Merritts, who now numbered seventeen, owned any part of a mine or railroad. Mr. Rockefeller owned everything.[3] Perhaps the late Charles N. Thomas, the noted economist, summed up what happened in a generality. "In times of financial stringency," wrote Mr. Thomas, "many properties inevitably change hands."

The Merritts' property did in 1893, anyway.

All of the seven brothers are dead, and none died rich. Lon Merritt lived on until May 9, 1926. He left no will. His estate hardly called for legal aid in its disposition. It consisted of household goods worth all of $1,500, of miscellaneous items of value to $800, and of hard cash exactly $150.

Mr. Rockefeller outlived Lon Merritt, and when he died he left considerably more money.

---

[3] Everything, apparently, was legal and aboveboard. The Merritts sued and won; the case was reversed, and did not go to trial again, being settled out of court. The Merritts retracted their charges of fraud. Rockefeller paid them approximately $500,000, every penny of which the Merritts turned over to their creditors.

9 The Great Mesabi Pox

THE three big ore strikes made by the Merritt boys on the Mesabi, one after another, brought about the greatest iron-mining excitement this country has ever known. Stories of mine strikes seldom lose much in the retelling. By the time news of what the Merritts had found had filtered out into the world, it was to the effect that all northeastern Minnesota was one huge field of soft but solid iron. All one had to do, it seemed, was to drive a few stakes, get mineral rights to the land, and start shoveling out pretty ore.

Men are large-sized children, and nowhere are grown men so childlike as in their readiness to believe stories of hidden treasure, whether the treasure was hidden by a Captain Kidd or by the glacial drift of unknown centuries. So, men came in a hurry and overland to the Mesabi from the end of the Vermilion mine railroad at Tower, or they fought their way through eighty miles of forest from Duluth. They came by the score for a few weeks, then by the hundred for a few months, and lastly, at the height of the rush in 1892, by the thousand. No one knows how many they numbered. Old-timers put it between fifteen and twenty-five thousand. It was the nearest thing to a Klondike rush the iron business has known.

The Mesabi rush was the usual army of adventurous

men—loggers, timber cruisers, timber barons; miners who wanted to be mine operators, college men from New York and Boston, and gamblers, fancy men and women from everywhere. With billions of savage mosquitoes droning in their ears and biting, this mob fought its feverish way from Tower or Duluth to the new range, over treacherous muskeg and through brush that clutched at them like barbed wire, packing on their backs everything from dismantled diamond drills to the umbrella that a "prospector" from Philadelphia thought would be a handy thing to have along.

When the brief northland summer was gone, the rush continued on foot and sleds, to the light of high-flickering aurora borealis and the music of frost crackling like a corps of hidden sharpshooters. Men lived that Mesabi winter through in a condition akin to savagery. It killed a host of them. It sent more hurrying back to the places whence they came, telling the world they would not stay in such a bitter and forlorn land for all the iron in the earth. With the tenderfeet now in ebb tide back to their farms and cities, the soon-to-be-fabulous figures of the new range began to take shape. Frank Hibbing was one.

Hibbing was a young man out of Germany by way of Beaver Dam, Wisconsin, where he had worked in a shingle mill and so, naturally, had lost three fingers. This loss did not prevent him from becoming a dependable timber cruiser—which was only a step, in that day and place, from being a prospector for iron ore.

The big strikes of the Merritts had occurred on what Hibbing came to believe was the eastern end of the Mesabi Range. Leaving the sheeplike to huddle around the known rich fields of Biwabik and Mountain Iron, Hibbing struck out alone through the forest. Some twenty-five miles west of the center of activity, he found likely-looking ground. Here, as they said, he drove his stakes.

With a lease on his hunk of howling wilderness, Hibbing got a crew of men, and they swamped out a road from Mountain Iron, end of the Merritts' new railroad. All the wise boys around the saloons in Biwabik and Mountain Iron were sorry to see the genial Hibbing act that way. "Bughouse," they said. They were sure the Great Silences had got him. They liked Hibbing, and no one enjoys seeing a friend go stark mad and cutting a road directly away from "where all the ore is."

Less than a year later the likable Dutchman with the walrus mustache had struck by far the biggest deposits of iron on this or any other range—deposits that were to make Mountain Iron look like something that had got under your finger nails; and soon he was busy platting what was to be the rip-snorting mining town of Hibbing.

The town of Hibbing, as related, was far west of the first big doings. It had to wait for the railroad. Meanwhile, Virginia City was growing rapidly as the social center for the hundreds of miners who were scooping up the soft ore at Mountain Iron, Mesabi Mountain, and Biwabik.

Cornish mine captains were in the vanguard to the new range, as they had been elsewhere. One of the most notable was Captain John Gill, pure Cornwall in lineage, birth, and speech, and perhaps the biggest man on the Mesabi. It is impossible today to say exactly how big and tall Captain John was; but he was likely just under seven feet and weighed three hundred pounds, with no pasties in his pockets.

Strangely for a Cornish mine captain, Captain John was sometimes as reckless as he was tall, and he loved a good blast. None of your piddling two-stick blasts for him. When he was clearing the forest of pine off Mountain Iron for the Merritt boys, Captain John ran afoul of a huge stump that refused to be moved by an orthodox blast of powder. Captain John swore a complicated Cornish oath and went into the powder house. When he emerged he was lugging half a box of 90 per cent stumping. With his own hands he placed this twenty-five pounds [1] of dynamite under the stump, attached a fuse, and warned all to get out of the way.

The ensuing blast is still remembered. It was said to have been the mightiest ever to shake the Mesabi since the range was formed by the convulsions of erupting volcanoes. No part of the stump was seen again—at least in St. Louis County. The blast stunned five miners who were a hundred yards away and running like the wind. It also blew rocks, timber, and a boulder through the cook shanty where Mrs. Gill, Captain John's wife, was getting midday dinner. It was a bigger blast than Captain John had expected. He ran to the cookhouse to find his wife on the floor with a broken hip. What she said about it isn't of exact record, but she is known to have passed a few remarks about blowing an honest woman out of hearth and home. "Ah, mother," replied Captain John soothingly, "but it was a mighty fine bla-ast! You should have seen it go."

Not many mine captains became wealthy. Captain Marcus Fay was an exception. He came to the Mesabi in 1892, wearing a big black beard, to take charge of mine

---

[1] Doubtless an exaggeration of the poundage. But it was a blast violent enough to be famous forty-five years afterward.

interests at Biwabik for what was known as "the Saginaw crowd." Captain Fay did some thinking as well as mining and managed to secure a fee of one dollar a ton on all ore he produced from the Kellog mine. There was a good deal of ore in the Kellog. But wealth didn't unseat Captain Fay and send him to live in Duluth or New York City. He remained on the ground that had made him rich. Captain Fay stayed and built the most elegant residence in Virginia City, a fine hotel, a theater, and was glad to put on a white vest and shake hands with Ruby Robert Fitzsimmons when the noted fighter appeared at Fay's Opera House.

A year or so after the opening of the Mesabi Range and the coming of the railroad, those men who had "walked in" were rated as pioneers. That was how fast life moved in the mine towns. Captain A. H. Stevens was noted because he walked in, all the way from the Menominee, and led twenty-five horses. It was probably Captain Stevens, too, although veterans still argue about it, who first used a steam shovel to mine Mesabi ore. The rig Captain Stevens contrived was a formidable contraption, something like a cross between a small bunkhouse, a locomotive, and a dredge. When it took a bite out of a bank of ore, the tail end reared up like a bronco; the stack shivered and belched fire, cinders, and smoke, while the noise was enough to frighten even the stolid Finns. As for the engineer, he hung on for dear life and hoped for the best. Anyway, Captain Stevens' rig started a trend.

Not in the van but a little later, old Captain Tom, the famous Captain Tom Walters of the Marquette, showed up on the Mesabi. Captain Tom had mined all the way from Cornwall, including Pennsylvania in the days of the Molly Maguires. He found mining with a steam shovel sort of silly; but Captain Tom had iron in his blood, and he had to work where there was plenty of ore.

A veritable prince of the range for many years was the late Mike Godfrey, who had charge of the great Oliver-Frick properties and bossed more mine captains —some of them as temperamental as opera stars—than any superintendent up to that time. Godfrey was rated a genius on the range and had a mine named for him, a positive accolade either of stature or of wealth. In God-frey's case it was stature.

None of the common cousinjack miners, the men who had dug all those deep holes on the Marquette, the Me-nominee, the Gogebic, the Vermilion—none of these lads thought much of surface mining. They actually *liked* working underground—a more "heven" tempera-ture, they said—and they refused to admit that a man on a steam shovel, out in the open air where sun and rain fell on him, was a miner at all. "Bloody ditch-diggers!" said the Cornishmen.

Many cousinjacks came to the Mesabi, of course, but they were never to dominate this range. Nor were the Irish. By the nineties Scandinavian and Finnish immi-gration was in full flood. Blond-haired giants from Nor-way and Sweden and smaller but tough and wiry men from Helsingfors took over the job of digging ore.

Getting soft ore out of an open pit wasn't much like blasting hard ore out of solid rock two thousand feet down and hauling it to the surface. One steam shovel could mine as much Mesabi ore in an hour as five hun-dred miners could bring up in a day from the old deep mines. It made production cheaper. There were no ex-pensive shafts, no pumps, no air compressors on the

Mesabi. Not nearly so many men were needed as formerly.

By the time the Mesabi was all set to produce in a big way, Finnish miners had taken the place of the cousin-jacks. The Finns brought their wives to the range, and they also brought an idea new to the iron country: Finns liked to have a piece of ground to live on, to have a garden. Maybe a hayfield, too, and a cow. Certainly some pigs and chickens.

Many a Finn's spare time from the pits was spent grubbing an acre of stumps; but even before this he built his *sauna*,[2] the classic bathhouse of Finland. Into this little cabin he moved, with his wife and family if they were present, and there they lived until he, with his wife swinging an ax, too, could build the main living quarters. The Finns set a pattern for life on the range, and other races who followed them to the Mesabi largely adopted this manner of mining and small farming. About the only Cornish custom to survive was the pasty for midday lunch. That, and Cornish wrestling.

The tempo of mining, of life itself on the new Mesabi was not to be compared with the rather leisurely way things had gone forward on the older ranges. It began with the first strike of the Merritts. The rush, the competition to get in on the ground floor, took on terrific speed. Greedy, which is to say natural, men of large means en-

---

[2] This was usually about eight by ten feet, of logs, with two rooms: the outer, a dressing room; the inner, the bath proper. The bath was a stove covered with stones. When the stones were heated, water was thrown on them, making steam. Soap and brushes were used, and cedar boughs with which the bather stroked himself. The old-fashioned Finns of 1939 may have a conventional bathroom in their home, but they also have the *sauna* outside, and prefer it.

tered the scene early and fought for likely iron-bearing
lands with every weapon they could devise. No holds
were barred.

Lazy or dull-witted fellows were bribed by the thousand, and for paltry sums, to apply for homesteads and
make a feeble gesture at living on them. Mineral and
timber rights to these "homesteads" were of course
transferred to the holding companies of wealthy men
who wanted either to get cheap timber, or to acquire ore
lands to peddle at fancy prices to the huge combines—
the Olivers, the Fricks, the Rockefellers—which were
then being formed. These were scandalous doings which
required not only bribers but bribees.[3] The common
man's part in them was no prettier than that of the
damnable capitalists—and not nearly so intelligent.

Fate seemed to loom particularly large in making
many of the big fortunes that came out of the Mesabi
open pits. There was that Saginaw crowd of lumbermen.
They had acquired vast stands of timberland in northeastern Minnesota before they ever knew there was more
wealth underground than in the trees. By the mid-
nineties these lumbermen were surprised, and doubtless
pleased, to find their names as important in ore as they
had been in timber—the fabulous Wellington R. Burt,
and Temple Dorr, Ezra Rust, Clarence M. Hill, Aaron T.
Bliss, Elbridge M. Fowler, George C. Robinson, Simon
J. Murphy, Elisha Flinn, and the hard-boiled old lumber

---

[3] This homestead skulduggery was too widespread even to be estimated.
In a single group of cases investigated by Federal land agents, several
hundred Canadians had crossed the border into the mineral and timber
belt of Minnesota, declared their intention of becoming American citizens, acquired free homesteads which they commuted to large concerns
for a few dollars each, then returned to their former homes in Ontario.
The entire proceedings required only fourteen to eighteen months.

concern of Wright & Davis. Mesabi ore also played a big part in making the huge Yawkey and Boeing fortunes of Detroit and that of Morton Hull of Chicago.

You'll find all those names stamped on the Mesabi today, in 1939, although many of them begin to fade somewhat.[4]

Still more lumbermen stumbled unwittingly into the flood of purple ore, and rode it out successfully. As early as 1875 the Pillsburys of Minneapolis, who were lumbermen as well as makers of flour, had begun buying Minnesota timberlands. Twenty years later, when most of the timber had been cut, the Pillsburys were mildly interested when H. M. Bennett, who was cruising the Mesabi, informed them that there was good ore under some of their land. They told him not to bother about it unless he was positive he could uncover at least a hundred million tons; if he could do this, he might have a half-interest.

What Bennett found, with the expert aid of John M. Longyear, totaled to many times the stipulated amount. It piled an iron fortune on top of the Pillsburys' milling and timber interests, and it permitted Longyear and Bennett to build not mansions but castles.

A timber cruiser who got well paid for a summer's work was Marshall H. Alworth of Saginaw, Michigan. Sent into the Minnesota woods to buy timberlands for the Messrs. Hull and Boeing, Alworth purchased 7,500 acres for $22,500. Alworth was to have one-third interest in any profits from resale of the timberland. No one ever knew what the timber brought, if anything; but the ground proved to be almost solid iron ore, and ten mil-

---

[4] Even one of the Merritt boys, who did nothing but discover the Mesabi Range, has a mine named for him—the Leonidas, near Eveleth.

lion tons were taken out as a starter. Alworth put away his small ax and hung his compass up behind the door. He never had to cruise white pine again.

Even an Empire Builder got into the iron business without suspecting what was going on. James J. Hill was engaged in building and buying railroads all the way from Lake Superior to the Pacific Coast. Some of Hill's lumbermen friends had logged off a large tract of timber out of Grand Rapids, Minnesota. With the timber all gone, they found themselves with a haywire railroad left over. Somehow, they prevailed on Hill to buy the road and the cutover land.

Hill was rather surprised, when he inspected his new property, to find that the road didn't go anywhere at all; it started at Grand Rapids but soon petered out in the middle of thousands of acres of stumps—desolation as far as the eye could see. He muttered something under his breath, then went away and tried to forget it. Shortly afterward prospectors discovered that Jim Hill's hedgehog railroad rambled over some of the richest property on the entire range. Hill didn't sell. He hung on, and in a few years the worthless cutover land became known as the Great Northern Ore Properties. It paid out pretty well, too.[5]

Affairs on the Mesabi Range had moved very fast indeed. By the mid-nineties virtual control of the entire range and its railroad was in the hands of two concerns: Mr. Rockefeller's Lake Superior Consolidated Iron Mines, and the Oliver-Frick-Carnegie combine.

As for mining itself, nothing like it had been seen. To

[5] Up to Dec. 27, 1923, stockholders of this concern had received $47,-625,000 in dividends.

begin with, it was easier now, and quicker, to locate deposits of ore. The diamond drill took care of that. This
device operates on the principle of an apple corer. The
cutting face of the first drills was made of the famous
"black diamonds" of Brazil, carbons of great hardness
that could bore through anything, and in early days cost
as much as ninety-five dollars a carat.

Boring down into the ground, the drill brings up a
core composed of samples of strata encountered by the
drill head. These samples will tell a man exactly what is
beneath him, down there out of sight, and how thick it
is, too. It is sure, and quick—just what the boys wanted
on the Mesabi.

Frank Hibbing himself is said to have packed in the
first drill used on the new range and to have discovered
his Lone Jack mine with its aid. In a little while, men
set up exclusively as drillers and became important figures on the range. Henry O. Johnson bossed the Longyear exploring crews. Henry Osterberg became a noted
diamond drill man, and so did the Moe brothers, Tom
and Martin. Shortly after the turn of the century the
Cole & McDonald Exploration Company of Virginia
City claimed to be "the most extensive diamond-drill
operators on earth."

If it was easier to locate ore now, it was ten times as
easy to mine it. The first crude steam shovels were soon
improved and enlarged until one of them at a single bite
picked up no less than thirteen tons, and was literally
equal to the hand shovels of an army. When the mines
were stripped—that is, the timber out of the way, the
stumps gone—the shovels went at it, going around and
around, then down a bit, and around and around again,
following the ore wherever it went, like a hound on the

scent. It was hardly mining in the accepted sense of the word. There were no shafts, no skips, little blasting. This was merely excavating, like digging a gigantic cellar in broad daylight.[6] No wonder the cousinjacks were disgusted. A "miner" here was the engineer of a rig that puffed and tooted, a rig that was fed on coal and not on good pasties and honest beer. Nobody wore a sconce and candle in his cap any more. . . . The bloody bleeding world was upside down.

The world may have been upside down to the Cornish old-timers, but it was moving very fast in these early Mesabi days. Three years after the Merritts' railroad came to Mountain Iron, the Mesabi output of ore had passed that of the Marquette Range, until then the biggest producer. The steam shovels were making holes in the ground, holes deep and wide and long enough to astound the visitor.

Shortly after the turn of the century there were one hundred and eleven of these gigantic pits, seemingly an endless though scattering chain of pockmarks, yawning red and blue under Minnesota's bright sun, and brooding mysteriously in purple and brown under twilight shadows. It was as though a great pox had broken out all along the Mesabi's fifty miles of now bleak and treeless iron hills.

Out of these vast chasms, every few hours, rolled long trains that whistled mournfully across the high tableland, then dipped into the slant that wheeled them down to Duluth and the ore pockets with scarcely a pound of steam expended. The trains were loaded high with the soft rich stuff that the snorting blast furnaces had by

---

[6] A very few mines on the Mesabi were worked underground-style, but the range was and still is known as an open-pit range.

now learned to digest and were finding excellent food indeed. They called much of it Number One Bessemer, down at South Chicago and Gary and Rankin and Youngstown, and ore could have no higher compliment. The Mesabi had been opened up just in time to supply what was needed to make the United States the greatest steel-producing country on earth.

The purple ore also was making some pretty lively towns back in the hills.

10 *Boom-Town Life*

AFTER one winter spent in Virginia City, Minnesota, P. H. McGarry, who ran a hotel there, told a hardware salesman from Chicago to send him a stove guaranteed to heat a forty-acre lot in 40-below weather. The stove came forthwith and is said to have required the best part of a flatcar for its transportation. It was the daddy of stoves, fit to heat all Valhalla. It took four-foot sticks, and old-timers vow that you could ram about half a cord into its cast-iron belly. Two hard-working Finns labored ten hours a day to feed it.

McGarry was right in thinking the Mesabi country cold. For three months no man there expected to see the mercury rise above zero. Much of the time the quicksilver hung sluggishly around 20 to 30 below, and nobody spoke about the weather except when temperature registered 60 and, at least once in a ten-year period, 62 below zero. It was then said to be fairly brisk and coolish.

Mostly, the mines were open pits. By early December they froze so hard that dynamite made little impression; and they remained that way until spring, which might come in April but more often in May. Thus a miner had a good deal of time on his hands.

The Finns had their little farms, of course, but there wasn't much farming to be done in a Mesabi winter. As for the few Cornish and Irish and plain Americans, they did the best they could to entertain themselves during the long dark winters.

There was timber on the range, in early mining days, and many of the boys turned logger at first snow-fly. Neither camps nor mines were very far from the lively cities that were growing up around the pits and underground mines at Biwabik, Mountain Iron, Virginia, Eveleth, and Hibbing. There was to be no shortage of entertainment in any of them.

There is a free and easy atmosphere about a mining boom that amounts almost to a continuous festive mood. There are plenty of hardships, of course, but hardships are expected and are never considered as such at the time. Life in boom country takes on a zip and a zest that comes only once to any region and can never be recaptured. It's because men are without root. Once they have their roots in the ground, and build brick banks and churches and schools, and put up lace curtains, and have a Ladies Aid and an Elks Temple, and erect a monument to Admiral Dewey, then the end of the boom era is in sight.

Every part of the Republic has had its great and sometimes red-eyed pioneer days. Those on the Mesabi were probably as stirring as any. A man got the feeling before even he had reached the range. He got it the moment he boarded a Duluth, Missabe & Northern passenger train at Duluth. For almost two decades there was hardly a seat to spare in the rattling wooden coaches. The cars had either the heat of hell inside, or the frosty breath of Minnesota, depending on the box-stove abilities of the brakeman and the condition of the coach windows, which were often kicked out by drunks who wanted a little fresh air.

The conductors were genial fellows, some of them "on the make" in a mild sort of way. One of them peddled a neat line of galluses as he went down the aisle taking tickets. They were the latest thing, non-button type, and cost only sixty cents a pair. This conductor did so well with galluses that he added a nobby line of celluloid collars, both bright and dull finish. He would stop punching tickets any time to make a sale. Another, who had a wide acquaintance and was said to be a shrewd judge of character, set up as a moneylender. He'd lend five dollars or so to a broke and thirsty miner or lumberjack, without security; and usually he got it back with interest the next time the boys went to town.

The mine towns at first were all of the boom type. They grew quickly—a long street of board shacks with false fronts for the business area, and side streets of rooming houses and homes. A saloon was opened first of all, naturally enough, and close on its heels came hotels, stores, banks, schools and churches, all of them whacked together out of green boards and timbers. All might come into being within sixty days.

The Mesabi towns developed an intense rivalry. They all had newspapers, like the *Mesaba Range* at Biwabik and the *Mesaba Ore* at Hibbing, whose very names proclaimed the dominant interest,[1] and the editors argued

---

[1] The use of "iron" or of some other word pertaining to the industry was a striking feature of mine-range newspaper names, here and elsewhere, and showed pride and singleness of purpose. Past and present newspapers include: *Mining Journal*, Marquette, Mich.; *Iron Ore*, Ishpeming, Mich.; *Gogebic Iron Spirit*, Bessemer, Mich.; *Montreal River Miner*, Hurley, Wis.; *Ely Miner*, Ely, Minn.; *Mountain Iron Manitou*, Mountain Iron, Minn.; and *Itasca Iron News*, Bovey, Minn.

without end, and lied famously, about growth, population, baseball teams, and prize fighters.

Virginia City was the first metropolis. Bill Hays' hall
there was enough in itself to make a metropolis on the
early range. It was a huge ramshackle building, un-
painted, and not large enough to hold the crowds which
came to see the varied entertainment offered, things like
dog fights, prize fights, minstrel shows, and "socials"
that turned into wild drunken orgies. Gambling continued unabated in Hays' hall throughout the week. On
Sunday mornings Mr. Hays kindly turned the place over
to any preacher who wanted to operate. It returned to
gambling in the afternoon.

Fire struck Virginia City hard in its infancy, laying
the town flat. It was rebuilt quickly and well, but lusty
young Hibbing, twenty-eight miles west, was offering
wilder entertainment and soon would be calling itself
"The Little Chicago of the Range." Hibbing, too, had
more open pits than any of them.

Where Frank Hibbing had driven his stakes became
technically a village because it retained that form of
government. In reality, it was a bawdy, howling mine
town that grew into a small city in less than five years.
The great pits—the Hull, the Rust, Sellers, and Mahoning mines—were right at its doorstep, in fact, under its
doorstep. As if these vast deposits were not enough for
one town, Hibbing miners could walk from their homes
to work in the Webb, the Susquehanna, the Boeing, the
Philbin, and the Longyear, any one of them a big enough
hole. Hibbing miners bragged that nowhere on earth or
the moon was the ground so filled with iron. They told
one another that here was enough ore to keep Finn min-

ers and Cornish mine captains busy until Kingdom
Come, and long after.

Hibbing from the first was the sportiest town on the
range. It had a professional baseball team and a racing
track. Prize fighting was popular, and even more attention was given to wrestling. Hibbing's enthusiasm was
such that the town seemed always on the verge of producing a world's champion in some line or other. An instance was one Scotty Scott, a young Cornish miner, almost a giant, who was billed as the Mesaba Terror; he
was a wrestler who threw his man or tore him apart.

The Terror was doing pretty well until Frank Gotch
came to Hibbing for an exhibition. Hibbing sports figured the Terror had a chance with Gotch, who was then
the world's champion wrestler. As for the Terror, he
merely asked the boys on Pine Street whether they
wanted to see him make a square knot out of Champion
Gotch—or would a bow knot look better? The boys
cheered and told him either kind would do. Then, they
bet even money that Hibbing's Terror would take two
out of three falls.

The match was all good fun for Gotch. He started the
thing off mildly by throwing out his incredibly hard
stomach so quick and roughly that it bounced the
amazed Terror across the ring. Then, Gotch laughed
good-naturedly and got down to business. He grabbed
the Terror by one foot and held the Terror's two hundred and sixty pounds high in the air, head downward,
while he spanked the Terror's vast behind quite hard.

It was a terrible evening for the Terror and his backers, and it wasn't over. Just to show how a really hard
guy performed when he got up a sweat, Gotch next put
a toe-hold on the big lad and tortured him into insensi-

bility. When the Terror could walk again, in two or three days, he was seen walking toward the Hibbing railroad depot. "That Gotch made a bloody ass of me," he said, and bought a ticket for Duluth.

An abler man than the Terror was Eric Nord, miner at the Mahoning pit, whose early exploits are celebrated forty years after. Nord hailed from Sweden and first came to notice in Hibbing when he beat the living daylights out of Jim Arnold, reckoned Hibbing's big-bully man. It was thought quite a feat to lick Jim Arnold, and Chief Jim Butchert, who saw the scrap, lost no time in getting young Nord a job as patrolman on the Hibbing police force. They needed men like Nord in the Little Chicago of the Range.

Nord is said to have lifted one end of a boxcar clear off the rails, just for fun. He never took up whittling but liked to sit and twist horseshoes; and he once cleaned out Dave Kelly's place of a crew of tough lumberjacks, throwing them through doors and windows. Patrolman Nord went on to new glory. Hearing that Jack King, the notorious champion of all Cornish wrestlers, was taking on all comers in a tournament at Iron Mountain, Michigan, young Nord went there, won his way up through a batch of contenders from four iron ranges, and was finally matched with King.

This Jack King was the John L. Sullivan of the iron and copper country, fully as fabulous as John L. and just as mean. In the big battle, Nord and King grappled and twisted for hours. Nord was obviously wearing the champ down when King sunk his big strong fingers around Nord's throat and started choking. The referee had to pound King to make him let go. He never would face Nord again.

It required the services of Nord and several other rather hard cops to keep Hibbing's gusto within any sort of bounds. The town had sixty-one recognized saloons, and how many "houses" not even the police pretended to know. The biggest and roughest place of all was a combination saloon and "dance hall" operated on the south edge of town by the aforementioned Dave Kelly. It catered to both miners and lumberjacks. Beer was twenty-five cents a glass, and Kelly's bartenders made sure that a glass did not contain too much beer. This system became famous and was known as "making it white for the boys." It consisted of using lots of air pressure with the draft beer, thus creating, as one oldster recalls it, "enough foam for Niagara Falls and a mouthful of beer at the bottom." The boys didn't seem to mind. They were usually so drunk by the time they got to beer that it didn't matter.

Two dozen well rouged charmers circulated in Kelly's saloon and dance hall. The girls encouraged the miners to buy large and expensive boxes of candy for them. These were displayed in fancy showcases, and any one of them cost a day's wages. The candy was sold over and over again, and no girl ever tasted it. Dave Kelly himself had carefully treated every chocolate and bonbon with kerosene—just to make sure. And besides, as Dave pointed out, he didn't want the girls getting too fat.

Every saloon in town had its snake room. Into these obscure dens, back of the barroom proper, the too-drunk miners and lumberjacks stumbled, or were thrown, to sleep it off on the floor, with boots and mackinaws for pillows. The snake rooms, too, served as employment offices. They still tell of the time Uncle Al Powers, the boss logger who cleared much of the timber around Hibbing, came into Bob Maxwell's Peerless Saloon to pick up a crew to drive logs down to the sawmill.

Maxwell took Uncle Al into the snake room. Perhaps fifty or sixty men were sprawled all over the floor in every condition of inebriety. "Boys," said Maxwell, "Uncle Al's here, and he is looking for men for the drive."

One of the sobering drunks sat up and rubbed his eyes. "Oh, he is, is he? Well, how much is he paying?"

"Five dollars a day and board," said the saloonkeeper.

" 'Tain't enough," growled the drunk, and "Where's his bitching stream at?"

"It's on Day Brook, boys," replied Maxwell.

"Tell him to bring his goddam brook in here and let's have a look at it," shouted a chorus of drunks. Then they rolled over and went to sleep again.

Lumberjacks added much to Hibbing's early life. They came in by the hundreds from near-by camps, staged gang fights on Pine Street, broke up dances, and were sometimes run out of town by Hibbing's tough constables and police. The lumberjacks' reign was brief, anyway. They cut down all the pine in a hurry, then moved westward into new timber.

But Hibbing continued to have its share of violence, jacks or no. Italians and Slovenes and other races from eastern Europe began moving in early in the new century. Stabbings and gunplay took the place of calked-boot encounters. It was in Hibbing that the only known and conventional duel of the iron ranges took place. It was an odd anachronism to hang over into 1910.

Sam Kacich and Pete Radovitch worked together in the Herald mine. They had been close friends since old-country days, and they lived together in a cabin near the mine. What started the affair was never known. It was probably the trouble that so often happens to two men living in close association: They simply got tired of seeing so much of each other.

Anyway, on the 28th of October in 1910 Sam and Pete cleaned up their little shack, putting everything in neat order. They walked the short distance into Hibbing together, and each bought a revolver at a sporting-goods store, at the same time. A bit later they went into a fruit stand, bought and ate some grapes, and meanwhile were seen writing on a piece of paper which one of them put in his pocket.

Now, the two friends made the rounds of Hibbing saloons, drinking moderately and treating all acquaintances they met. They said nothing of what must have been in their minds. Having a last drink near the corner of Third and Pine streets, the two men started walking down the Great Northern tracks, toward the Herald mine. At the Fifth Avenue crossing they stopped. Each loaded his gun. They stood back to back a moment. A horrified witness saw them pace quickly away from each other, stop, and turn. Fire belched from both guns. Pete went down with a bullet through his head. Sam suffered a slight flesh wound in his left arm. Leaving Pete bleeding on the tracks, Sam walked to the Hibbing police station and gave himself up to Patrolman Ryan. Pete was dead when police arrived.

The pre-duel document was produced at the trial. In it each man agreed that the survivor of the duel should have the other's property, both here and in the old country. The case didn't make any sense to the court at all.

But the Law didn't hang Sam Kacich. Vic Power saw to that.

If Hibbing never had a "hanging judge," it was probably because of Victor L. Power. Known all over the range as the "fighting lawyer," Power seldom lost a case, whether it was murder or merely assault and battery. As long as he lived, too, Vic Power was a hornet to the big mining companies. He served as village president for many years. He was quite influential in the Minnesota legislature, where he constantly lobbied for laws to soak the mine companies for all they could stand in the way of taxes, and he was very successful. Mine companies came to class Vic Power along with Big Bill Haywood, Elizabeth Gurley Flynn, and other "anarchists." And nothing pleased Vic Power more than to sue a mine company on the part of some injured miner. He was no shyster, though, and old miners recall him as a friend to the underdog on all occasions.

Vic Power liked to call Hibbing "The Iron Ore Capital of the World." The title fitted the town then, just as it does today. More material—that is to say, more of Mother Earth—has been removed from the Hull-Rust group of open pits alone than was removed in digging the canal across Panama. That's a heap of world. Indeed, the village of Hibbing was built so close to rich earth that something had to be done about it. What was done was one of the epics of the range.

Along about World War time, the open pits, which had been started well out of town, had eaten away to the very edge of Hibbing. Long cracks began appearing in the ground, well ahead of the army of steam shovels. Another thing was that the Oliver interests decided to change the method of working the Buffalo mine from underground to open pit.

On and on came the great shovels, snorting, and continually cutting away at the banks of purple ore. Buildings sagged. A dance hall buckled in the middle and cracked open. Deeper and deeper went the pits. Now and again the ground gave way wholly and a frame building, with the ground under it, went crashing down into one of the encroaching mines.

Engineers of the Oliver company reported there were indications that the main body of ore extended under the city, even beyond. It was a case of moving, of moving an entire city of 15,000 population. The mining company purchased some forty acres of the old town and undertook to move all the buildings to a new location it had prepared a little more than half a mile south.

One could say that moving all Hibbing was quite a job and still not tell a tenth of it. Moving began in 1918. Again, Hibbing took on pioneer aspect. Or, the new Hibbing did. The old town grew more ghostly each day; and each day, too, part of old Hibbing was scraped into a steam shovel to disappear forever—to be dropped into an ore car and go rolling down over the muskegs to Duluth, and on to Gary and Pittsburgh. . . . In a moment of fantasy, Hibbing folk used to wonder, as sometimes they still do, if part of their old cellars were made into steel beams for the Empire State Building or Sam Insull's Opera House.

Day and night for three years, over soft earth or frozen ground, old Hibbing trundled its way southward, two, four, ten buildings at a time, on rollers, and pulled by every sort of motive power—horses, gasoline tractors, steam rollers, and log haulers. Homes, stores, saloons, churches, barber shops, even hotels, all of them hit the trail, while kids hung out windows shouting to one another and stolid flax-haired Finnish mothers cooked dinner on stoves that heaved like ships' galleys.

Old Hibbing was on the move, perhaps the strangest trek of a people who have been on the move much of the time ever since the Republic was founded. Old Hibbing had been built of wood and could be moved. Much of it, anyway. The ancient Sellers Hotel, a rambling four-story structure, started the journey bravely, like a great ark, an ark inhabited only by the varied fauna a thousand miners had seen in delirium tremens. But the ride was too much. When part way to its new site, the creaking hulk was heard to give a long moan, as though in mortal pain. Then came a mighty tearing sound, like a thunderbolt splitting the range, and the huge structure collapsed into an unrecognizable mass of boards and timbers.

The mine company estimated that moving the town had cost them better than twenty-two million dollars. Doubtless it did, and it would have been cheap at half the price. Old Hibbing's cellars, and far beneath them, were almost pure iron ore. Not yet, twenty years afterward, have the big steam shovels eaten up all that was Hibbing. The hole that used to be Hibbing grows wider and deeper every summer.

By 1922 the new and present Hibbing had come into full flower, utterly unlike the older town. The mines were paying a plenty in taxes, these latter days. Every scoop of a shovel meant approximately one dollar and twenty-five cents in school taxes. So Hibbing, which was

ever a town of enthusiasm, built a high school that cost
between five and six million dollars [2] and is said to use
Haviland china in its domestic science courses. It's a
school building you aren't likely to find in any other
city of similar size in the country.

Hibbing built, also with mine taxes—and properly so
—some pretty fine public buildings, community halls,
and parks with monuments. It paved the least street in
town, and it put up lamp posts that would shame the
"millionaire towns" of Brookline, Massachusetts, and
Pasadena, California. In fact, Hibbing today is one of
the slickest small cities on view anywhere. Mine taxes
did it. Approximately ninety-five cents of every dollar
spent by the Village of Hibbing comes from these taxes.
You will have an idea of how much they amount to
when you know that Hibbing often spends as much tax
money in a year as huge Minneapolis.

Nor is the village of Hibbing alone in its splendor.
Virginia City, which fire destroyed twice, and which
came of age and dropped the pioneer-sounding "city"
from its title, has school and other public buildings almost as regal as Hibbing's. And so, on a lesser scale,
have much smaller Chisholm [3] and Eveleth, and even
tiny Buhl.[4]

Just about the only tax worry of citizens of Mesabi

---

[2] Hibbing has been ribbed so much about its tony school building that
citizens don't like to be asked about its cost. They point out that it isn't
just a high school, anyway, and explain that the building houses everything from kindergarten to second-year college.

[3] Platted in 1905 by Archie Chisholm, one of Frank Hibbing's partners. Chisholm, like most range towns, had to burn down at least once,
which it did in 1908 without the loss of a life, and was rebuilt within a
year.

[4] Named for Frank H. Buhl, a late steelmaster of Sharon, Pa.

Range towns has been how to spend the mine taxes. Happy politicians seemingly have taken care of that matter very well indeed, living in clover up to their ears. It is only in recent years that the clover has begun to show signs of drooping.

11 *Trouble on the Range*

REDHEADED woodpeckers drummed away at stumps on the Mesabi in the spring of 1916, and a young, red-scarved woman, handsome as a very she-devil, flitted over the range, too, drumming up trouble for the mine companies.

The mine companies had no inkling of what was ahead. Company officials had long grown soft and unsuspecting from a lack of labor troubles. All of the five ranges had been singularly free of them. Only twice in sixty years of mining had labor got out of hand, and neither uprising amounted to much.

It seems somewhat strange that the mechanization of the industry, followed in turn by the inevitable speed-up, was accompanied by so few strikes. During the eighties there had been a small number of local and unorganized strikes on the Menominee. Few men were involved. All the strikes had been quickly broken, with little or no bloodshed, and were never heard of. It was forest fire that spread on the ranges, in the early days, not unrest.

Just why miners on the iron ranges caused so few upheavals is difficult to understand. Some observers have laid it to the iron companies' policy of having their mine crews made up of many nationalities, speaking different languages and having racial antipathies that prevented them from working together to form a union.

130

This theory hardly holds water. There were as many different nationalities in Butte, Montana, as there were in Ishpeming, Iron Mountain, or Ironwood; and the Butte miners were forever raising a loud and often violent rumpus about wages and working conditions. Even more races were at work in the steel plants around Pittsburgh, and Pittsburgh was a notoriously bloody striking ground from Civil War days until late in the century.

Possibly, as some pollyannas have attempted to point out, it was because the miners were so content with their lot. But one can believe both in God and in Capital and still doubt that one.

The docility of iron miners was likely due to more complex causes. A majority of them had families, rather large families. Then, too, they were isolated in many small towns where an "agitator" was a marked man; once he raised his voice against a mine company, he might as well give up trying to get work as a miner in the Lake states. Iron itself were easier to break than the Black List of the mine companies.

Whatever it was, it surely was no mere love of mining as an occupation that kept the boys from going berserk more often than they did. You'll find proof of it in the second and third generations of the Irish and Cornish stock that opened the ranges: Very few of them are miners. They will tell you that their fathers, and their mothers, too, wanted them to be anything but miners.

The nearest thing to a genuine strike before 1900 began in August of 1895, when miners of the Cleveland Cliffs Iron Company at Ishpeming went out for higher wages. This was an organized effort. The men had quietly formed a union, collected dues, elected officers, and

formulated demands. William Cood was president of the
union.

The strike effected a complete shutdown of the Cleveland Cliffs mines. By the first of September the mines
were steadily filling with water, and still there was no
sign of a break in the ranks. The situation was serious
enough to bring William G. Mather, head of the mine
company, to Ishpeming.

Conferences between Mather and the strikers' committee came to nothing. Mather determined to open with
imported strikebreakers. Early in September they arrived—along with five companies of the Michigan militia. The strike was quickly broken.

Again, this time on the Mesabi, organized trouble
flared up. The match was struck by Tapilo Petreila, a
short barrel-chested Italian who came to Hibbing from
Calumet, where he had succeeded in partially organizing the copper miners.

Petreila had some of the gifts of his illustrious coun-
tryman Garibaldi. He was a perfect orator for the range.
He spoke well and loud in three languages, and he was a
good organizer. Moreover, he had the backing of the
Western Federation of Miners, one of the most powerful
groups in the West. He soon had Mesabi miners talking
about the comparative philosophies of Mr. Marx and
Mr. Carnegie, and the strike began in mid-July of 1907.

The miners apparently had been nursing a great deal
of secret dissatisfaction, at least around Hibbing, for
they came out of the open pits in droves. Two days later
there was scarcely a steam shovel at work in Hibbing,
Chisholm, or Mountain Iron. The mine companies swore
in deputies and armed them; more than five hundred

company men patrolled the pits. Clashes occurred at Chisholm, with any amount of clubbing and a little shooting.

The fiery Petreila seems to have started out well enough, but he needed outside help. The famous Mother Jones put in an appearance, but the record indicates that the striking miners got little help from the Federation. Petreila was arrested for carrying concealed weapons. The strike failed to spread to other mines. Mesabi pits outside the affected area continued to operate full-handed. Early in August a trainload of Italians, Montenegrins, and assorted Croats and Slovenes, all freshly arrived from Europe, rolled onto the range. Writing was plain on the wall. By the middle of August the striking miners were tumbling over themselves to return to work, glad to get their old jobs back before the newcomers took them. The Mesabi wasn't quite ripe for trouble. Not by almost a decade.

Ten years of quiet followed Petreila's attempt. Then, in April of 1916 the pretty girl with the red scarf flitted across the Mesabi. She was Elizabeth Gurley Flynn, organizer for the Wobblies, as the Industrial Workers of the World were usually known in the West.

If iron company officials had known that The Flynn was loose on the range, they might well have tossed fitfully in their sleep. Already an experienced agitator for the young and lively Wobblies, Gurley Flynn had succeeded in bringing war and chaos around city officials of Spokane in a free-speech fight that packed that city full of wild and howling lumberjacks, hard-rock men, and other violent working stiffs. She had also played a leading part in the Lawrence "Revolution," back in Massachusetts.

The Flynn loved trouble more than anything else, and
she was as capable an agitator as ever mounted a soap-
box.[1]

But the mine barons knew nothing of The Flynn's doings that April. They had grown, as related, very soft
and sluggish from the long quiet. So the girl spoke, without molestation, at hurriedly called meetings in Aurora,
Eveleth, Virginia, Chisholm, and Hibbing. She told the
miners that the war in Europe had sent the iron and
steel markets to the highest point ever known. She described the lush ease in which mine owners were supposed to live, and compared it with the stark life enjoyed by the miners and their families. When some
home guard [2] stood up in meeting to say that mine wages
were pretty good on the Mesabi, anyway, The Flynn
gave him and his wages a sneer. And when The Flynn
sneered, it was sneer enough to wither the head of a
diamond drill.

"And what *are* wages, anyway?" she demanded. Then
she told the boys about the pelican.

"Away back in the dim past," said the pretty girl with
the red tie around her throat, "long before even Andy
Carnegie and John D. Rockefeller were born, there sat
on a river bank in China an old Chinese. He was fishing,
and he wasn't having much luck. He didn't get a nibble
all day.

"Close by, a large pelican was fishing, too. The old
Chinese watched, and he saw that the bird was doing

---

[1] Long a resident of Portland, Oregon, where she lived in retirement
with Dr. Marie Equi, another militant woman, Gurley Flynn now makes
her home in Connecticut.

[2] A home guard in Wobbly language designates a good, steady employee who is not interested in the class struggle. He is said to be a
"company man," hence suspect.

very well. Down he would go, then up, with a big fish in his mouth, which he swallowed with satisfaction. Over and over again the pelican got a fish.

"Now, my boys, the Chinese are a reflective race. The old fisherman watched the bird all day, and he thought a good deal. That night he sneaked up on the sleeping pelican and caught him. He put a string on one of the bird's legs and next day the old gent sat on the river bank, this time with the pelican doing the fishing for him.

"But it didn't work out very well at first. The pelican continued to dive and catch fish, but before the Chinese could haul him in, the bird had swallowed his prey. A good idea, my boys, but it had gone haywire."

By now the miners sat up in their seats, and brows furrowed in an effort to connect pelicans with wages. The clear vibrant voice of the girl went on:

"But, m'lads, the Chinese are a very reflective people. The old fisherman thought awhile; then he forged a collar out of brass which he put around the pelican's neck. The collar, you understand, was large enough to permit the bird to breathe, and tight enough to prevent him from swallowing the fish—which, doubtless the poor pelican thought was his own fish."

A gleam of understanding, hardly bright yet but growing, flashed across the faces of the listening miners. The Flynn talked on:

"Well, boys, it worked like a charm. The bird caught the fish, the old gent hauled him in, took away the fish, and sent the bird back for more. Every once in a while—just to encourage the pelican and to keep him alive so he would catch more fish—the Chinese would give him fish heads and tails to eat."

By now the boys were sitting on the edge of their chairs. And The Flynn let them have it:

"And that collar around *your* necks, right under where you ought to have heads and brains—that collar is the Wage System. . . . The Boss gets all the best parts of the fish. You, you working stiffs, you get the heads and tails—the *wages*."

The working stiffs of the Mesabi also got the idea. Night policemen in the range towns must have heard the delighted applause and the cheering at Gurley Flynn's meetings, those April evenings, but like the mine officials, they had long ago ceased to think of labor troubles. Gurley Flynn waved her bright red scarf and went away.

Forty-five days passed, and all remained apparently quiet. Then, on the second day of June, miners at Aurora suddenly threw down their tools, and struck. They demanded, at first, complete abolition of the contract system of mining by which men were paid so much a ton; and a bit later the demands included just about everything the boys could think up.

It may have been coincidence, but a day or two before the strike, Arthur Boose, Wobbly organizer known as the Old Warhorse, appeared on the scene at Aurora. With the strike under way, he called a meeting and formed a committee. The Old Warhorse was immediately arrested on a somewhat vague charge of "inciting to riot"—a favorite one—and thrown into the Aurora jail. Doubtless the Warhorse expected this move, for he had laid his plans. He had told the committee that, no matter what might happen, news of the Aurora strike must be spread at once, like forest fire.

Some of the spreading fire was carried out of Aurora

by a young Finn miner. His name might have been
Revere, but he was known as Ormi something-or-other.
Unlike Paul Revere, Ormi had no horse; nor was a train
of cars handy just then. So, out of Aurora that June evening Ormi walked until he was well beyond the observation of mine police. Then he ran.

Young Ormi was in the prime of young manhood, and
he ran swiftly through the falling dusk, traveling like a
shadow blown along by a soft Mesabi wind. At Biwabik
he told the boys what was up, then ran on to McKinley,
stopped briefly, and continued into Virginia, rousing the
secretary of the Finnish Brotherhood lodge there. It had
been a good twenty-mile run through the night. Next
morning few miners showed up for work anywhere along
the eastern section of the range.

The fire ran fast across the Mesabi, traveling west.
Out of the open pits and underground mines swarmed
the Finns, the Italians, and that conglomeration of races
designated simply as Hunkies. Warhorse Boose had managed to get the word to Chicago and Cleveland, and now
the Wobblies sent their best organizers, among them
Sam Scarlett, Frank Little, and the celebrated Carlo
Tresca. In less than a week all mining was tied up across
the fifty miles of the Mesabi, from Aurora to Coleraine,
and striking miners had trooped over to the small Cuyuna Range, calling out the boys there.

If the mine companies had been slow in catching on,
they worked fast when the strike came. At Virginia,
where fifteen hundred strikers were meeting in the Finnish hall—and talking pretty tough—mine officials had
little trouble in persuading the Law to swear in hundreds of citizens as deputies. These were armed and put

in charge of David Foley,[3] chief of the Oliver Iron Mining Company's mine police and detectives. The scene was set perfectly for the violence to follow.

The armed deputies called themselves the Citizens Committee. One of their first moves was to post a proclamation ordering all "agitators" to leave Virginia before sundown. The agitators paid no heed. That night strikers and members of the Committee clashed. Guns belched readily, and a striker was killed.

At Biwabik, slugging and sniping and sabotage at the mines grew into a roaring battle. J. C. Myron, a deputy, and one Tom Ladvalla were killed. Several were wounded on both sides.

There was rioting at Gilbert, at Eveleth, at Hibbing. Leading strikers were clubbed and driven out of Coleraine and Chisholm, with threats of lynching should they return.

Police arrested Tresca, Little,[4] Scarlett and five more Wobbly organizers. They were charged with the murder of Deputy Myron and were taken to jail at Duluth.

The range was now seething. Hospitals were overflowing with the wounded and beaten. If mine guards relaxed a moment, steam shovels and other expensive equipment were sabotaged as if by magic. From all parts of the West—which included Oregon and California—footloose Wobblies moved in, bringing the number of outside agitators to an estimated seven hundred. It was

---

[3] Naturally hated by the strikers because of his job, David Foley, once of Negaunee, Mich., was rated a brave man, afraid of nothing, and a dead shot.

[4] Lynched a year later while leading a strike at Butte, Mont., by a gang of masked men who left the old Vigilante warning "3-7-77" pinned to Little's body.

a lot of trouble to be added to the already troublous range.

The mines themselves were quiet enough. Not a shovel stuttered. The drills were silent. No ore trains moved; there wasn't any ore. Strikers tried to dissuade D., M. & N. crews from operating passenger trains (they feared strikebreakers might be brought in), but the railroaders paid no attention. So the strikers lined the tracks and jeered, singing Wobbly Joe Hill's famous parody:

> "Casey Jones, kept his junk pile running;
>   Casey Jones, was working double-time;
> Casey Jones, got a wooden medal
>   For acting like a scab on the D. M. Line."

The trains continued to run and to bring in passengers, chiefly newspapermen and certain startled mine officials. No strikebreakers came. The trains also brought in thousands of copies of *Solidarity*, the I.W.W. paper published in Cleveland. *"Sol"* fairly reeked with excitement and reported that the Red Dawn was imminent. Its banner headlines told the strikers they were battling against the Steel Trust for the good of all civilization.

Big Bill Haywood, general secretary of the I.W.W. and then at the height of his power, issued a "Declaration of War" on the United States Steel Corporation. Big Bill knew how to declare war in a large way and to leave no doubt about it. Wobbly linguists, of which there was never a shortage, put Bill's manifesto into eleven languages. Then they printed a ton or so of the proclamations and had them distributed by night in every iron-mining town in Minnesota, Wisconsin, and Michigan.

The Wobblies hoped and expected that a general mine strike would grow out of the Mesabi uprising.

Clubbing and shooting continued in the Mesabi towns. So did sabotage. Organizers rushed to Ironwood on the Gogebic and Iron Mountain on the Menominee; but they were met by city and mine police, promptly beaten up, and hurried out of town.

Early in July, Gurley Flynn appeared on the Mesabi again. This time the police were fully alert, and they made every effort to catch the elusive woman whose voice and presence had touched off the greatest iron-range strike in history. They never did catch up with The Flynn, but they got into hot water trying to. Six different women were arrested by mine detectives on suspicion of being the she-firebrand. The six women didn't like it and threatened to sue.

No wonder mine police had the jumps and jitters. For the first time since iron ore had been mined in America, more than twenty thousand miners were on strike, and not a wheel was turning on the Mesabi. Gurley Flynn staged two big meetings in downtown Duluth at which she told the world of the "brutal and high-handed methods of Steel Trust gunmen and thugs." Then she went on to St. Paul to plead with Governor Burnquist to do something "to stop the illegal attacks on strikers by tools of United States Steel." The governor said he would look into the matter. He didn't, and it was too late, anyway.

The Wobblies had their shortcomings, but they always had a fine sense of timing. In September organizers began to feel that the strikers were tiring of the struggle. The strike was not spreading as it had been earlier in the summer. Wives were pleading with their men to return to work. Winter was coming on. So the Wobblies held local union meetings in the mine towns. The locals voted to call off the strike and return to work.

The timing was perfect, everything considered. Even though the strike was lost, as it certainly was, its ending was marked, definite; the strikers had voted to end it. Much better that way, from the Wobbly viewpoint, than to have it peter out, with men drifting back to work and thus "scabbing." None of the demands had been won, but the Wobs seemed content: They had fought U.S. Steel to a standstill for three months, a thing none of the conventional unions had ever managed to do.

The effects of the Mesabi strike, however, were to be felt gradually on all the ranges. Wages were increased. Some claimed this was due entirely to wartime and a shortage of help. But many miners who were not Wobblies believed that wages wouldn't have gone quite so high if it had not been for those three months of battle on the Mesabi.

Working conditions, too, were better after the strike. More attention was paid to the safety of miners. But not nearly enough.

12 *Death Calls at Milford*

THE small mine settlement of Milford stood out sharp and desolate on the hill, that winter afternoon, and a wan February sun slanted long shadows on the snow. The longest shadow was that from the shaft house, a hulking mass of boards and timbers covering the entrance to the hole in the ground. Two rows of miners' shacks began not far from the shaft and marched away for a hundred yards across the white blanket, orderly enough and stark as only a Minnesota mine town can be stark.

It was a quiet winter day on the surface. Kids were at school. Miners' wives were busy in their tiny kitchens, and white smoke from sixty stoves rose straight up from sixty pipes guyed with haywire. The single telephone line to Crosby hummed loud in the silent cold, as lonesome a sound as the moan of a great horned owl.

One hundred and twenty feet below the bleak Minnesota winter, the day shift of the mine crew was busy digging out manganese ore. The Cuyuna Range was noted for its fine manganese. Forty-eight men were at work today, which was the 5th of February, 1924. The air down there was still and warm, the temperature about what one might expect on a fine autumn day. No mittens, no earmuffs down there.

It was a good safe mine, too. It had been in operation

seven years and had never had anything approaching disaster. Opened by Franklin Merritt of the famous mining family, it was owned by George H. Crosby, the big manganese man of Duluth, and operated by the Whitmarsh Mining Company. More important to the miners was the fact that Captain Evan Crellin was in charge. Captain Crellin was only thirty, but he had long since earned his title, both here and on the Mesabi. Son of old Captain John Crellin, Captain Evan was reputed one of the best men to work for on any range. Today, this 5th of February, Captain Crellin had a company official in the mine, the well known Roland McDonald, engineer of Duluth.

As for the miners themselves, they were all experienced men, mostly young, and the forty-odd represented every race and nationality on the Cuyuna Range.

Matt Kangas was one of the miners. Late that afternoon Matt began to get hungry and, as men will do at such a time, he took out his watch. It was exactly half-past three. Before he had returned the watch to his pocket, he heard a sound that stopped him dead in his tracks.

From far off somewhere, it seemed—his ear couldn't place the direction or distance—Matt Kangas heard a roaring sound, but such a roaring as he had never heard before, above or below ground. It wasn't a noise that grew; it was a noise both mighty and full-grown when it struck his ear. It couldn't be thunder, down there, and it couldn't be a thousand locomotives bearing down on him at once. For a flash Matt thought of it as a noise such as God might make, if God ever visited mines.

Matt didn't know what it was but he knew what to do: He ran like the wind for the shaft, shouting as he ran, and he saw that other men had heard the Thing and they were running, too.

The skip, the cage, was high above, on the surface. To get away from that noise, which now seemed to shake the very iron walls, a miner must take to the ladders. As Matt put his foot on the rung he heard shouts behind him. The shouts were mixed and jumbled from the echo in the shaft but they sounded like "Water—water!"

It *was* water, too. As Matt started his desperate climb up the first ladder, there came a roar louder than ever and Matt saw a rolling flood of black boiling stuff coming down the long drift. He saw Captain Crellin put a hand on the ladder, as if to mount, then turn to hurry away to a cross-tunnel where Matt knew four men were working—or had been working.

When he was perhaps twenty feet on his way up the interminable ladder, Matt saw something he never forgot; a leaping black wave thundered into the shaft below him and battered half a dozen screaming men against the manganese walls. Manganese is very hard. The wave seemed to recede, to rebound, then it leaped again to clutch at one uplifted arm and pull it down into a very devil's churn of water and mud and sand and ore and mine timbers.

The roaring noise seemed to abate a moment, but it was no time for a man to pause on a ladder. The shaft below was boiling, filling up as fast as a man could climb —indeed, it was filling faster. Matt saw it catch two climbing men, one after the other, and drag them under to be seen no more.

Matt climbed on. So did Emil Kaim and young Frank Kravaten, who had brought his father's dinner bucket that noon and had tarried in the mine. Those three and four others made it to the top. They were safe, but only by a margin so slim they never liked to talk about it.

Down below, down there one hundred and twenty feet, forty-one good men, including valiant Captain Crellin and Engineer McDonald, remained. They were to stay for days, for weeks, until the mine could be pumped out—but they wouldn't mind the delay in the least.

By the time Matt Kangas and the six others had come up into the frosty air, the time was three thirty-five. The mine, which was eighteen hundred feet long, was filled to within a few yards of the top of the one hundred and twenty-foot shaft. The filling had seemed a lifetime to the men who had climbed the ladders. It really had required but five minutes, scarcely long enough to have electrocuted a man in a chair.

But the rumble underneath their two rows of shacks, a rumble that had rattled tin dishes on the table, had told the women that not all was well in the mine. Miners' wives are like that; they are very alert to noises underground. They dropped everything and came a-running to the shaft house, Mrs. Majnarich with a kerchief over her head, the others with hair flying, and all with dry terror in their eyes. The weeping would come later.

All that Matt and the six with him could tell was "Water . . . flood . . . water all over." Mrs. Maki put her head into the shaft house to look. It was water, all right —surly, black, and gurgling—hardly a good jump below. Mrs. Maki turned away quickly, and all the women had to look. One of them became hysterical and had started to climb down the ladder when men seized her. The shaft house was roped off.

What was so ironically called "relief" came almost immediately to Milford Location. All mine towns are quick that way. Men and pumps came hurriedly from Brainerd and Crosby, and other men came from the range villages—Ironton, Cuyuna, Manganese, Wolford, and Riverton. Women came, too, and women were better than men at this kind of disaster. They found thirty-two widows, some of them with fingers frozen, still clinging to the rope that barred their way to the mine head. Others were sitting silent beside stoves in which the fire had long since gone out.

Thirty-two widows and eighty-two children whose fathers were still at the bottom of Milford shaft. Two of the widows didn't yet know of their new status. They couldn't leave their beds. They fussed, unknowingly, in the mine company hospital because the proud fathers had not come to see the hour-old babies who whimpered beside them in bed.

There was plenty that women could do that night.

As for the men, they got the great pumps going long before midnight. All that day and the next and the next, for weeks on end, the pumps never ceased their chugging at the Milford shaft. Enough water came out of that black hole to make a lake. And why not? It had been a lake, until half-past three on the afternoon Matt Kangas looked at his watch.

A little way north of Milford was a large pond, a quarter of a mile wide and some twenty feet deep in spots. By five o'clock on the day of the disaster, this body of water had shrunk to less than a third its normal size. The covering of ice had slumped and fallen. The pond was reduced to a frozen mire. The Milford shaft had taken a very long drink of it.

Reports always follow such disasters and Milford's

was no exception. The mining inspector of the State of Minnesota said simply that the mining operations had opened up a large area under the sand bottom of the pond. The bottom had given way, and—well, the bottom had given way.

Nobody but God was to blame at Milford, and if anyone got the blame at Ishpeming, two years later, it was God, too.

The Barnes-Hecker mine of the Cleveland Cliffs Iron Company ran its shaft into the ground some five miles west of Ishpeming, Michigan. It was a fairly deep mine, a little over one thousand feet down, and as safe as they made them. At 11:20 in the forenoon of February 3, 1926, the subterranean chambers of hard black magnetite suddenly shook as if with palsy, and a frightful rumbling filled the ears, and the hearts, too, of a hundred men who were at work on the 800-foot level.

All these men knew of what had happened at Milford; it was mine history. They dropped their tools instantly at the first strange rumbling and ran for the shaft. The mine cage was down-shaft and ready. Into it piled a herd of men before it shot upward to safety. Young Wilfred Wills, motor runner, didn't make the cage. So, he shouted warning to three men working near and the four started climbing ladders.

Eight hundred feet is no distance at all, on a sidewalk or across a green field. It is an ungodly long way to walk upward, in a mine where the lights have gone out and Death is mounting the ladder close under your feet.

It seemed a long way to Wilfred Wills, anyhow. He couldn't see what was behind, under him, but he could hear plain enough. He heard Death catch up with the three lads who were climbing for dear life, too—heard it catch up with them and pull them down in an agony of sound and horror that would wake him in his sleep ten years after.

Fifty-one men stayed below in the Barnes-Hecker, including the boss, Captain Tippett. A few days later ten bodies were recovered, all at the 500-foot level, which meant that the boys had been better than halfway up to safety. But halfway to safety in a mine isn't anywhere near enough. When the flooding water had ceased its gurgling it was precisely 815 feet deep in the Barnes-Hecker shaft. Deep enough, so some miner remarked— although it hardly seemed apposite—to have drowned even Andy Carnegie.

A number of the bodies were never recovered, but fifty-one funeral services were held in Ishpeming, a town that had long since become used to proxy corpses in its sixty years of mining iron.

What had happened? It was very simple, as simple as the affair at Milford. A good-sized pond—some called it a lake—had broken through the mine ceiling. State Geologist L. P. Barrett came to have a look. Said he: "Prior to any attempt to mine ore from the property, a large lake, actually over the ore body known at that time, was drained and ditches constructed to carry away any surface water from the territory immediately above the ore body." Geologist Barrett, known as an eminently fair and honest man, said that all possible precautions had been taken.

Lakes, however, have a way beyond the comprehension of man. They have an affinity for mines seemingly not to be reckoned with, even by geologists, engineers, and other experts. William E. Hill died with Captain Tippett and the forty-nine others in the Barnes-Hecker. Mr. Hill was Inspector of Mines for the State of Michigan.

13 *Tales Told in a Dryhouse*

MEN of the iron ranges have never lacked for something to talk about. Mine disasters, if they are well in the past, are favorite subjects. A lot of "stove mining" is done, too, when veterans who date back to the days of Captain Tom Walters and Captain Ed Florada tell of the candlesconce and mule-power era.

They talk of sudden death and of incredible rescue, and they are sure to tell about the ghost of Harley Harris. When a whole lake burst into that mine at Milford, Minnesota, Harris, one of the miners, gave the alarm by sounding the mine siren, and then tied the siren's cord around his waist so that the weight of his body would hold the whistle open. That was the way they found him, months later, when the mine was drained. But when operations in the mine were resumed, miners quit one after another, and drew their time. They told that they could still hear the wailing of the siren. Some of them claimed to have seen the wraithlike figure of Harley Harris, too, a-holding of her down and wide open.

They discuss the hardness of ore at different mines, and mighty drilling feats. And all Minnesota miners like to recall that feverish summer and fall of 1929 when thirty million tons of Mesabi ore went out of Duluth in seven months' time, a record.

They have their legendary heroes, become marvelous

with the years and much retelling—Jack King and such.
There are tales of the vast amount of sin on tap in Hurley, Wisconsin, and of wild doings in the past at the port
of Ashland, and at Iron Mountain and Gilbert. Men who
have worked in the copper mines of the Keweenaw Peninsula will speak up to say that Houghton, a copper
town, was the livest place in which a man could spend
his money. Old-timers are sure to argue about the speed
with which certain mine towns came into existence.
Many claim the record should go to Nashwauk, on the
west end of the Mesabi, and others say it was near-by
Marble. Both were built quickly. They talk of ghosts
that were once towns, too.

There is no end to the talk. Most of it is to be heard in
the great rambling dryhouses near the tipples of underground mines.

To a miner this building is "the dry." It is a combination bathhouse, warehouse, locker room, and club.
Sometimes, when feeling runs high on a subject, a dry
has something of the United States Senate about it.

Miners put their street clothes in steel-meshed lockers
in the dry. Their heavy mine togs, their helmets, lamps,
and boots, hang from the high ceiling in long rows,
hauled up there by chains and small pulleys, and left to
dry for the twelve hours between shifts. It is quite a
sight to see the clothing and equipment of four hundred miners hanging from steel chains, all in one room.
It is more interesting to hear the talk that goes on there,
talk that is continued in the shower rooms and possibly
carried on to some beer parlor in town.

There is something about a dry that makes for talk.
It is here that the real history of mines and miners is
passed down from the Nestors, many of them compe-

tent if unlettered historians, to the young fellows. The youngsters today think more of World's Series baseball, and automobiles, than they do of history, but they manage to get no little of the latter in the course of a year or so schooling in a dry.

No man can say of history where it leaves off and folklore and legend begin, for there is little documentation possible for what one hears in a dry between shifts. But it is probably as accurate as the history taught in colleges. It is often far more entertaining. There are no stuffed shirts in miners' history, no Millard Fillmores, no Cal Coolidges.

The aforementioned Jack King still looms large in mine-range history, forty years after his fabulous exploits, as a sort of combined Jesse James, Robin Hood, and John L. Sullivan. Although the countless tales of Jack King run off in all directions, they agree on certain items regarding him: He had worked as a copper miner at Hancock, Michigan; he was six feet tall, handsome as a leading man; he was for years the champion of all Cornish wrestlers; and, like Jim Fisk, he was "always kind to the poor." King was also a leading actor in what still is known as the Great Pay-Train Robbery, at Boston Siding, near Hancock.

Beyond these few facts, the listener can take his choice from literally thousands of tales of Jack King. The man has grown almost to Paul Bunyan stature. There is hardly a saloon on the older iron ranges wherein Jack King didn't beat somebody up. He felled oxen with his fist. In the woods near Michigamme he tangled with a big black bear, which he strangled with his naked hands.

At Republic, Michigan, Jack threw a big tough mine

captain over an ore car. At Champion he fought and
licked eight Irish miners single-handed, and on St. Patrick's Day. Over at Bessemer, he went sissy, attending a
dance there and ordering everybody off the floor while
he waltzed round with the belle of the ball. He seems to
have been on the move for most of his earlier life, and
his wrestling feats are recalled by old-timers on every
range except the Mesabi. By the time the Mesabi went
into production, Jack wasn't doing much roaming. He
was in the Big House at Marquette.

The Great Pay-Train Robbery occurred in 1893 near
Hancock on the Mineral Range Railroad. When the
northbound train pulled into Hancock that day, three
men got aboard as passengers—King and two other fellows. As the train was pulling into Boston Siding, at the
top of a long grade out of Hancock, three masked men
suddenly appeared in the locomotive cab. Each had a
gun in his hand. They forced the engineer to stop, then
had the fireman uncouple the train at the rear end of
the combination baggage and express car. Leaving the
remainder of the train stranded at the top of the grade,
the locomotive and one car pulled ahead about a quarter of a mile.

The boys knew what they were after. In the express
strongbox was $50,000 in cash for payday at the Calu-
met & Hecla copper mines. They tossed the box into the
bushes and told the engineer he could go along about
his business.

The affair had been well planned. On the road near
by was a man with horse and buggy, waiting. The boys
put the box under the buggy seat, and all four drove to
Laurium, then doubled back on their tracks to Houghton. Here they went to a boarding house where a con-

federate had a trunk. This confederate was, of all people, the engineer of the train they had held up. Into his trunk they put the cashbox. LeLiberty, the engineer confederate, had the trunk taken to the Houghton depot and requested that it be shipped to Marquette, where he had been transferred in line of duty.

The box, still unopened, got to Marquette without trouble. So did the robbers. Trouble came when the gang started to divvy the spoils. Two brothers named Hogan, who were later credited with having planned the robbery, put in their claims for an extra amount of loot. This was at the rendezvous of the gang in Marquette. Argument grew into a good-sized and rather noisy fight. Police were called. They came and toted the boys off to jail, along with the $50,000, still intact. The Great Pay-Train Robbery was over, except for sentences to be served in the Marquette pen and for tales about the affair, which never cease.[1]

After his release, Jack King appeared briefly in Hurley, Wisconsin; but his great days had passed, just as Hurley's great days now have passed. This town was the miners' Mecca for more than fifty years, a lewd and lively anachronism, a hangover into comparatively recent times from the days when Sin was barefaced and unblushing, a combination of Butte and Nome that existed well into the present century.

The Montreal River separates Hurley from its larger

---

[1] This version of the robbery, sedate compared to most, was given the author by D. S. Coon, of Escanaba, Mich., who got it from his father and other old-timers of the Copper Peninsula. The records of the State House of Correction and Branch Prison at Marquette, Marvin L. Coon, Warden, show that King got five years. So did John Butler, Edward Hogan, and Dominick Hogan. LeLiberty turned State's evidence and went free.

and highly respectable neighbor, Ironwood, on the Michigan side of the stream. For half a mile Hurley's main thoroughfare, Silver Street, ran between almost solid rows of saloons and bawdyhouses and combinations of the two. It was the toughest place on the range, any old range, and it seemed to glory in its reputation for assorted depravity.

Hurley's heyday passed twenty, some say thirty years ago. It has grown more seemly, and parts of its ancient face have been lifted and streamlined with chromium-fronted bars and night clubs. Here and there, however, one may still see architecture of the old backwoods frontier, even if the Hurley spirit is vastly subdued. There is the Old Office, with mirror and mahogany to dazzle the eye; and the Montreal, the Flame, and the Turf Exchange, remnants of the classic day of drinking hard liquor.

Perhaps the wondrous Marble Hall is the best sample of what drinking emporiums were like in the era of ten-cent whisky. It's in Hurley yet, and it cannot have changed much from the day it was built in 1888. Its back bar and walls are covered with large murals—a scene of two deer fighting; a man driving a pung-sleigh home with a fat buck in the seat; and a lone wolf baying under a bright Wisconsin moon. The colors have faded a little, and the artist—who was C. H. Peters and is not remembered today—painted in the genre of his time, with crude bold strokes in his human figures but with amazing care in detail of animals and trees.

Hurley's most notorious joint of former times was the Klondike, now no more. It stood on Silver Street, not far from the river, and was operated by one Joe De Caire, a fellow reputed as strong as an ox and lots quicker. Joe seldom needed any aid from bouncers.

Anything that a miner or logger wanted could be had in the Klondike. Old-timers think it would be running today had it not been for the mixture of bad booze and even worse women. They point out that the life of a "combination place" is never so long as that of a straight saloon.

Anyhow, a young miner who thought he was something in the way of a barroom fighter came into the Klondike one day with the idea of throwing the powerful and mean Joe De Caire into the street. Joe paid little attention, telling the lad to go away and forget it. The youth persisted, starting around one end of the bar to get at Joe.

One of Joe's many girls was leaning on the bar, having a drink with a customer. Why she did it isn't understood to this day, for big Joe was capable of taking care of himself. The woman drew one of those pearl-handled .32-caliber revolvers from her kimono and shot the lad down. He died.

They tell that Joe De Caire was never the same afterward. The killing sort of bothered him. Then, fire visited the Klondike in 1901, burning it flat along with Bartender Tim Ryan who ran into the flaming building to rescue money from the till. The Klondike was never rebuilt.

More feared than Hurley's thugs, these latter days, feared even more than accidents, is the disease called miner's consumption or silicosis. It is caused by dust from the drilling machines, and from blasting. You hear quite a bit of talk about it in the dryhouses.

There are few hospitals on the iron ranges that do not have one or more silicosis patients. One of these victims has kept track of deaths of members of a crew he worked with in a mine near Hurley, in 1931. They number twelve in the past eight years.[2]

The United States Bureau of Mines says that there is no known cure for silicosis, once it has a start. Hence, prevention is the answer to the problem. Wet drilling, while causing less dust than dry drilling, does not completely remove the dust nor the danger. Various dust-prevention devices, for use with drills, have been tried out. Some of them seem to do the job, but they require time to adjust; and many miners do not like to bother when they are working on a tonnage basis. The disease has become so prevalent that twenty-one states now recognize silicosis and related dust diseases in their workmen's compensation laws.

Iron miners have had few ballads of their own, although a man will occasionally raise his voice in the dry with "Section Sixteen," quite authentic and sung to the tune of "Ta-ra-ra-ra-boom-de-ay":

> If you want a lively time
> Take a trip down Sixteen Mine,
> Ride the cage that goes so fast
> You can't see the drifts go past.

---

[2] My informant is Donald Gerry of Ironwood, Mich., flat on his back for many years. Names and ages of Gerry's crew who have died since 1931 are given as follows: Victor Spear, 56; Tom Hollien, 58; Andrew Hollien, 57; John Oliver, 38; Charles Noviek, 35; Pete Tummey, 44; Pete Obert, 34; Louis Didiana, 43; Joe Schiavo, 50; James Leach, 50; Tony Steela, 48; Frank Schwab, 36.

Clamber off at Stop Fifteen,
Queerest place you've ever seen.
Lumber, mules, an' everything,
Taper off now, while we sing:

(Ta-ra-ra-ra, etc.)

Perk your ears up, pardner mine,
Cap'n coming down the line;
Scratch the dirt a little more,
Cover up the low-grade ore;
If he saw it he'd be sore;
Close down Contract Twenty-four.
Once that he is safely by,
Then our little song we'll try:

(Ta-ra-ra-ra, etc.)

When we're just about to blast
And it's quitting time at last,
Then we scrub our hands real white,
Wash away the hem-a-tite;
Sit beside Pa Stevens' ditch,
Chew the rag with Shift Boss Rich.
Cousinjack and Irishman,
Finnish and Italian.

(Ta-ra-ra-ra, etc.)

Cornish miners, and the Irish, too, were great singers
in former days. They seem to have had few songs dealing
with iron mining,[3] however; and nowadays there is little

---

[3] Only the most ancient of iron miners recall a ballad about a fancy
woman who operated in many of the range towns of the seventies and
early eighties. None can sing it today. Briton C. Prout, 71, of Virginia,
Minn., remembers of hearing both of the song and of the lady. He re-

singing of any kind heard in a dryhouse. The phono-
graph, then the radio, have silenced the warblers.

Item: Cousinjack miners had a saying that God made
at least one great mistake when he didn't make a man
entirely hollow; so he could hold more beer.

Item: Everywhere on the several ranges you will hear
about the cousinjack mine captain who asked a clerk to
order a "hay-frame." A telegram was immediately dis-
patched to Ashland—or Marquette, or Duluth—for
"one hay-frame." It required days and a number of tele-
grams to get the thing straightened out. What the Cornish captain wanted, of course, was an A-frame.

Iron miners have never been overly "radical," but
they often like to talk about things that must worry mine
officials. For instance, they like to talk about mine taxes,
especially on the Mesabi where taxing the mines has
reached a science, not to say an art. They know that
mine taxes are the Great Menace to mine companies, so
the boys like to chuckle over the thought of company
officials lying awake nights, troubled at the thought of
the two-to-six-million-dollar schoolhouses built in mine
villages; at thought of the Haviland and Crown Derby
china, bought with tax money for the schools' domestic
science departments. Says one jolly old skip tender in
the dryhouse: "Wouldn't it make Henry W. Oliver toss
in his grave to think of little Angela Campopiano crashing some of that china while learning to make a welsh
rabbit!"

Even in these later days there is often talk about rats

---

ports she was known as Mother Two-Tubs. In time, she became so
dusky red from so much iron ore, according to the song, that she was
adopted by an Indian tribe and became a princess. It is regrettable that
so charming a ballad has been lost.

and how rats "always" leave a mine just before a mine fire, cave-in, or other disaster. Most miners still believe it and will not work in a ratless mine. Not long ago the J Shaft of Cleveland Cliffs mine at Ishpeming was shut down for three months. It suddenly occurred to somebody that no one had taken the trouble to feed the rats during the shutdown. A group of miners purchased a sack of oats and took it to the mine head. One of the group, Axel Johnson, agreed to take the oats down-shaft. About ten minutes after he had been lowered into the mine, the men on the surface got the emergency hoist signal. The hoist was thrown into gear. Up came Axel, half a dozen great rats still clinging to his clothes. His face, neck, and arms were terribly chewed. "Eff yu vant dem so-and-so's fed again," he said, "yu go on down an' feed dem yurself."

Axel was taken to the mine hospital. There he related that the moment he got off the skip, what must have been a million rats came at him from every direction. He threw down the sack of grain and gave the hoist-quick signal. Rats swarmed all over him, squealing and gnawing, before he could get away.

Item: A rat in a mine can detect any change in atmospheric pressure. Hence, he knows when a cave-in is coming; or if gas is present.

In the older days teamsters were important and noted men on the ranges. Before railroads came, the arrival of a six-horse wagon in town was an event. It meant food, clothing, tobacco, liquor and mail. One of the most noted horse- and mule-skinners was Alec McKillop, weighing two hundred and twenty pounds and as broad across the rear as any prize Percheron, who drove supply wagons into Virginia, Mountain Iron, and Hibbing.

His voice was powerful enough, and it carried like thunder, rolling for a mile or more through the forest that covered the Mesabi. It acted like a locomotive whistle. Half an hour before he was due in town, Alec would roar loud and long, thus assuring himself of a good audience at the local post office.

Alec was drunk much of the time, a condition he laid almost wholly to his wooden leg. "Alcohol eases the chafe on my stump," he liked to say, as he poured down another four or five fingers. One time Alec went berserk in Duff Campbell's Midway Saloon in Hibbing. He didn't like the way the roulette wheel set. He picked it up and threw it into a corner. Then, he stopped at the stud table. He didn't like that, either. He turned it over. Then he turned half a pint down his throat, sat down on the barroom floor, and went to sleep.

Unhappy at the broken roulette wheel, Proprietor Campbell got a saw and cut off ten inches of Alec's peg. When Alec awoke he roared loud for a drink of liquor and got to his feet. As he started, automatically, toward the bar, the ten inches of leg that wasn't there threw him flat. The boys told him his leg had shrunk, on account of the good quality of whisky he had been drinking. Content with the explanation, Alec nailed a piece of two-by-four onto the end of his leg and went away to feed his horses.

Item: The larger mine cities were always good show towns. Sarah Bernhardt played them; so did Chauncey Olcott. Arthur Deagon, young miner at Hurley, went away to the city and became quite a noted singer and actor. Favorite of Scandinavians and many others, in all the range cities, were the Färm sisters, Tekla and Klara, born on the Marquette Range at Ishpeming, who sang sweetly in Swedish and English.[4] Much of the drama, in pre-movie days, was cared for by Miss Myrtle Vinton's Players, who had a fine repertoire for a week, including "East Lynne" every Friday evening; and Bob and Eva McGinley's company of troupers.

Any newcomer to the iron country was likely to ask where the Cuyuna got its odd name. This was the last iron range to be discovered. It was discovered when an owner of much land around Deerwood, Minnesota, attempted to run his boundaries. He soon found that his compass needle was greatly disturbed, and he at once sought iron ore. His name was Cuyler Adams and he owned a dog named Una. Hence, Cuyuna. Drilling on the Cuyuna did not begin until 1903. The range was "opened" in 1905, when United States Steel acquired property there.

Item: Winter? There never was such a winter in the iron country as that of 1880–1881. For three weeks not a train moved on any railroad north of Lake Michigan.

Item: A favorite smart-aleck reply to the question "Where you going?" is: "I'm going back-shaft." This reply means nothing at all. You can go up-shaft and down-shaft, never back-shaft.

Talk in the dry, these later years, more often turns to the constant introduction of new and largely automatic machinery, which supplants man power; and the efforts of mine companies to utilize low-grade ores. And always, of course, the boys in the dry wonder how many years of life are left to the iron ranges.

---

[4] Klara Färm, now Mrs. Lawrence Muehling of Manchester, N.H., is still heard in the range cities on occasion. Tekla, who became Mrs. Burt McKinnie, died in 1923.

14 *Rusty Ghosts Are Walking*

NO IRON miner of twenty-five years ago could have dreamed of the host of machinery that would soon change his ways or put him on the shelf, show him that he must become a mechanic or leave the range. Picks and shovels and horses and mules are no longer symbols of mining iron.

Nor are hand drills or hammers. Augers driven at high speed by compressed air drill powder holes in underground mines. After a blast the loose ore is loaded into cars by power-driven scrapers. Long trains of cars glide away down the endless levels to the smooth hum of an electric locomotive. At a shaft station the gable-bottom cars flop open to let the ore fall through a grate into the pocket below. From this pocket skips are automatically loaded by gravity, one after another, and hauled to the surface to be automatically dumped into loading hoppers at the tipple.

Instead of a murky hole in the ground, a mine is brilliantly lighted by electricity on the main levels; only at the working faces do miners need head lamps, and these are of carbide or battery. Shafts are of steel. Canvas tubes run everywhere, even in the deepest mine. They are part of the ventilating system. Mine cages are huge double-deck affairs, holding seventy-five men and much material. They are operated by electricity and can be hoisted at the rate of one thousand feet a minute.

In open-pit mines, the "steam" shovels aren't steam any more. They are run by electricity, weigh 350 tons, and pick up sixteen tons of ore at a dipperful. The shovels are moved either on rails or on caterpillar treads.

A big pit like the Hull-Rust at Hibbing will have some seventy-five miles of standard railroad track in the pit alone. But gandy dancers, as track crews are called, don't lay and move the rails any more. It is done by a machine that picks up the track, lays it down in a new place, and sets and drives the spikes that hold the rails. Even this method of getting ore out of an open pit may be passing. The ore conveyer has arrived.

At the Spruce open pit, at Eveleth, ore flows uphill and for a distance of one mile, on nine separate belt conveyers, each feeding the next, and travels at the rate of five hundred feet a minute. That's fast mining. The vertical lift from pit bottom to the loading dock is four hundred feet, which is quite a grade, but ore tumbles into the hoppers at the rate of seven hundred and fifty tons an hour. . . . It's enough to make an old-timer dizzy. There is no place around here for a man with a puttering hand shovel.

If open-pit ore is hard, or frozen, the boys wheel up one of the big blast-hole drilling machines, a tower set on a caterpillar, which makes the hole and sets the charge in no time at all. It's one reason that hand-drilling contests seldom are a feature of Fourth of July celebrations any more.

Not everybody knows that iron ore is more carefully graded than coal, peas, or tobacco. This is done because the various kinds of ore are the ingredients that compose the soup from which steel is made. Three days before an ore boat is due to arrive, say at Duluth, the grader at a

Mesabi mine will know what sort of ore is wanted. The grader's crew takes samples from the top of the loaded cars of ore, one from each car. Five samples are combined to make one sample, which is sent to the laboratory at the mine. The train then pulls out for its trip to the sorting yards, at Proctor, near Duluth.

Before the train has arrived at the yards, after a run of sixty-odd miles, the laboratory man has completed his analysis and telephoned the information to the boss man at the sorting yards. With the chemical composition of each car in front of him, the grader distributes the cars into lots known as "blocks," according to the tonnage and grade ordered.

Because the two major steel-making processes are the Bessemer and the open-hearth methods, ore is put into two general classifications—Bessemer and non-Bessemer. Chief difference is that Bessemer must not contain more than 0.045 per cent phosphorus, always termed "phos." Ore from the different ranges, even mines, is put into subgrades.[1] Great care is taken in grading and sorting, for no chef was ever more careful of his materials than are the men who boil ore to make steel.

Digging has gone on at such a rate since 1900 that the iron content, except in a few rich open-pit mines, is nowhere near so great as it used to be. Much ore has to be treated by a process known as concentration. This is expensive business. A huge plant must be built and filled with machinery. Into this the ore is taken for washing

[1] The Oliver Iron Mining Co. classifies its ore as follows: Mesabi Range Bessemer is graded into Groups 1, 2, and 5; non-Bessemer, into Groups 3 and 7. Vermilion Range ore is Pioneer (Bessemer) and Frontier (non-Bessemer). The Marquette Range produces Bedford (non-Bessemer); the Gogebic, Norden (non-Bessemer); and the Menominee, Barton (non-Bessemer).

with water in agitating machines. Sand and other impurities are thus removed. Even after washing much of the concentrated ore does not contain so much iron as in the days when the ranges were young. A time is coming when iron ore is going to cost a lot more than it does today.

How great a supply of iron remains in the ground of Michigan, Wisconsin, and Minnesota, no man knows. Some say it will last fifty years. At its annual meeting in 1938 the American Institute of Mining and Metallurgical Engineers reported that the main known bodies of ore will be exhausted in about thirty-five years. They pointed out that the Lake Superior district furnishes 85 per cent of the iron ore used in this country today, and that "all who know the terrain are convinced that the chances for discoveries of big new deposits are nil." The Institute seems to believe, however, that there will always be a supply of ore for the furnaces but that ore will cost much more in the future.

Ghosts already are walking on the ranges. At Babbitt, on the northeastern tip of the Mesabi, is an ore concentration plant that cost six million dollars to build. It is deserted, and so is the mine and the town of Babbitt itself. For 364 days in the year a watchman makes his rounds. Once a year mechanics come to oil the machinery, turn it over a few times, then go away leaving Babbitt to the watchman and the blue jays. Babbitt ore became so low in iron content that it had to be processed.[2]

---

[2] The Trout Lake plant of the Oliver company, near Coleraine, Minn., continues to concentrate ore to the extent of some 3,000,000 tons a season. Much sand and rock has to be washed out of the western Mesabi ore. The Trout Lake plant uses approximately 240,000,000 gallons of water every season.

And roaring old Biwabik, once the queen of the Mesabi, dims and grows ghostly. No ore has come out of Biwabik since the Mary Ellen mine was closed down almost a full decade ago. There is ore yet in the Mary Ellen, but it is not being mined today.

Eight miles north of Brainerd, Minnesota, the mine town of Omaha is deserted, its pits fenced off to keep stray cattle from falling into them. The same is true of Cuyuna, Northland, Trommald, Manganese—once lively little towns with stores, banks, post offices. Grass and brush grow high in their streets in 1939. The holes that once were the plate-glass windows of buildings are boarded up.

Doubtless there will be more of these as time goes on. Yet all isn't so black as it sounds. Many people think that if the range had low-cost fuel, to be used in processing ore, many a mine ghost would come to life.[3] Professor E. W. Davis of the University of Minnesota School of Mines ought to know what he is talking about, and he says that the United States has "an almost inexhaustible supply of iron ore . . . if concentration of the lean ores continues to make progress. . . . The greatest need is for cheap natural gas."

A Minnesota group known as the Range League of Municipalities thinks as Professor Davis. The League and other organizations are supporting plans for a natural gas pipe line to the iron ranges from the Baker field in Montana; or gas might be brought in from southwest Kansas. Either line would require piping for some

---

[3] In the spring of 1939 a new "sink & float" process was announced. If as successful as its sponsors believe, it would extend the Mesabi's life by many years.

eight hundred and fifty miles, which would be nothing unusual in this age.

Thus, evolution of the iron-mining industry has rolled along swiftly since the first big deposits were discovered, only ninety years ago. Every least change in mining methods has been recorded in a host of technical books. Production and costs have been analyzed in countless pamphlets and reports. Of the thousands and thousands of men who dug the ore out of the ground, not much has been written. Who were they?

Well, for the first three decades after 1850 they were mostly Irish and Cornish from the old country, together with a seasoning of Germans. French-Canadians were in the crews, too, but they worked only on the surface.

By 1890, however, the Murphys, the Lyons, the Maloneys, as well as the vast family of Jones, were becoming a minority. On the Marquette Range that year, more than eight hundred Swedes, Norwegians, and Finns "took out their first papers." The Nordic flood continued for another ten years.

After them came Italians, to be followed by Poles, and the Poles by a horde of races from southeastern Europe. Indians seldom worked in the mines. Negroes never became a problem; it was too cold up there.

At least one exact record of the ebb and flow of mine-town populations has been kept. You'll find the record, clear and easy to read, on the Deer Lake road out of Ishpeming, Michigan, which was one of the first iron towns.

The Deer Lake cemetery has two enclosures. On the left are the Catholics, on the right the Protestants, the heathens, the unbelievers. One enters either by the same stile over a fence, and the both of them together form a valuable record, one well worth the seeing.

There they are, the lads who dug the Marquette Range, the boys who found the stuff to be boiled into cannon for Vicksburg, armor plate for Santiago, shells for Saint-Mihiel; they had to dig deep before other Irish, and many Chinese, could lay the Union Pacific's rails; and a lot of their sweat went into New York's Flatiron Building and Chicago's Rookery. There they are, they and the women who cooked their pasties and bore their children. On the left and at the front are the headstones of the Celts who had dug salt in Ireland before they came to dig something harder in America. Back a little, the Murphys give way to a scattering of Duponts who cut the Ishpeming forest into mine timbers. The Duponts give way to a few Schmidts, while back of them are many Italians. Beyond the Cicalas are Swioteks. Beyond Swioteks, the names of Slovaks, Bulgarians, and Hungarians that no American can pronounce.

On the other side of the stile are at first the unnumbered men and women of Jones and King and other cousinjacks. They sleep well, after their hard labors in Cornwall and Wales and Pennsylvania and Michigan. Many of them went to sleep in the seventies and eighties. After them come the innumerable Nelsons and Swansons, who laid down their picks in the nineties and after; and the Wirkulas and Puttonens from distant Helsingfors.

One wonders if they found poetry, found beauty, in their hard murky lives. Probably they did. Most men do, no matter at what they labor, or where. One can believe that these underground men had a feeling for the darksome stopes; that blinking, bobbing candles in a long drift were a kind of poetry to them, and that the dripping of water in some remote cave served them as a rippling brook has served other men above ground, a kind of music. One can understand the thrill of a well set blast that shook the dark metallic walls until they trembled. They were, at least, working in the very midst of nature. And when they came up to look at the sun, the sun may have seemed more beautiful to them than ever it is to those who are never where they miss its rays.

The brewers of iron, the steelmakers, down in Chicago and Pittsburgh, never knew these men of the range. To them, these miners were as a vague race, possibly human, but far off as the moon. All the steelworkers knew was that somebody, somewhere, sent them a great deal of ore.

As for the miners, they knew little of what became of their ore, once it was dug and put into a ship. True enough, as everybody knew, the ore was made into iron and steel, but how, where, and by what sort of men, the miners had no inkling. When the ore had left the mines, it went out of their lives. And much of the ore had to voyage a thousand miles before it entered the lives of the steelworkers.

15 *Red-Bellies Down the Lakes*

A MINE engineer on the Mesabi, digging himself out through high snowdrifts around his cabin and longing for the ease and comfort of the city, once remarked that God always took care to hide His iron deposits well, placing them in ground far remote from centers of civilization.[1]

It is true. Much of the ore of the Lake Superior district travels a thousand miles, or more, before it reaches a blast furnace. But if God hid His ore so well, He was thoughtful enough to plat an inland sea, a handsome if not always calm highway, with the ore at one end, and plenty of coal at the other. Moreover, midway of this inland sea route are large deposits of limestone.

Ore, coal, and limestone—it's all you need to make iron and steel to span a nation and to start a nation to building forty stories high. The three must be brought together by some industrial link.

The red-bellies form the necessary chain. All ships on the Great Lakes aren't red-bellies. The term came into use with the first of the larger ore ships, built of steel and painted red, boats that could stow six thousand tons of red stuff in their holds and be away down the Lakes. The term is often heard today and may be applied to any ore boat, large or small.

---

[1] Lem Bradley was the genial and reflective man who made this observation. He pioneered on the Mesabi Range and now lives in Duluth.

They had a steamboat on the upper Lakes as early as 1818, when the famous *Walk-on-the-Water* plied fairly regularly between Black Rock, New York, and the hustling trading post at Detroit. She was a marvel in her day, being 135 feet long and making as much as eight knots an hour in good weather. It was sail and not steam, however, that moved most of the early ore from the Marquette and Menominee ranges.

Captain Alva Bradley's fleet of brigs and schooners was one of the first to handle ore. Captain Bradley started with the *London* in 1858, and a bit later added the *Exchange* and the almost legendary *Wagstaff*, which sailed with ore in its small stomach every season for more than a quarter of a century, a long life for a windjammer on the Lakes.

Steam began driving sails from the ore-carrying fleet in the eighties, and by 1900—although they were not completely extinct for another two decades—a sailing schooner was a curiosity, fit for a little piece in the local newspaper.

Both sailing ships and the earlier steam vessels left a ghastly record of tragedy, a record that is hardly suspected except by those who have sailed the Lakes or have lived close enough to their shores to know the fury of a storm on the inland sea. Men have kept that record. During the twenty years between 1878 and 1898, 5,999 vessels were wrecked on the five Big Ponds, and of this number 1,093 were complete losses—ships, cargoes, and often men.

Veterans of the Lakes remain calm when "deep-water men" call them patronizingly "fresh-water sailors," with an implication that sailing the Great Lakes is no sailing at all but a mere sissy outing. The fresh-water men point to the record and ask the salts if anywhere, in their Atlantic or Pacific, there is an expanse of 90,000 square miles to muster such a record of death and destruction. It is probably an argument that never will be settled.

No few of the wrecks on the Lakes have been caused by the desire of shipowners to get in just one more trip, late—too late—in the season. An average season on the Lakes is from about April 25 to December 10. It was during those "last weeks of navigation," as they are called, that many of the wrecks occurred. Winter comes down very quickly in those periods—in an hour, perhaps—and more than one ship has foundered and gone down by reason of the very ice that formed all over her. This is known as getting the little ice devils.

It was the little ice devils that caught up with the *W. F. Sauber*. Steaming out of Duluth with a load of Mesabi ore late one season, the *Sauber* was met by a gale of sleet off Whitefish Point, near the eastern end of Lake Superior. Weighted with the tons of ice that formed on her so quickly, and wallowing in a high sea, she was starting to sink when the steamer *Yale*, probably the only other ship on the lake at that moment, came up.

Captain James Jackson of the *Yale* hove to. For eighteen hours he stood by in the pounding seas, waiting for a moment when he could put over a small boat to reach the sinking vessel. By dawn it was seen that the *Yale* too would sink if she didn't get away from there; the ice devils now encased her in a heavy crystal plating.

At last, Captain Jackson himself with volunteers was lowered in a boat. They made the side of the *Sauber* and took off every man—every man but Captain W. E. Morris, who chose to remain. Thirty minutes later Captain Morris and the *W. F. Sauber* were well out of the storm by being well beneath it.

It was one of the countless classic rescues on the Lakes. Captain Jackson was given a gold medal, and sailors from Duluth to Buffalo contributed to a purse of gold that was presented to the brave officer.

The ore-carrying fleet has had its mysteries, too— ships that never made port and left no record of what happened. There was the *Bannockburn*, a great steel hulk of a ship that cleared Duluth with a cargo late one season. She was sighted next evening, and all seemed well. She was never seen again, nor were any of her crew of twenty-two men. Nearly two years later an oar with her name scraped in the wood was found among reeds on a shore of Lake Michigan.

Belonging to legend but doubtless founded on fact is the deathless story of the Two Lost Tows. You'll hear it everywhere that old-timers get to talking: One night on Lake Huron the line between a freighter and its two barges in tow snapped during a storm. Neither barge and none of their crews of six men was ever found.

There was the ill-fated *Chicora*. She wasn't an ore boat, but she often carried mining men as passengers, until January 21, 1895. Early on the morning of that day she put out of Milwaukee with one passenger and crew of twenty-three men. The weather was very mild. It looked like an easy, quick trip across Lake Michigan to St. Joseph. Weeks later parts of her wreckage were washed up on the shore near South Haven, Michigan. No one ever knew what happened.[2]

---

[2] Before he died in 1937, the late J. S. Morton, one of the *Chicora's* owners, told a newspaperman the "inside" story of her loss: "The reason

Old-time sailors of the day didn't like the looks of the first ships built of steel, and their dislike was only strengthened by what happened to some of the early steel boats. They sprung bolts and rivets in bad weather, and their plates came apart. Woodship sailors vowed it was against nature to keep a steel ship afloat.

The steel ship was delayed only briefly by these troubles, however. In 1890 the stanch *Manola* was built. She toted 3,000 tons of ore in the worst of storms and rode them all out easily. Two years later the 4,100-ton *Maritana* went into service, to be followed in 1896 by the *Sir Henry Bessemer*, rated good for 6,700 tons. By the turn of the century one of the proudest carriers on the Lakes was the great *Malietoa*,[3] reckoned a veritable ark, whose skipper considered 7,500 tons about right for a decent load of ore.

A great deal of attention was paid to the interior fittings of the earlier steam freighters, both wood and steel. The artistic efforts were of course confined to the captain's quarters, the dining and smoking rooms, and to two or three staterooms for the accommodation of mine barons and their invited guests. These were gorgeous, often even gaudy. To be a guest on one of the big red-bellies was considered a mark of distinction, as it is today.

Captain Stines pulled out of Milwaukee so early that day was that he was the victim of a physical disability that required constant medical attention. He wanted to get to Dr. Scott at St. Joseph. Had he remained in Milwaukee long enough to see a doctor there, he would have received the wire from us telling him to remain in port because of impending storms."

[3] Still an able ship, according to Capt. R. C. Caughell, who was in command when the author went aboard her at the Gary docks in the summer of 1938, to watch 7,500 tons of Vermilion Range ore from Two Harbors, Minn., unloaded in less than five hours.

Only invited guests were carried on ore boats, and no
Atlantic liner was more elegantly fitted. Panels of but-
ternut or walnut were set off by walls of polished white
mahogany, smoother than the satin—often brocaded—
of the draperies. Wherever there was a chance for wood-
carving, it was carved—carved into lions' heads and
claws, into flying sea gulls in half-relief and into profiles
of seductive Harpies and mermaids. Scrollwork hung
everywhere like gingerbread lace.

The lounges, you may be sure, were of the red plush
that marked the period, both ashore and afloat. Polished
brass glittered in a greater expanse of mirror than most
barrooms could boast. When a Samuel L. Tilden or a
plain Sam Mather or a Colonel James Picklands went up
the Lakes to see how his ore was doing, he rode, sir, in
style and at ease.

The size of the steel freighters continued to increase
with the years. In 1904 the *Augustus B. Wolvin* slid
down the ways. She made a mighty splash. She was 540
feet long and could carry 10,500 tons. Eight years later
she was dwarfed when the *W. P. Snyder, Jr.*, fifty feet
longer, took to the water and steamed away with 12,200
tons. A Goliath of modern-day ore carriers is the *Harry
Coulby*, second ship named for an English immigrant
boy who made good in a big way on the Lakes and became general manager of the Pittsburgh Steamship fleet.
The present *Harry Coulby*, launched in 1925, is 607
feet long and has a beam of 65 feet, making her a good-
sized craft on any man's ocean. She can tote 14,000 tons
of the stuff they use in Gary and Pittsburgh.

There is no red plush in the *Coulby;* but each stateroom is enameled in delicate tints, and each stateroom
has a tiled bath. The captain's quarters might well have

pleased an old-line Steel Baron, except they are rather in too good taste. As for the crew, they live in splendor compared to the quarters and mess of a freighter of twenty-five years ago.

Today, the ore-carrier fleet numbers some three hundred and fifty vessels, most of them much finer than a landlubber would expect; and a sizable fleet of ships is engaged almost wholly in transporting limestone from the Michigan quarries to the blast furnaces.

Ore-loading ports have one thing in common—a long dock, often a mile of it, lined with hopper pockets out of which thunders the ore, down into the hatches of the ships. First of the ore ports was Marquette, with a short haul of from twelve to thirty miles from mine to dock. Menominee ore, after a haul of from forty to eighty miles, is loaded at Escanaba. The Gogebic ore comes from fifty miles inland and is loaded at Ashland. All the Vermilion ore, together with some from the eastern end of the Mesabi, is hauled to Two Harbors from mines sixty-five to ninety miles distant. Duluth-Superior, newest and greatest of loading ports, ships most of the Mesabi ore after a haul averaging one hundred miles.

Loading became simple and quick enough, once the bumper beam was devised to spread the ore evenly in the hold. Without undue effort any carrier on the Lakes can be filled full of ore in less than two hours. It is often done much faster. The *Augustus B. Wolvin* once took aboard 10,500 tons in a bare ninety minutes.

Unloading takes longer but not nearly so long as it did before the Hewlett machine was invented. This device can be likened to the arm of the biggest crab that man could imagine, if he sat right down and imagined

hard for a long time. The Hewlett unloaders usually
work in a series of five or six units which travel on rails
along the dock and are spotted in position with hatches
on the ship. The huge arm unfolds, bends, reaches out—
and down into the hold it goes with the operator riding
it in an inclosure just above the jaws. Its mouth is wide
open when it strikes the ore in the hold. It can twist,
turn, perform every evolution possible to a shovel in the
hands of a man. Only the Hewlett picks up fifteen tons
instead of pounds at a bite.

With its maw filled and dripping with ore, the giant
arm comes up out of the hold, swings surely over a car
on the dock, releases its mawful, then unfolds again and
returns to the hatch.

As the cars are filled, they move automatically up an
incline to the top of the stock piles of ore, dump their
loads and return for more. Six of the Hewletts will un-
load seven thousand tons in from four to six hours. . . .
It gives an idea of what has happened to the man with
the No. 2 hand shovel. The Hewlett is the chief reason
that a round trip—Duluth to Chicago and return—requires but seven days. In pre-Hewlett days it took three
weeks.[4]

There would have been little need of inventing the
Hewlett unloader if there had been no canal and locks at
Sault Ste. Marie. Most of the ore was landlocked up
there beyond the swift and rocky falls that barred Lake

---

[4] An idea of sailing distances of the red-bellies can be had from the
following table, in miles (Buffalo is the basing point): to Ashtabula,
117; Cleveland, 173; Lorain, 194; Detroit, 256; Escanaba, 695; Sault
Ste. Marie, 602; Marquette, 760; Ashland, 949; Two Harbors, 973;
Duluth, 996. Sailing distance between Chicago and Duluth is 810 miles.
On Lake Superior alone, and in a fairly straight line, a ship can sail
394 miles between Duluth and Sault Ste. Marie.

Superior from the steel mills. The canal that Charles T. Harvey and his men blasted out of rock back in the fifties let the ore boats through. It has not to this day been given its rightful place among American historical events.

It is passing strange that so few Americans know anything about this canal. They will travel far to brag of having seen the Suez and the Panama canals, yet right at home is a gateway for commerce that has no peer, anywhere. The amount of cargo carried through the Suez is piddling compared to the burden that goes through the Soo. It has always been so. In 1915 it was fifteen million tons for the Suez, seventy-one million tons for the Soo. In 1935 it was thirty-two millions and forty-eight millions respectively. And remember, the Soo Canal operates only seven months in the year. As for the famed Panama ditch, it carries about half as much as the Soo.

Historians seem not aware of it yet, seventy-five years after, but the canal at the Soo has played a bigger part in America's development than the Erie ever did. It was a big factor in making good steel cheap and in putting the United States away out front in steelmaking. The Soo Canal is the greatest gateway of commerce on earth.

The Soo Canal can be a picture, too, one that will not readily be forgotten, with a score of big freighters, plated sheer white with ice and belching black smoke straight up toward the frosty sky, waiting their turn at the locks. It is a beautifully grim picture, mostly blacks and whites, with a dash of red, and it still cries aloud for an artist to paint it.

Freighting on the Great Lakes, no less than on salt water, has ever attracted all manner of men, from saints to scoundrels hiding from the law. In older days the crews were doubtless a rather rough lot. There are capable sailors today, only less rough. They have a leaven of college boys in the summer months. Fighting becomes rare. Discipline remains good, probably much better than in the American merchant marine, although the Great Lakes captains are not nearly so hard-boiled as they used to be—skippers like the redoubtable Fighting (John) Parke who could hear the least whisper of disrespect to his authority in a thundering gale. Fighting Parke scented trouble at far distances and always went to meet it, head on. Other noted skippers of the old school were Captain John Burns, and the genial Captain Frank Sealy, a notable teller of tall tales of the Lakes.

As for ports, old sailors seem to agree that for wild entertainment, plus downright thuggery, there was nothing quite like Ashtabula Harbor, Ohio. Not even Canal Street in Buffalo, long a Mecca for Great Lakes sailors, could equal Ashtabula Harbor. The sporting houses were so close to the docks that the ladies could and did sit on their own porches and display their charms to sailors even while the boys were engaged in docking the ship.[5]

Ashtabula Harbor's attractions have dimmed somewhat, or at least changed their outward appearance, and in later years Superior, Wisconsin, with a street of dives that would have done credit to the mining town of Hurley, became exceedingly popular with Great Lakes sailors.

---

[5] R. C. Rattray, who has served many years as a chief engineer on ore carriers, recalls one sailor who could not contain himself until his ship was docked. Leaping to the wharf before the lines were made fast, he disappeared and wasn't seen again for three days.

On the whole, however, the boys on the ore carriers have tamed down, immeasurably. They still have reason to dread the Pictured Rocks of Lake Superior, where so many storms have blown down a host of good ships, and men; and they breathe more easily when they have passed the notorious St. Clair Flats, where many a carrier has dragged her bottom and come away with all her plates loose.

But the boys eat like kings, sleep in quarters that would have seemed baronial to old-time Lakes mariners, and both the wages and the treatment they get are good. They do not work overly hard, and they are far more acceptable as insurance risks than their fathers and grandfathers. Both as men and as sailors they will stack up with any salts of the seven seas.

Part II

STEEL

16 *Kelly Takes Cold Air*

IT WAS common talk around Eddyville, Kentucky, that William Kelly had a disordered mind. Eddyville felt rather sorry about it, for young Kelly was a genial sort. He had a pleasant wife, and he was doing well—but not so well as to create envy—in his small iron business, making large black kettles that were used for boiling cane sugar in the Deep South.

Kelly's derangement was harmless enough so long as he confined it to mere talk, but even his talk finally became irritating to ironmakers of the Cumberland valley. It was so preposterous—against God and Reason, they called it. Kelly's idea, in short, was that he could make steel out of molten iron simply by blowing *cold* air into it. It was a heresy terrible enough to warrant a thunderbolt on Kelly's head, straight from an Old Testament Jehovah startled and angry at such thinking.

The heresy had its inception one day in 1847 while Kelly was brewing iron in his furnace near Eddyville. He noted that one small spot in the iron was glowing with a white heat, so hot it was almost invisible, and that no fuel heat was causing it. Only cold air played on the incandescent bit of metal. It gave Kelly pause.

Young Kelly was only thirty-six years old, but already he was a reflective man; and if early environment had anything to do with it, his birthplace was Pittsburgh,

Pennsylvania, where for a long time men had been giving thought to metals. For several weeks, after that incident at the furnace, Kelly mulled over in his mind an idea so revolutionary that he hesitated to speak it aloud; men had been burned at the stake for less. But it had to come out at last, and he talked it publicly to the ironmongers of Eddyville.

Iron contains carbon, said Kelly in effect, and air contains oxygen. The two have what learned men term an affinity. I propose to blow a blast of common cold air into a batch of molten iron. I believe the oxygen will *burn* away the carbon, leaving something pretty much like good steel.

They laughed uproariously, or sadly, according to their nature. They didn't burn Kelly at the stake, doubtless only from fear of the law, and he went ahead to build a pot in which he might prove his blasphemous theory. "It will be a converter," he said.

A few months later Kelly sent invitations to all interested to come to see his device convert molten iron into steel by the introduction of cold air. Men quit their forges up and down the Cumberland and came prepared to laugh at Crazy Kelly. He gave them a laugh, and a scare. Filling his devilish pot with molten iron, he turned on a blast of cold air. There came a roar, as fire, smoke, and hot metal belched out of the converter's mouth and splattered sizzling iron all over two acres of good Kentucky soil. Nobody was hurt, and everybody went home shaking his head over poor Crazy Kelly.

Kelly didn't cease his efforts for a moment. He immediately began work on a new converter. It was at about this time that his father-in-law, who took no stock in William's fantastic ideas, stepped in to prevent further ridicule. He had Kelly confined to the house and called a physician to "administer to William's disordered mind." He felt sure that he must commit his son-in-law to an asylum.

In those days mental cases were understood hardly at all, and Kelly might well have been taken forcibly to an asylum to be chained and fed like a wild beast. Fortunately for the steel industry, the doctor was a highly intelligent man. He listened attentively while Kelly explained his theory about steel. "My idea is perfectly sound," said the patient, "but I didn't build the converter correctly. I see what was the matter now; but I may have to build two or three more before I get one that will do what I want."

The physician became convinced that his charge wasn't crazy at all but might be on the verge of making a revolutionary discovery. . . . There was Mr. Whitney's machine that had made cotton king in the South.

Kelly, free from the shadow of the madhouse, went ahead along the lines he had laid out. He had plenty of time, now, to carry on his experiments; his best customer, the Cincinnati concern that bought his iron kettles, wrote him coolly that they wouldn't be wanting any more of his product. They had heard of Crazy Kelly's aberrations. They could not afford to handle kettles made by a man who harbored idiotic ideas of making steel out of iron and cold air.

Kelly was desperate now. He built four, possibly five more converters, none of them quite the right thing but each one getting better. Then, in 1850 or 1851—the date isn't certain—he announced to the Cumberland valley that he was ready to give another demonstration.

There wasn't a great deal of excitement around there,

so the ironmakers and the curious idle came to Kelly's
works to see what it would be like this time. Those who
had attended Kelly's previous demonstration were careful to stand well to one side of the mouth of the converter. The crowd was even larger than it had been at
the 1847 fiasco.

Years afterward an old man who was an eyewitness
recalled what happened that day. "We saw a middling-
sized vessel," he said, "that had a mouth open on one
side and near the top. The whole was shaped something
like an egg, only bigger than a barrel. We saw molten
iron poured into the vessel. Then, Kelly he turned on a
blast of cold air, blown from a rig he had devised himself. The vessel set up a large noise, a roaring like you
don't often hear, and fire belched furiously from its
mouth, making many colors. But only for a few minutes.
The noise and fire died down. We then saw a blacksmith
take a small part of the iron, which had cooled, and with
a merry ring of his hammer, he contrived and threw at
the feet of the amazed spectators, a perfect horseshoe.
. . . Next, the smith took some more of the cooled metal,
made it into nails forthwith, and shod the horse of one
in the crowd. No one laughed at Kelly, now."

The horseshoe wasn't steel, but it was malleable iron,
which is very close to being steel, and the magic of it was
that it had been converted out of crude pig in ten minutes and with no fuel other than cold air from a blast.
That ten minutes of William Kelly's was a moment to
rank with the best periods of Whitney, Morse, and Edison; that horseshoe, something to rank with the message, "W-h-a-t h-a-t-h G-o-d w-r-o-u-g-h-t."

It is doubtful that anyone present quite realized the
importance of what he had seen, unless it was Kelly—

Kelly and two Englishmen who had been working for him. They had come all the way from London to Eddyville the year before, saying they had heard of his experiments. They were ironworkers, they told Kelly, and they wanted to enter his employ. Big-hearted Kelly not only hired them but readily told them everything about his experiments. He apparently had no idea in mind of doing anything with his discovery—if discovery it was— other than of making steel by a new cheap method.

Now, with Kelly's first successful converter in blast, the two Englishmen suddenly disappeared. They left so quickly they didn't even wait to collect wages due them. Kelly thought this rather odd, and made efforts to find out what had been the cause. He managed to trace them to Cincinnati, then on to Pittsburgh and New York City, where they had taken ship for England. Kelly then forgot the matter.

That is, he forgot it for a time. Four years later Kelly, who had done nothing about his process other than to continue to improve it (carrying on his experiments in a corner of the Cambria Iron Works at Johnstown, Pennsylvania) read in a daily paper that an Englishman named Henry Bessemer had arrived in the United States for the purpose of patenting a process he had devised for the making of steel without fuel. Reading on, Kelly came to the conclusion that the process described was identical with his own. He also wondered if the two Englishmen who had left his employ so hurriedly had any connection with the matter.[1]

Heretofore Kelly had given no thought to applying

---

[1] He never found out. John Newton Boucher, apparently the only American who ever tried to give Kelly his due, wrote that the two mysterious Englishmen never again appeared on the scene.

for a patent. It is doubtful that he would have done so in 1856 if it had not been for friends who urged him, on patriotic grounds, to prevent a hated Englishman from getting credit for something a good American had accomplished years before. Patriotic feeling, as well as inventor's pride, probably caused Kelly to go to Washington. Here he produced evidence sufficient to secure a patent for himself in advance of the Bessemer patent.

In applying for his patent Kelly displayed the lack of showmanship that might otherwise have made his name secure. He called his invention "A Pneumatic Process for Making Steel," without any thought of putting his own name on it. He termed his process "pneumatic" because it was cold air that did the trick, and honest, literal Kelly felt that cold air should get the credit. He received his patent a year later, in 1857.

Now began the famous Kelly-Bessemer controversy, which was active, and sometimes bitter, for almost two decades and lasted another twenty years or so as a subject to argue about between shifts.

Henry Bessemer was just as much a mechanical genius as Kelly and a far abler man in other ways. He had had his discouragements, too. During the Crimean War he devised an artillery projectile that revolved in flight; but the metal of the cannons of the day was not strong enough, either in barrel or in chamber, to stand the strain of Bessemer's shell and its charge. He began experimenting with a process to make better steel than England's crucibles of the time were turning out.

Bessemer got no more encouragement in England than Kelly had received in Kentucky. The tight little island had gone into its long era of smugness, and it was tight against any new idea. One of its great Navy experts,

Sir Henry Chads, was indicative of the English mind of the period. In 1848, Sir Henry told Bessemer that "iron is a material not calculated for ships of war." Six years later England was plating its men-of-war with that metal.

So, faced with such expert opinion on the limitations of iron, Bessemer crossed the Channel to France, where Napoleon III gave him both encouragement and financial aid with his experiments.

Bessemer's next appearance in England was when he read a paper before the Association for the Advancement of Science, in October of 1856. He described to this body how he had converted pig into malleable iron by blowing cold air through it. It was the identical process William Kelly had hit upon in 1847 and had carried out successfully in 1850 or 1851.

Bessemer, unlike Kelly, was a first-class business man. He secured a British patent at once, and he also got strong backing. It required some doing to get the pig-headed British ironmongers to adopt the new process, but Bessemer and his backers did it. It made Bessemer a fortune, and in 1879 he became Sir Henry.[2]

Neither Bessemer nor Kelly had succeeded in making pure steel. What their process lacked was supplied by Robert Mushet, an Englishman who with his sons contributed many improvements to the iron and steel industry. Mushet was experimenting along the same lines as Kelly and Bessemer. He discovered that by partially recarburizing the liquid after it had been blown with cold air, the result was pure steel. Mushet secured a pat-

---

[2] Contrary to common belief, Bessemer was knighted not for his steel-making process, but specifically for one of his earliest inventions—a device for stamping deeds and other official documents.

ent on this part of the process. It got him a medal, and little else. . . . One wonders if Mushet and Kelly ever met to talk it over.

With Mushet's patent to help him, Bessemer went ahead and made his process a dazzling success in England and on the Continent. Bessemer steel rails were being laid in England as early as 1861.

Not in the United States, though. Unfortunate circumstances due to the dual patents, along with the necessary Mushet patent, and the fact that Kelly was beset with domestic and financial troubles at the same time, brought on a chaotic period. Bessemer rails made in England entered the booming American market.

Kelly and associates formed the Kelly Pneumatic Process Company to perfect a type of converter. They built an experimental plant at Wyandotte, Michigan, and here in 1864 the first commercial ingots of Kelly-process steel were cast. A year later these ingots were rolled into the first American steel rails at the plant of the North Chicago Rolling Mills.

The Kelly-Bessemer situation was further complicated. Alex Holley and his company at Troy, New York, had secured the American rights to the Bessemer-Mushet process and had started to make steel rails, too. The resulting confusion was not cleared up until 1870. In that year Bessemer's patents in the United States ran out and the Patent Office refused to renew them. Kelly, on his showing that he had received almost nothing for his device and his long years of work, was granted a renewal for seven years. Many steelmasters fought tooth and nail to prevent Kelly from getting the renewal. They wanted to use the process without paying for the right.

Whatever its name—and the name of "Bessemer" adhered to the method, chiefly because English Bessemer rails were used in large amounts by American railroads —the process was cleared up in time to furnish cheap and good rails to lay up and down and across America. The roads were laying six thousand, often seven thousand miles of new track each year. Within a year after the patent mess was straightened out, production of American Bessemer steel tripled. In another three years it had tripled again and in less than a decade the annual figure increased to more than one million gross tons. The price of steel rails dropped from a high of $166 a ton in 1867, to $45 ten years later. And in 1880 the United States was the greatest steelmaking country on earth.

Bessemer's, or Kelly's, process alone didn't bring all this about. It was merely one, if perhaps the most important, of the factors that were doing away with the Iron Age and bringing on the Age of Steel. Many an operator of Bessemer converters in the seventies and eighties bore an Irish name, and they did the best they could by William Kelly—they called his rig a Kelly Converter and nothing else. But the Irish soon were swamped by a horde of Poles and Hungarians and Italians who cared little what it was called, and Kelly's name dimmed a little every year until it was wholly forgotten.

Before he died, however, Kelly had the satisfaction of knowing that the nights and murky days of his home town were streaked and lurid from the belching volcanoes of Kelly's Pneumatic Process. Pittsburgh had taken his converter to its heart, if Pittsburgh had a heart, and was making a big thing of it.

17 *Pittsburgh Buds and Blossoms*

THE perpetual half-night in which Pittsburgh has lived most of its life fell over the city long before the Republic was born. John Frazer came there in 1749 to erect a forge and to make, among other things, very handsome and fairly accurate flintlock muskets. The smoke Frazer's forge sent up was some of the first seen around those parts.

What became Pittsburgh was at first Fort Duquesne, an outpost of the French. When the British took over, they renamed it for William Pitt. It was an odd choice, as things turned out. Pitt was a man of vast mental activity, but his physical powers were weak. It was going to take a prodigious amount of strong back and hard muscle to build the kind of city Pittsburgh became.

Fort Pitt was an ironmongers' paradise from the beginning. Two big rivers met at a point of level land to form the Ohio that flowed west, in the direction the country was building. The hills round about contained no little iron and a huge amount of coal. Some of the hills had limestone deposits. There was a forest from which charcoal could be made, until men discovered that coke was better. Natural gas hissed out of the ground.

Not all of these things were discovered at once; but by 1805 the Fort Pitt Foundry Company was doing business, and a bit later it cast some tough cannon balls for Commodore Perry to use on Lake Erie, and General Jackson blew a lot more of them at New Orleans. The Government took cognizance of this new supply of ordnance and established an arsenal at Pittsburgh in 1814.

There were setbacks for the "New Birmingham," as Pittsburgh liked to call itself, but there was no stopping it. The remarkable Schoenberger family, ironmakers of Petersburg, Pennsylvania, saw what was ahead, and in 1824 they built the Juniata Iron Works at Pittsburgh and began making bar and sheet iron, boiler plate, and cut nails on a large scale. Another German, the fascinating Christopher Zug, came to build the Sable Iron Works. Zug dressed like a Quaker, but his habits were far from Quakerish. He drove a stable of fast-steppers and was said to have lived a life as fast as his horses, until disaster struck his business and changed his ways. The Sable Works blew up from a boiler explosion one day. Zug sold his horses and thereafter lived soberly, driving a sorry mule whose hair had been burned off in the explosion. It is worth marking, for Zug was probably the only ironmaster ever to feel chastened.

On November 2, 1849, the *Pittsburgh Gazette* reported:

A messenger boy of the name of Andrew Carnegie, employed by the O'Reilly Telegraph Company, yesterday found a draft for the amount of five hundred dollars. Like an honest little fellow, he promptly made known the fact, and deposited the paper in good hands where it awaits identification.

Four years later one Benjamin F. Jones and one James Laughlin formed a partnership to take over the American Iron Works, which was having rough going.

Two rising business men of the town were William Thaw and Thomas Mellon. A British family named Schenley had married into a sizable Pittsburgh fortune. Both whisky and bottles to put it in were being manufactured in the city. Coke ovens and charcoal pits smoked all day along the surrounding hills and glittered all night. A rolling mill was crashing its way into the innermost consciousness of citizens. A man who went there to live at this period never forgot his first sight of the new Birmingham:

We reached Pittsburgh on a clear day, so that we did not see it at its worst; but, oh! the misery of that sight. . . . After traveling for two weeks through clean, white, cheerful-looking villages and towns, to come all at once upon dirty streets and dark filthy looking houses stretching away in rows continuously ahead and all enveloped in an atmosphere of smoke and soot which blackened everything in sight. . . . I soon became familiar with my environment, however . . . the gloom passed away, never to return.

Perhaps that's why they could stand Pittsburgh at all, in its early days, and in its great days, too. One by one, through the years, the steel barons moved out of town, to build country places in suburban Sewickley, and often to New York City. But many of the old and important families remained in the soot to the end, living in mansard-roofed horrors on Penn Avenue until encroaching skyscrapers shut out what little sun managed to penetrate the gloom.

An event of 1861 was the building of the Eliza Furnaces by Jones & Laughlin, two of the most famous stacks ever to brew ore into iron. At about the same time the Kloman Brothers, who had been making iron in a small way, built the Iron City Forge on Twenty-ninth Street. This forge, although neither the Klomans nor Andy Carnegie knew it, was the foundation of the Carnegie Steel Company which, in turn, became the colossus known as United States Steel.

The scene was set.

Down below, down in the ranks of the working stiffs, all was aboil and abubble, too. Skilled labor, at least, was noting that employers seemed to combine to further their interests. As early as 1830 five leading iron manufacturers had got together to set a scale of prices for their products. They were also in agreement on the subject of wages to be paid, and on company stores as well. The policies laid down were not peculiar to Pittsburgh or even to the iron industry: They were simply to pay the least possible wages for the most work, and to gouge the employee wherever it could be done. Company stores, in theory operated to help employees to live cheaply—as they damned well had to, to live at all—were nothing like that in practice. An employee was urged to run "a bill of goods" at the company store, and he might be sure the bill of goods cost him as much and usually more than he would have paid in an independent store. A dollar a day for skilled labor was considered a fair wage in the ironworks, and this not always in cash.

Such conditions brought on unorganized strikes which broke out sporadically between 1840 and 1850. In the latter year puddlers and boilers staged a determined effort. They struck hard and held meetings and parades which were orderly until strikebreakers were imported from Virginia and New England. The scabs were kept behind locked doors to prevent them from hearing the pleas of the strikers. Then the boys got tough. With a number of screaming women in their ranks, they in-

vaded many of the ironworks, committing sabotage on
the forges and furnaces. Rioting broke out all over town.
For the first time the militia was called out to put down
a Pittsburgh strike, an event that became all too common with the years.

In the next few years Pittsburgh employers had labor
eating out of their hands, even those "aristocrats of labor" the iron puddlers. But the puddlers were holding
secret meetings.

A puddler was quite a fellow during the latter half of
the nineteenth century. The puddling furnace was a
brick oven with two compartments—one, a receptacle
into which some five hundred pounds of pig iron was
put at a time; the other, a fuel chamber where melting
heat was generated. Drafts were so arranged that the
flames swept directly upon the surface of the iron.

With the pig iron in its place and the heat turned on,
the puddler went to work with a long rod. Through a
hole in the furnace door he began stirring the mass of
iron in order to bring as much of it as possible into contact with the air. Heat brought out the impurities in the
iron, and these, in the form of slag, rose to the top and
were drawn out of the furnace through a hole called the
cinder notch.

The temperature kept mounting, and gradually the
mass began to solidify into granules, something like butter in a churn. It was at this point that the puddler
started to show his skill. Yes, and his brawn. With his
rod through the sweltering hole, he worked the mass of
iron into three balls, each about the size of a bushel basket. These were taken out of the furnace with iron tongs
suspended from a trolley. The tongs carried the balls of

red-hot iron to the squeezer, where the remaining slag was forced out and the iron formed into a bloom, which was a bar three to four feet long.

As the bloom fell from the squeezer, it was grabbed in tongs by a "rougher," the man who shoved it into the rolls of the muck or roughing mill. This was to compress the iron still more and to remove any slag the squeezer had missed.

It was all a hard and colorful business. As the bloom hit into the rolls of the roughing mill, there was a crash to deafen, while a shower of sparks flew over everything. On the other side of the rolls, the bloom emerged slightly longer in shape and was caught by the "catcher" in his tongs and put through an even tighter roll. So the bar passed back and forth until it had gone through the last and tightest opening. It was then known as a muck bar.

Such bars were cut into lengths; several were piled together, and all put into a heating furnace. Here they were heated to a welding temperature, taken out to be rolled again, and were then cooled. This bar was merchant iron, the finished iron of commerce.

Puddling iron was done in a temperature hotter than an African jungle. It called for constitutions as tough as merchant iron itself, and killed off the others in no time. Working one charge was called a "heat." It required from two to three hours. Five heats were considered a day's work. Two, sometimes three men took turns at stirring the hot metal. Puddlers drank enormous amounts of beer with their work, ate much salt to supply what they had lost in the heat, and ever worked in puddles of sweat. When off duty, they drank beer with a slug of whisky added and gave their name to an honorable drink—the Puddlers' Cocktail. Working always in high temperatures, puddlers had a high mortality rate from pulmonary diseases.

Making merchant iron by the puddling process was big business in Pittsburgh of midcentury. Puddlers were the most important men in an ironworks. So, when they were so violently put down by the militia in 1850, they began to brood.

Puddlers did some of their brooding in the back room of a hotel saloon on Diamond Street, in downtown Pittsburgh. It was a ramshackle old place, but the beer was good; and out of the beer and brooding came talk. The boys discussed everything from the large fortunes doubtless being made by their employers to the need of a union for themselves. In 1858 a handful of these puddlers formed the United Sons of Vulcan.

The Sons were at first a secret organization. They continued to meet in the back room, but not everybody was allowed to join. They posted a man at the door and went on with the planning. They discussed the merits and faults of this or that puddler before he was asked to become a member. They devised secret handclasps, signs, and passwords. All the hocus-pocus of a lodge was used.

The idea spread rapidly all over town. Several groups were formed. A local lodge was called a Forge. The master of a forge was a Grand Vulcan. The membership was composed largely of American, English (Welsh), Scotch, Irish, and German puddlers. In 1862 they came out into the open.

For a time the Sons managed to get a number of concessions, sometimes by striking, often by negotiation. In the summer of 1867 they struck hard, crippling or shutting down every furnace in the Pittsburgh area. The em-

ployers replied by declaring a lockout of local puddlers
and sending to Europe for experienced men. There was
the usual amount of violence, and the strike ended in a
compromise. For the next decade the Sons held their
own pretty well, and then merged with two other unions
to form the Amalgamated Association of Iron & Steel
Workers.

Pittsburgh grew like a mushroom on its diet of soot
and cinders. In 1820 it had been a straggling village of
ten thousand population. Forty years later one hundred
and thirty thousand people lived on The Point between
the two rivers, or handy by. Steamboats were taking iron
products down the Ohio for shipment to the new towns
and cities of the West. The Pennsylvania Railroad had
come to town from Philadelphia and was bringing
hordes of immigrants to work in the mills and furnaces,
and was taking away Pittsburgh iron to invade the old
markets long held in the East by New England, New
Jersey, and Virginia manufacturers.

The magnificent character of the ironmaster, the
baron of smoke and fire and slag, was being formed. One
could see it emerging from the murk along the Monongahela.

Whether or not Andrew Carnegie was a real ironmaster is a matter of debate, but there is no doubt concern-
ing his ability as an organizer, salesman, and financier.
He never knew a great deal about the product he made,
and he didn't need to. He simply hired men who did
know.

Soon after his messenger-boy days Andy went to work
for the new Pennsylvania Railroad. He did very well,
both for the company and for himself, and he saw that

railroad iron of all kinds was going to have a boom market for a long time. Through friends he got to know the aforementioned Kloman Brothers who were making the finest railroad-car axles that could be bought.

In a desire to enlarge the production end of their business, the Klomans needed more capital. Andy Carnegie and his brother Thomas, a railroad purchasing agent named Thomas Miller, and Henry Phipps furnished the capital by buying into the Kloman firm. The axle business was so good that Andy resigned his railroad job to give all his attention to his new interest.

While he was still employed by the railroad, Andy had bought into a firm engaged in making iron bridges—things that any railroad might need; and he combined the bridge concern with his Kloman interests to form the Union Iron Mills. Miller, the railroad purchasing agent, managed to throw a good deal of business to the mills. Henry Phipps watched the company's coffers and expenditures. He was good with bankers, too. It was said Phipps could "float a check in thin air" longer than any man living. As for Tom Carnegie, old-timers who knew the Carnegie brothers said that Tom was by far the abler man. Better liked and trusted, too.

Andy did not remain in Pittsburgh long. He established his home in New York City, but he was everywhere—entertaining politicians and railroad men, seeing the right people, and traveling all over the country, around the world even. He always sent back plenty of orders to keep the Union Iron Mills busy.

Remaining on the job, Tom Carnegie married Lucy, the daughter of William Coleman, a pioneer Pittsburgh ironmaster who also had made a fortune in oil speculation. Coleman often helped the Union Mills over a lean period with a loan, and his advice to young Phipps and Tom Carnegie was worth much more than the money.

With the cost of bringing Lake Superior ore to Pittsburgh constantly decreasing, a group of Pittsburgh ironmasters proposed to build their own blast furnaces and thus save a part of the $40 a ton they were paying the various local makers of pig iron. They invited the Union Mills to join the group.

Old Coleman advised against joining. "Why don't you build your own furnaces?" he asked Tom Carnegie and Phipps. They asked Andy. He agreed. The firm of Kloman, Carnegie & Company was formed to build and operate an independent furnace. It was the first time the Carnegie name appeared in a company title.

The Lucy Furnace, named for Lucy Coleman Carnegie, went into blast in May of 1872 at Fifty-first Street. The Isabella Furnace of the other group was completed at about the same time. It was named for a Mrs. Herron, sister of one of the partners.

Taking raw ore and making it into pig iron was something new to the Klomans and Carnegies. They had always bought their pig ready-made. The new Lucy worked well for several weeks and then came down with a sudden "chill." A chill in a blast furnace is no joke. It means that the mixture of ore, limestone, and coke has been allowed to cool, through some breakdown of the machinery, and has formed a solid mass inside the brick stack.

The Lucy, it turned out, was chilled to solidity. The crew started in at the long slow job of digging out, from below, the mass of metal and flux. When the digging was perhaps six or eight feet up, Skelding, the Lucy's boss, remarked that if he only had a cannon he'd shoot all hell out of the chill.

The Allegheny Arsenal of the United States Government was near by. Somebody went there and talked the officer in charge into loaning a small siege mortar. Skelding let out a whoop of joy. Putting the piece at the bottom of the stack, he shot three balls—all they could get—upward into the mass. Each ball served to bring down some of the chill, but much remained. The cannon balls were now stuck high up in the stack. With a magnificent oath, proper to the occasion, Skelding put an extra large charge of powder into the snub-nosed cannon, rammed it near full of cotton waste, and on top of this placed a fifty-pound hunk of hard iron ore that had come from the Republic mine in Michigan. Then he touched her off.

The ore shot did the trick. Down crashed tons and tons of the "hang" and the Lucy was soon clean and running on another blast. Skelding's feat gave blast-furnace men an epic to talk about for the next hundred years.

No less epic was the constant battle for a record cast between the opposing Lucy and Isabella furnaces. The average daily output at first was fifty tons at each furnace. A few months later the Isabella was casting sixty-five tons. The Lucy went to seventy. So it teetered back and forth for two years, with Pittsburgh newspapers taking notice and the crew of each furnace working like madmen to beat the other's record, a desire that was not discouraged by the furnace companies. Then, on October 24, 1874, the Lucy up and smelted one hundred tons of pig iron in ten hours, and its crew got gloriously drunk on free beer and whisky. Ironmasters from Chicago, Johnstown, Wheeling, and Bethlehem soon came to Pittsburgh to see with their own eyes, incredulous at the news of a hundred tons a day from one furnace.

Served by the snorting Lucy, the Union Iron Mills was soon operating two plants, known as the Upper and the Lower mills. They were making many items, including iron bridges, and they were rolling iron rails. Old Bill Coleman, who had a most active mind, asked the Carnegie boys why they didn't look into this new business of making not iron but steel rails. Tom Carnegie was interested, but not Andy. "Pioneering don't pay," he said.

Pittsburgh had been lagging. There wasn't a Bessemer converter in town, although Coleman had read that steel was being made elsewhere by this process, both in England and in America. Coleman made a trip to Chicago and Joliet. Here he saw the wonders of the converter that blew molten pig iron into bright steel in ten minutes. He saw the same thing at the Cambria Works in Johnstown, again at the Cleveland Rolling Mills.[1] Coleman returned to Pittsburgh convinced that the day of iron, so far as rails and bridges were concerned, was a thing of the past.

Tom Carnegie was convinced, too. He and Coleman immediately began planning a company for the manufacture of Bessemer steel and nothing else. They took an option on a large farm at Braddock's Field, the spot twelve miles up the Monongahela where General Braddock was defeated by the French and Indians in 1755;

---

[1] Mr. Coleman might also have seen other Bessemer converters in action at Newburgh, Ohio, Bethlehem, Pa., and Worcester, Mass. Pittsburgh was singularly backward.

and they interested a number of wealthy men. Andy
Carnegie was still sour on the idea.

The new company went ahead without Andy. But he
was weakening. On a trip to England he was shown steel
rails that had done service for five years. Iron rails, he
knew, had to be junked or re-rolled every few months.
When he returned to the United States he went directly
to Pittsburgh and told Coleman and brother Tom that
he wanted to buy into the company. Little Andy was like
that; often he was dragged by the tail into new enterprises that added to his fortune.

Ground was broken and work going ahead at Braddock's Field when Jay Cooke & Company failed and the
Panic of '73 hit the country. Pretty nearly all work of
any kind stopped, and for a time it looked as though the
Union Iron Mills and Kloman, Carnegie & Company
would go down in the crash.

The Carnegie end of the business survived: the Klomans were frozen out by methods which even then were
characteristic of Little Andy. With the return of better
times, the work at Braddock was resumed. During the
panic J. Edgar Thomson, president of the Pennsylvania
Railroad, had taken $100,000 worth of bonds in the
Braddock venture. The new firm emerged as the Edgar
Thomson Steel Company.

When the huge plant was done—largest in the world
at that time—Mr. Thomson was hardly pleased to learn
that the company which had honored his name, and in
which he was a stockholder, had built it within as
easy distance of the Baltimore & Ohio Railroad as it was
of his own Pennsylvania. But Little Andy performed a
neat piece of flattery which softened the great man. On
the founding-stone corner of this "Leviathan of Steel,"

as local newspapers termed it, he placed a bronze marker of quiet dignity: "The J. Edgar Thomson Works."

The man in charge of building the Edgar Thomson was one of the real geniuses of steel, Alexander L. Holley, the same who had erected an experimental plant at Troy, New York, to show that iron could be made into steel by the Bessemer process. He also had a hand in putting in the Bessemer departments at Joliet, Johnstown, and Bethlehem.

Holley probably knew more about making steel than anyone else in the United States, and as much as anyone in England or Germany. It was he who first suggested that a chemist would be a good man to have around where iron and steel were made. He even proposed that steel be made to certain chemical standards, a heresy of the worst kind. These and many other of Holley's heresies soon became orthodox practice.

At Braddock on the Monongahela, Holley built what was doubtless the finest steel plant in the United States if not the world. One of his helpers was young Bill Jones, an ex-foreman from the Cambria Works at Johnstown. Holley found Jones an exceptional man. He told the Carnegies that here was the proper superintendent for them at Braddock.

This Bill Jones was thirty-four years old. Born in the sooty hamlet of Catasauqua, Pennsylvania, of Welsh parents, he had gone to work in the Crane Iron Works when he was ten. What education he acquired came from reading his father's collection of books, which included Plutarch and Shakespeare. Coming of age, he married and went to work at the Cambria Works in Johnstown, where he received an excellent schooling under Daniel J. Morrell, the "Quaker Ironmaster," who knew how to pick good men and was always the first to adopt any new process.

The Cambria Works of the time, indeed, amounted almost to a university of iron and steel. William Kelly was conducting his queer experiments in a corner of the plant. John Fritz, another great name in the industry, was chief engineer at the Cambria and already had invented and built his marvelous three-high rolling mill. And there was Captain Lapsley who knew more about rolling steel rails than anybody else. A bright young man could learn a good deal in Johnstown.

When the Civil War came on, Bill Jones enlisted as a private, was cited twice for great bravery; he returned to Johnstown a captain, and the title stuck to him ever afterward. Captain Jones resumed work at the Cambria in 1865, being made foreman of a department.

A shake-up in the management put Daniel N. Jones, no relation, in charge. Bill may have thought that he and not Dan should have been given the boss job, but he continued in his place as foreman. Then Holley gave him a chance to help him at Braddock, on the new plant.

As related, Holley found Jones to be a truly remarkable young man. Many suggestions made by Jones were incorporated by Holley in the Braddock plant.

Meanwhile, and before the Braddock works was ready, trouble broke out back in Johnstown. It was a bitter labor dispute, and news of it got into the newspapers. Andy Carnegie, always a great reader, saw the item. He hurried at once to Pittsburgh and proposed to his partners that they make Bill Jones superintendent at the J. Edgar Thomson, and that Superintendent Jones invite such workmen as were dissatisfied at Johnstown to come over to the Monongahela and bring their working clothes.

It was a brilliant idea, and it worked wonderfully. Bill Jones was a popular leader at Johnstown, and most of the departmental heads of the Cambria felt that he had been given a raw deal. Also, the Cambria boys were disgusted with the local labor trouble. Inside of two weeks pretty nearly every top-grade man at the Cambria Works had moved, bag and baggage, wife and children, into Braddock.

On the 26th of August, 1875, the J. Edgar Thomson Works—Captain William R. Jones, superintendent— made its first Bessemer blow, and a few days later Pittsburgh's first steel rails were crashing through the rollers.

Captain Jones was happy to have his old gang with him on the new job. So was Andy Carnegie. He had raided a competitor of all its best men, and every one of them had had long training in making what the Braddock plant was designed for—Bessemer steel. And although Little Andy couldn't have known it then, he had brought to the biggest steel plant in the United States the greatest steelmaker of all time, either in America or in foreign parts.

18 *The Mighty Men of Braddock*

NOT since time began had there been such doings in the iron and steel industry as went on after Captain Bill Jones pulled the starting whistle of the Edgar Thomson Works that first day at Braddock. Within a year the plant on the Monongahela was rolling more Bessemer rails than all the mills in the country put together. It was little less than a revolution.

The steel plant faced the river. Back of it on the hills the town of Braddock huddled in long rows of new shacks. They looked ancient and forlorn six months after they were built, for Captain Bill and his men made soot and grime twenty-four hours a day, every day in the week. When a local divine took him to task for working his men on the Sabbath, Bill roared that he was making steel for this world—let the preacher attend to what would come after.

Bill was a large man, generous and good-natured for the most part, but given to violent fits that reminded his men of the blast of a Bessemer when the cold air was turned on. But Bill's men would go to hell and back for him. He was terribly hard on weaklings and incompetents, and the lazy feared him like the Devil himself. To those who could and would follow him in his driving frenzy, Captain Bill was a boss without a peer.

When the Edgar Thomson Works started operating

Bill unquestionably had the finest crew of steel men in the United States. They got better and faster and more efficient year by year. In 1876 the works turned out so much steel, and did it so cheaply, that the company had a net profit of $181,007. Four years later Jones and his men were rolling 10,000 tons of Bessemer rails every month, and the company's profit that year was $1,625,-000, doubtless the biggest return to a steel concern in the United States.

The public was amazed at the huge steel production of the Carnegie company, and everywhere there was talk of the genius of this small Scotchman. But inside the steel business, where men knew the hows and whys of things, the boys talked of Andy Carnegie hardly at all as a steelmaster. They talked endlessly and admiringly of this dynamo of a Captain Bill Jones. The like of him had never been seen.[1]

"I'm going to drive America hell-whooping into first place as a steelmaker," he liked to say. "We Yankees have been dragging 'er—dragging 'er worse than a bunch of Joliet farmers, but by God we're going to get there." He swore prodigiously and often classically by combining the best efforts of the Bard of Avon, whom he knew by heart, with his own profane fancies, which had sulphur enough to glow in dark places.

Captain Bill sat up nights to watch the roaring converters blow fire that made the black waters of the river glisten. He sat up nights, too, to invent and to build the first Jones Mixer, a stupendous pot of an iron box into which Bill had the boys dump *all* the molten pig from the blast furnaces. The gigantic box was then rocked to

---

[1] And his like hasn't been seen since, according to all old-timers who worked under Captain Bill. He is put down as in a class all by himself.

and fro until the metal was fused into a homogeneous mass, ready to pour into the Bessemer vessels. This mixer assured an even quality of steel and was so good it is still used half a century afterward.

The mixer saved time, too. Captain Bill thought as much of a second as most men do of an hour. He stalked the plant from end to end, every day, his eye on everything, not only to cut out waste motion but to make his mighty men as comfortable as possible. He'd tear down a shed or building and have it rebuilt if he would give better ventilation that way. He set departments to working against one another, but he had them all working together for the glory of the Edgar Thomson as against any other steelworks, Carnegie or not. When the Braddock furnaces first hung up a world's record for production of pig iron, Captain Bill had a piece of sheet steel cut into the shape of a broom and fastened in a prominent place on one of the cast houses, thus signifying that the Edgar Thomson broom had swept away all previous records, here or on the moon. "I don't want to have to take that broom down," he roared at his crew, and they roared back that hell would freeze over first.

Nothing around Braddock ever got a chance to freeze over—the pace was too swift; but in spite of the speed none of the machinery ever wore out. Bill wouldn't give it a chance. Improvements in rail making were coming fast in those days, and soon there grew a monstrous pile of junked machinery at Braddock—machines that Bill had thrown out a few months, sometimes weeks, after they had been installed. "By God!" he often swore. "I'll have no haywire around these parts." And if Little Andy or any company official presumed to take Bill to task for junking machinery that was far from worn out, Bill promptly sent in his resignation and remained home for a day.

Captain Jones early became convinced that human flesh could not stand the pace of the daily twelve-hour drive at Braddock. He put the plant on three eight-hour shifts. But he was fifty years ahead of the times. Other steel mills, both Carnegie's and of other concerns, continued to work twelve-hour turns; and in 1888 Captain Jones regretfully returned his men to the longer workday, but not without a strike that lasted five months. It was the only serious labor trouble they ever had at Braddock under the reign of Captain Jones, and it was no doing of his.

It didn't take Little Andy very long to know that in Captain Bill Jones he had the peerless steelmaker. He tried to have Bill buy stock in the company. Bill wasn't interested. "I don't know anything about stock, and I don't want to be bothered with it," he roared loud enough to be heard above the rolling mill. "Tell you what you can do, Andy—you can pay me one hell of a big salary."

Little Andy did so. He paid Bill the same salary that the President of the United States then received, or $25,000.

Bill cared nothing for money. Men who knew him estimate that he gave away at least half of his salary to members of his crew or their families. If he learned that there was illness, or a new baby, in any of the poor homes in Braddock, Bill never bothered to tell the company about it. He simply sent the family ten, fifty, or a hundred dollars of his own money. It was one of the many reasons why men swore by Captain Bill Jones.

Under stress or strain Bill would fire men right and

left, sometimes a whole department at a lick. And he usually took them all back next day.

Little Andy had a habit of making sarcastic remarks to his officials, writing them on little cards and sending them through the mail. Most of the men who wore Andy's collar took them without a yip. Not so Captain Bill. He resigned at least twice on this account, swearing audibly that he would never work another hour for that oatmeal-eating son of a bitching Scotchman. On these occasions Little Andy hurried from New York and gave Bill a raise and also made him an apology. It was known inside the company that Bill Jones was the only man living to whom Andrew Carnegie would apologize.

To make the production records the Edgar Thomson Works was forever achieving, Bill preferred Germans, Irish, and Swedes. These men, and American country boys, whom he called "Buckwheats," were his favorites. Of his own race, the Welsh, Bill said that a small number in a crew was enough. Englishmen he held to be troublesome. "Always wanting more wages," he said. Whoever he was, and no matter what the wages, a man earned his keep at Braddock.

Andy Carnegie never ceased to marvel and delight in the rough-shod yet efficient way Captain Jones ran the works at Braddock. Andy was a celebrity collector, and he often brought great men to meet Captain Jones and to see him and his men perform. Herbert Spencer of *First Principles,* one of the intellectual giants of the world, was pleased to shake hands with Captain Jones and watch his men in action. So were Matthew Arnold and a host of lesser fry. It was no condescension, for Captain Jones was a giant in his own right, the giant of steel. He never got around to go to England, but his fame reached there. Asked to do so, he prepared a paper that was read before the Iron and Steel Institute of Great Britain, in which he presented facts so startling that the Birmingham ironmongers could scarcely believe them.

But Bill Jones's facts were facts. His paper showed that the average British worker produced 420 tons of iron a year, while the average American worker turned out 555 tons. He ascribed America's greater tonnage to employment of young ambitious workmen; a strong but pleasant rivalry between plants; the employment of mixed nationalities, and the use of the most up-to-date machinery.

One of Captain Bill's last feats had to do with something other than steel or iron. In May of 1889 a dam broke near Johnstown, his old stamping grounds, and flooded the city in one of the worst disasters of modern times. When the news came to Braddock that night, Captain Bill called for volunteers from the Edgar Thomson. Men fell over themselves to get their names on the list. Bill chartered a special train, packed it full of men and supplies, and was away to the Johnstown Flood. In the stricken city, Captain Bill took charge of his crew and did heroic work in rescue and relief, being later commended publicly by Johnstown citizens.

But the sands of Captain Bill Jones were running out. On the 28th of September, 1889, one of the record-breaking furnaces at Braddock got to acting badly. Apparently, it had a "hang," and the molten metal was not flowing to the bottom of the stack as it should. Captain Bill went down to see about it. He got there just in time. With a roar that was heard across the river in Homestead, the furnace exploded. Sizzling white-hot liquid

metal flew over everything, burning six men to cinders
where they stood, and splattering the captain. Bill leaped
or was blown backward at the blast, and he fell into the
pit, striking his head on the edge of a steel car. His
burns alone might well have been enough to kill him,
but officially he died from a fractured skull.

It was a proper way for death to call for Captain Bill
Jones, in a slag pit, and with his boots on. The furnaces
did not make a new record that day, but the Bill Jones
Steel Broom still hung high on the plant, secure. Next
day, for the first time in fourteen years, or since operations began, the Edgar Thomson Works were silent. Ten
thousand men, many of them weeping openly as they
marched over the slag and cinders, saw Bill Jones laid
in his grave. Bill might have appreciated the honor, but
he never would have approved of shutting down those
Braddock furnaces for twelve long hours.[2]

Probably the most notable character at Braddock after
Captain Jones's death was a gigantic Irishman named
Mike Kileen but usually known as the Pusher. He
weighed two hundred and fifty pounds and often was
ugly. He came to Braddock as a common laborer, with
his toes sticking out through his shoes. Ignorant as a
yearling bull, he had many of the bull's attributes; but
he was a sort of genius, too. The Pusher became one of
the great blast-furnace men that old-timers still talk
about.

---

[2] In the head offices of the Carnegie-Illinois Steel Co. at Pittsburgh, a
faded photograph of Capt. William R. Jones hangs on the wall amid
those of such moguls as the two Carnegies, the Messrs. Phipps, Shinn,
Peacock, Corey, Gary, and Schwab. His strong, good-humored face, with
a slight squint to the eyes, might remind one of the Hon. Winston
Churchill of England.

By the time Mike Kileen had worked up to being boss man around the Braddock furnaces, he was a privileged character. When Andrew Carnegie visited the plant, Mike used to show him around and always called him "Andy" and nothing else. Mike the Pusher could get away with anything. It was told and believed among the Braddock crew that Andy had given orders that Mike Kileen was never to be fired, no matter what happened.

Plenty happened. Once when the company had imported a German expert, one Herr Whitman, to do some experimenting at Braddock, Mike walked in one morning to find the scientific man at K Furnace. Without a word he grabbed the German by the collar and threw him out into the yard.

Mike was feared everywhere for his violent temper. He was always beating some one up. Even his brother Jack was scared of him. On one occasion Mike told Jack, who was a molder, not to make a cast in some new molds until the next day. "The molds are too wet," he said. But Jack wanted to be away on a picnic. He went ahead and made the cast in the damp molds, hoping that Mike wouldn't be around again that day. The cast was ruined, just as Mike had said, and Jack saw Mike approaching. Jack hurriedly put on his coat, stepped out a side door, and wasn't seen around Braddock again for two years.

Mike's temper finally got so bad that the boys used a system. They knew it was Mike's custom to enter the plant every morning at the door to K Furnace cast house. At this door the gang always stationed one of their number, to observe Mike's temper and pass along the word when he was unusually vicious.

There was one fellow on the plant who got tired of Mike's toughness. He was Gus Rose, an inoffensive little man who stood about five feet. Mike always took a delight in riding little Gus. One morning Gus walked spryly into Mike's office, took a small revolver out of his pocket, slammed it down on the desk close to his right hand, and looked Mike in the eye. "Good morning, Mr. Kileen," he said meaningly. "And how does every little thing look to you this morning?" Mike was horribly afraid of guns. He looked at what Gus had near his hand, then laughed nervously. "Oh, everything is fine and dandy, Gus," he said, "just fine and dandy. Have a cigar?" It tickled everybody except Mike, and Gus Rose seemed to grow six inches taller. Mike never went near him again.

Mike contributed one great improvement to the steel industry—the Kileen Skimmer, for skimming slag from hot running metal, which is used to this day; but his peculiarities eventually convinced the company that he was a dangerous man to have loose. He was committed to a Pittsburgh hospital where he remained twelve years, crazy as a loon and happy. He had been pensioned off at $9,000 a year, and he felt very wealthy. Every day or so the old urge to be at the plant would take him. "Hitch up my rig, boy," he would shout at the top of his voice, which was still that of a bull. "Hitch up my rig. I've got to meet Little Andy. They're having trouble with the furnaces at Braddock." It took three strong orderlies to hold him in the room. Old Mike the Pusher finally died, and his last words were mutterings about the Braddock furnaces.

They had a number of toughies at Braddock. One of them was another Mike, known as Block Brennan, an ugly customer who appeared even worse than he was, with his horribly burned face, the result of an explosion of metal. Maybe that was why he liked to pick on men under him. One day he picked on a new hand named Anderson, who couldn't even speak English. Anderson said something in Swedish, picked up a long tapping-bar and struck Block over the head so hard that he died on the spot.

Many of the future great got their early training under Captain Bill Jones, too, among them young Charlie Schwab, Julian Kennedy, James Gayley, and James Scott.

The Edgar Thomson Works was a huge success from the day it began operating. The timing, thanks to Tom Carnegie and old Bill Coleman, had been perfect; railroads were now shouting for rails made of Bessemer steel. Iron had had its day; iron rails would soon be a drug on the market.

Andrew Kloman had seen it coming. He was the man who had been frozen out of the Carnegie concern. Not long after Braddock had gone into production, Kloman started building a steel plant across the river about a mile below Braddock. The site chosen had once been Amity Homestead, the fancy country place of a Pittsburgh pioneer named John McClure. At about the same time Kloman broke ground, a group of Pittsburgh steel men, angered because Carnegie would not sell them billets any longer, decided to build their own mill to make steel. Kloman and this group put in together, erecting a plant to make both rails and billets, together with the newfangled structural steel. Kloman died before the mill was ready, but in 1881 it began operations under the name of the Pittsburgh Bessemer Steel Company.

In charge of the new mill was one of the stockholders, William Clark, who prided himself on his successful opposition to labor unions. One of his first acts was to issue an order requiring all employees to sign an agreement renouncing their right to join any union. Most of the employees were members of the Amalgamated Association of Steel & Iron Workers. They soon struck. A compromise was made. Then came another strike. It was like that for the best part of two years. Manager Clark was relieved of his duties, but troubles at Homestead, which had by now dropped the "Amity" from its name, continued.

Homestead stockholders tired of the troubles. The mill was losing money, anyhow. The price of steel was dropping. So was the price of shares in the Pittsburgh Bessemer Steel Company. When the shares got low enough, the Carnegie company bought control, very cheaply. A strike at Johnstown had furnished the Carnegies with their crew of mighty men at Braddock, and now another strike had presented them with what was to become their biggest steel mill.

The Carnegies at once began enlarging the Homestead Works. Julian Kennedy came over from Braddock to take charge. He added a row of Bessemer converters, and he also installed one of the first open-hearth furnaces in America. This was not only keeping up to date but almost getting ahead of the times. From now on, Bessemer had a real competitor in open-hearth steel.

By the time Homestead had got into its stride, pneumonia, which was rather common around steel mills, removed Tom Carnegie from the company. It was a great loss, and on top of this Captain Bill Jones soon died in his boots. Little Andy looked around for somebody to run the whole shebang.

In 1882 the Carnegies had bought an interest in the coke company operated by young Henry Clay Frick at Connellsville, Pennsylvania. Only thirty-three years of age, Frick had built up a coke business that had almost a monopoly in the Pittsburgh area.[3] Andy invited him to join the Carnegie company. Frick did so and soon was put in charge of all the various properties. It was unquestionably the most brilliant move Little Andy ever made; and few of his moves were witless.

Frick began at once to consolidate the many Carnegie interests into one company under his management, and he also kept one eye on competition, for a new threat to the Carnegie rail monopoly had risen on the Monongahela—the Duquesne Steel Company, backed by Pittsburgh capital, which had erected a plant on the river bank just above Braddock. This wouldn't do at all.

The Duquesne rail mill was even more efficient than those at Braddock and Homestead, but the Duquesne management lacked a sense of reality. In a day when the Amalgamated union was very powerful, the Duquesne began operations with large grim signs in its yards and shops proclaiming "No Union Men Allowed on These Works."

The sign caused trouble from the first day—breakdowns of machinery, poorly rolled rails, and one thing or another. There was also a great deal of bickering in

---

[3] Born in 1849 at West Overton, Pa., Frick was a grandson of the founder of the famous Overholt distillery, and at nineteen Frick was working in his grandfather's office. Between 1871 and 1882, young Frick had the amazing career from which he emerged as the colossus of coke.

the crew, some of whom possibly carried cards in the
Amalgamated. In spite of these difficulties, the Duquesne
works cut into the rail market by underselling the Carnegie product. It could do this because it had adopted
the then quite revolutionary practice of running ingots
from the soaking pit through the rail mill without re-
heating. At the Carnegie mills, steel passed two or even
three times through the furnace before it became a finished rail.

But after a brief period the Duquesne company discovered that there wasn't a very lively market for its
good and much cheaper rails. Perhaps a letter sent out
by Carnegie himself had something to do with it. Andy
drafted this circular and sent it to every railroad purchasing agent in the United States. It was a truly alarm-
ing circular, and it gave the railroad boys the jitters. It
did not, of course, mention the Duquesne works by
name, but it shouted a grave warning against the use of
rails made by the direct rolling process. It said such rails
were very dangerous and intimated that derailment of
trains and consequent loss of life could be expected
where they were used.

This letter had an effect and so did the labor troubles
at the new Duquesne works. When Mr. Frick, Carnegie's new manager, proposed to the Duquesne people
that they sell out to him—direct-rolling dangers and all
—that company was glad to sell. In its first year under
Frick the works paid back their cost price. Nor was a
stop put to the "dangerous" direct-rolling process. It not
only was continued at Duquesne, but was adopted in all
the Carnegie plants.

Frick continued with his consolidation plans. In an
amazingly short time he had constructed a railroad con-

necting the various Carnegie properties, some on the Monongahela, others on the Allegheny. Frick could pick men as well as Andy, and he placed each of his plants in the hands of a capable manager.

In 1892, Mr. Frick's consolidations were made into the Carnegie Steel Company, with a capitalization of $25,000,000, and Mr. Frick took time off to build a mansion in Homestead, where he would be in the center of things. Whether or not he looked ahead a few months and saw it, Homestead was indeed to be in the center of things.

19 *War on the Monongahela*

THE man on the Smithfield Street bridge over the Monongahela didn't see much to interest him until just before dawn. He had watched there all night, walking back and forth, now in solid darkness, now in lurid light as some Bessemer went roaring into blow and revealed Pittsburgh, outside the steel mills, to be quiet and asleep. It had been a rather dull night.

But now, in the murky half-light before dawn, at a quarter past three, the watching man sighted a procession coming up the river. It was a flotilla of two tugs and two scows. In the lead was the *Little Bill,* towing the *Iron Mountain;* close behind, the *Tide* towing the *Monongahela.* The man recognized the tugs easily; he knew they were of the Carnegie Steel Company's fleet. And the names of the scows were familiar, but not their shapes. If these were the same ungainly tubs which were ordinarily used for moving the Carnegie company's steel rails, then monkey-work had been performed on them. They looked less like rail scows than they did like ships of war. Instead of open vessels, their holds were now enclosed with rugged woodwork, or something possibly even more resistant.

The man on the bridge couldn't know what the scows contained, but he must have felt that they contained no good. The man's name is lost to history. What he did is well known: he hurried from the bridge into drowsy Pittsburgh, and at the nearest telegraph station sent an eight-word message to Mr. Hugh O'Donnell, Homestead, Pennsylvania:

WATCH RIVER. TWO STEAMERS WITH SCOWS LEFT HERE.

Neither the watcher on the bridge nor Hugh O'Donnell knew what the two strangely covered scows contained. In them were an even three hundred well armed fellows who were soon to be only too well known as the "Pinkerton men." They were said to have been recruited by Pinkerton's National Detective Agency [1] from the ranks of ex-convicts and others unemployed. Assembled at near-by Youngstown, Ohio, they had been transported by rail to a point below Pittsburgh, and now they were being towed through the night to their destination.

Their destination was Homestead, eight miles above Pittsburgh. Homestead was already known as the biggest steel plant in the world, only it wasn't making any steel just then. It had been closed down five days before by Mr. Frick. Mr. Frick didn't like unions. He had fought his coke workers to a bloody finish at Connellsville, and he was determined now to smash the steelworkers' union in his Homestead plant.

Mr. Carnegie didn't like unions any better than Mr. Frick did; but Mr. Carnegie had long enjoyed posing as the Workingman's Friend, and so he went away to hide at Loch Rannoch, in Perthshire, Scotland, leaving Mr. Frick to do the smashing.

There was one thing about Henry C. Frick. He posed

---

[1] The Pinkerton Agency denies that ex-convicts were in this crew, and states that all its guards were agency-trained and responsible.

as nobody's friend, and the steel he made at Homestead was no tougher than Frick himself. When the Amalgamated Association of Iron & Steel Workers had refused his proffered scale of wage reductions, earlier in the summer, Frick shut down the plant. He also built a high fence around it—a fence with small holes, just about the right size for a Winchester barrel, bored through it.

By the time the big fence was completed, the steelworkers had become alarmed at the thought of strikebreakers. They placed pickets all around the plant. Other pickets watched roads leading into Homestead. Both town and steel plant, in fact, were actually in the hands of the strikers. But before all this had happened, Mr. Frick had asked Mr. Pinkerton to send "three hundred watchmen" to Homestead. They were almost there now.

The flotilla of trouble steamed slowly up the dirty yellow water of the Monongahela. The two scows were really more like *Merrimacs* than rail boats. Their tops were covered with stanch planking; inside, they had been specially fitted for the job in hand—sheets of armor plate, such as Mr. Carnegie made for the United States Navy, lined the top and sides. One of these men-of-war had been rigged up as an eating place, the other as a bunkhouse. But the Pinkerton men weren't to do any sleeping and not much eating.

At a lock below Homestead, the tug *Tide* dropped out because of engine trouble, and the *Little Bill* took both scows in tow. Just as the armada came abreast of Homestead, and could see the fitful glimmering of the Carrie Furnaces through the murk, a long sinister moan roused the sleeping town. It came from the whistle on the Homestead Electric Light Works, blown by Hugh O'Donnell, chief of the strikers' forces. O'Donnell had just received the message sent by the man on the Smithfield Street bridge in Pittsburgh. It was 4:25 in the morning of July 6, 1892. It was going to be quite a day.

No Paul Revere roused a countryside quicker than that Homestead blast. The horrible stark town back of the steel mills leaped to sudden life. Shouts and yells came from the sable-clapboarded shacks huddled close to the river, and doors banged on the slightly less grimy houses that clung to the bare steep hills which rose quickly from the river bank.

Out from the city wharf darted the small *Edna,* a launch chartered by the strikers for use as a patrol boat. The *Edna* circled the *Little Bill* and its ominous tow, hailing her. There was no answer. The tug steamed straight for the landing dock inside the steel plant's fence.

Again the *Edna* circled, while its crew shouted to know who and what was this ark of a cargo, cursing the *Little Bill* and all it contained and towed. By now, the near-by shore was alive with the figures of running men, many of them carrying rifles.

All was ready now.

The *Little Bill* steamed on to the water entrance of the big plant, silent now inside its hulking grime. A gangplank was put out from a scow, and somebody's nervous forefinger pulled the trigger of a rifle that was loaded and went off promptly.

Whose finger is not known, and although Congressmen were later to argue about it for weeks on end, it doesn't matter in the least. Here was a naval force of three hundred armed men who were being paid $1,500 a day to take charge of a steel plant and to guard it. And here was a land force of four thousand men, many of them armed, who believed their jobs, their very existence, were at stake. The only sure thing at such a moment is that someone will pull the trigger of a gun.

All hell broke loose immediately. Captain Hinde, in command of the Pinkerton men, went down in a welter of blood on the deck of the *Iron Mountain*, and the dry sinister crackle of rifle fire rattled all along the shore. On shore, too, four men were seen to throw up their hands and go down, one of them gushing blood horribly from his mouth.

The big whistle that had set all the town astir now boomed again, sending its hoarse bellow into every mouse's nest in Homestead and causing dishes to rattle in the cupboards of Rankin and Braddock, across the river. It served, as one man recalls, as a suitable bass for the staccato tenor of Marlins and Sharpses and Remingtons and Winchesters.

Women screamed high in twenty-two languages that morning, but it took no linguist to understand them: They screamed hate and terror, and long before noon many of them screamed anguish. They grabbed their kids, now, and started up the bare hills, the better to see their men shot down.

The Pinkerton men were hopelessly outnumbered, and they did the only thing they could. They remained in their armored scows, taking pot shots through portholes at any strikers who exposed themselves.

During a lull in the shooting, the *Little Bill* hurriedly took aboard several badly wounded Pinkerton men and backed out into the river, gunfire from the shore raking her full length. She chugged away to Braddock Hospital with her bloody cargo.

The whistle and shooting had aroused the workers at the Carrie Furnaces on the north side of the river. In midmorning, watchers on the Homestead side saw a puff of smoke rise up from near the furnaces, and soon they heard the scream of a cannon ball. It was a poor cannon and a poor ball, both of them cast for a war thirty years gone, but they tore a ragged hole in the side of the *Monongahela*. The ordnance had been taken from its place in front of the G.A.R. Hall in Braddock.

The Homestead army and their women on the hills cheered loud for the Braddock artillery. Here was something new. They cheered loud but not long. A second shot from the cannon went too far to hit a scow and exactly far enough to strike and to shear off clean the head of young Silas Wain, one of the strikers, who was crouching in the steel plant's yard.

It was a fearful death in full view of the mightiest audience ever to watch death on the Monongahela. It mattered not that it was strikers' cannon that had killed a striker. There in two pieces lay the quivering form of one who would have been alive except for the damnable Pinkerton men. The Homestead fighters and watchers went into a murderous frenzy.

From the Grand Army Hall in Homestead men, with women helping them, pulled still another old field piece of '65. They wheeled it to the pumping station just above where the scows were moored. They poured powder down the ancient's throat, followed the powder with a cast-iron pill that may have been meant for Richmond, and rammed it home with old newspapers. A fuse burned close, and the ancient roared and vomited fire.

It was good drama but not practical war. The shot went wild, away over into the middle of the river. Try as they would, the artillerymen could not depress the gun's muzzle enough to hit the scows. The ordnance was abandoned.

Not the battle, though. Fresh ammunition and arms had arrived from Pittsburgh for the strikers, and they swarmed toward the scows from three sides. But they hadn't yet learned the strategy of siege warfare, and the lesson was terrible in its cost.

A breath of flame from a scow porthole took an eye and a life out of George Rutter as he monkeyed with his own rifle. Another breath caused John Morris to grab at his stomach and to crumple up queerly in his middle, and go down to stay.

No, the boys on shore hadn't learned that a fortress isn't to be taken head on and by infantry alone. Peter Farris was running forward with a bright new Marlin in his hands when a porthole flame breathed at him. A watcher said Peter Farris whirled full around, threw his Marlin high in the air, and went down in a heap. A moment later, Harris Striegel kneeled to take aim at a porthole. The porthole flared briefly and the top of Striegel's head spattered a pile of pig iron behind him. A witness wondered if the iron had been made in No. 2 Blast, where Striegel had worked so long. . . .

This kind of battle wouldn't do. The strikers changed their tactics. Working warily, they piled iron pigs and steel rails and billets to make breastworks that no rifle could penetrate. Sharpshooters crouched in the shadow of huge ingots. And meanwhile new strategy was afoot.

Moored in the river at the up-end of the steel plant was a small raft of lumber. Strong hands rolled a barrel of oil from plant to raft and an ax swung to break the head. The green ooze poured out over raft and water. A hunk of burning waste was thrown into its middle, and men with long tapping irons gave the flaming raft a push in the right direction.

By now more than fifteen thousand persons watched from the bare open hills that were gallery seats. The amphitheater was larger than Rome ever had. The show was just as stirring. With flames shooting high in the air, the barge of fire slowly moved downstream toward the hapless scows, cheered on by more voices than Homestead had ever heard.

The raft, for a moment, seemed to be the answer to the siege. Making a heat that could be felt even on the streets of Homestead, it moved slowly, ruthlessly down toward the scows. Then it stuck on something and burned itself out to the groans of the gallery.

"Then," said Myron Stowell, who saw it, "then, many of the strikers could be seen dragging their bodies like snakes along the ground inside the plant yard." They were working their way to a single and exposed flatcar that stood on a railroad spur inside the plant. The short spur of track, as everyone could see, led directly down to the wharf where the scows were moored.

Moving the flatcar a bit, to get it behind a pile of pig iron, the men quickly loaded it with barrels of oil and bundles of waste. A torch was applied. Up leaped the flames as a man released the hand brakes. Fifty sweating bodies heaved hard at the car. It moved, it rolled, it was away down the slight incline to the wharf. The gallery on the hills went stark mad.

Down went the car loaded high with fire, gathering speed as it approached the water. It never got there. A spread rail, or something, sent it reeling off the track and into the sand alongshore, to burn futilely to an accompaniment of curses in twenty-two languages.

The deep-throated voice of the Homestead whistle warned strikers that some new danger was present. It was the *Little Bill* back from her trip with dead and wounded to Braddock. What the *Little Bill* meant to do, no striker or Pinkerton man ever knew. Before she was little more than in midstream a long rattle of gunfire broke out from behind the pig iron and ingot breastworks. In a moment there wasn't a pane of glass in her pilot house, and bullets ripped long neat splinters in her side and decks.

The pilot was Captain Rodgers. He lay on the floor and steered as best he could, which wasn't very good. The *Little Bill* steamed around in great drunken arcs, careening this way and that, while her smokestack was made into a sieve and her sides and lifeboat broke out with a great pox of lead bullets. But Rodgers managed to keep her off the Homestead shore, and presently she got out of range, to steam fast for Pittsburgh.

It was hell all around the two scows that day. It must have been no less inside. More than fifty Pinkerton men had been struck by bullets. Two of them, J. W. Klein and T. J. Connors, lay dead and covered with canvas in a corner. The bottom decks were slippery with blood. It was late afternoon when a pike pole with a fairly white shirt on its end was poked up from the scow nearer shore. The shirt was promptly torn and the slim pole shattered by gunfire from the pig-iron forts.

"We gotta kill them Pinks,[2] every one!" It was the

---

[2] Non-English-speaking strikers corrupted it to "Fink," and fink has since been a word calling for a smile—if you don't mean it.

shout that went up and down the breastworks. Old John
Monroe remembers it well today, in 1939, for he got a
bullet in his left leg just then, a Pinkerton bullet that
came along as John ran for the Carnegie pumphouse to
help unpack some dynamite.

John Monroe isn't sure, but he thinks the giant blasting powder was brought into Homestead from near-by
coal mines. Anyway, there was a lot of it, and a lot of
boxes of little brass caps, and roll upon roll of dirty
white fuse.

In 1892 many a steelworker had started life in the
coal mines and was more familiar with blasting powder
than with guns. *This* was simple as breathing. The
Homestead boys got out their knives, made holes for the
caps in the brown sticks, bit the caps with their teeth to
hold them firmly to the fuses, then rammed them into
the powder.

A man ran out of the pumphouse, a bundle of sticks
with a smoking tail in his hand. He waited a moment,
watching the fuse, while bullets of the Pinkerton men
zipped past him. Then he heaved.

A spume of water shot up close to the scows. When it
fell, watchers could see a long jagged hole just above the
water line of the *Monongahela*. Another bundle of death
fell smoking to the top deck and puffed fitfully. Men
prayed to God it would explode. It did. It went up with
a roar that sent planks flying in every direction. It made
a hole large enough for men on shore to see human
forms inside the scow.

The dynamiters continued. Another mob of men,
moved by a new idea, stormed uptown and raided the
Homestead fire hall. In a moment they came tearing
back down to the plant, yelling like all the devils in

hell and dragging a hosecart behind them. One of the big Carnegie water tanks was drawn off, and into the tank a hundred men poured oil, barrels of it, rolling them upward on inclined planks.

Soon, they were flushing oil from the hose onto the surface of the river around the scows. It swirled sluggishly, then spread out to make gaudy colors all around the besieged men-of-war. Bundles of flaming waste were thrown onto the oil. It fired the slime to burn bluishly in spots for a few moments, then went out. The scows weren't even scorched.

While the hosecart attack was going forward, President William Weihe of the steelworkers' union tried to address several hundred strikers back of the breastworks. Big Bill, seven feet tall and known as the Giant Puddler, was a commanding personality. But there was no commanding this mob. What Big Bill attempted to say was drowned in shouts for more and bigger and worse war on the Pinkerton men.

The men at the pumphouse were dynamiting the scows into another try for truce. Again the pike pole with the frayed shirt on it went up. It was close to nine o'clock in the evening.

This time Hugh O'Donnell, who had received the telegram sent by the man on the Smithfield Street bridge, walked alone and unarmed down the embankment to the scows. He and the Pinkertons parleyed. They asked only for safe conduct out of town. O'Donnell, who was an honest and an earnest man but who must have been unduly optimistic, agreed. He called and appointed a guard of men who first made sure the Pinkertons had no arms. And then the doomed men were formed into double file and began the march uptown.

As they left the scows they were forced to throw away their hats.

The plan was to escort the strangers four blocks to an old skating rink where they would remain under guard until they might safely be moved out of town. It might have worked, had Homestead been deserted. Instead, the town now swarmed with probably 20,000 persons, most of them hostile to these outlanders. It was a terrible gantlet, and no credit to Labor.

The mob surged at the Pinks all along the four blocks. Women clawed at them, screaming as only women can. One harridan ran the sharp end of an umbrella into a Pinkerton man's eye. It stuck there and he had to pull it out himself. A group of wild-eyed women tore a Pinkerton from the ranks and fell on him with awful fury. They left him less of a man than before. . . .

Boys threw stones and all manner of filth. Large infuriated men hauled Pinkertons from the line of march and beat them unmercifully. Various sadistic obscenities were performed on the hapless strangers. Forty-odd of them did not finish the march at all; they had to be dragged and carried, some of them mere pulps of flesh, to the skating rink guardhouse.

Down at the boat landing a mob ransacked the scows, then fired them, pouring oil into the holds. Flames spread to the pumphouse, and the blaze rose higher than the stacks of the steelworks. It all made a lurid and fitting end to what was America's greatest industrial battle, before and since. Fourteen men were either dead or about to die. The seriously wounded numbered one hundred and sixty-three.

By now the press had heard about Homestead. Newspapermen were pouring in from Chicago, New York, everywhere. For another five days the strikers ruled the town. State troops moved in on July 12 and took charge. The Battle of Homestead was over, or almost. One piece of violence remained. It happened eight miles away in Pittsburgh, and, for the strikers, it was a greater tragedy than anything that had taken place during those seething hours of July 6.

When the Homestead smoke had cleared, public opinion may not have been wholeheartedly with the strikers, but it was wholeheartedly against Henry C. Frick, Andrew Carnegie, and the steel company. The two men and the company were damned publicly by press and pulpit. A song [3] favoring the strikers at once became popular and was sung in every beer garden in the eastern states. In time, had it not been for this last piece of idiotic violence, public opinion might well have supported the iron and steel workers' union.

On July 23, then, Henry C. Frick sat in his office, the office of general manager of the steel company, in the Hussey Building, in downtown Pittsburgh. Suddenly a slight dark young man entered the room. "Frick—" he began. Then he pulled a revolver from his pocket, aimed at the steelmaster's head, and fired.

Blood poured out of Frick's neck and ran down over his well trimmed beard as he staggered to his feet. The young man fired again. The bullet took off part of Frick's left ear. Attendants came running to grab and tussle with the young killer. He tore partly away, a knife in his hand, stabbing Frick viciously.

They had the assassin collared now. Frick was all bloody, but game. "Let me," he said to his rescuers, "look at his face." He pointed to the fellow's mouth.

---

[3] "Father Was Killed by the Pinkerton Men," by William W. Delaney.

"What is he chewing on?" Frick asked. They choked the man and took a small capsule from his mouth.

The young man said his name was Alexander Berkman. The melodramatic capsule, he said, contained "enough fulminide of mercury to blow us all into bits."

They put Anarchist Berkman away in the pen for twenty-two years. He served fifteen, emerging to appear briefly in the limelight in 1917, when he and Emma Goldman were deported to Russia for conspiring to obstruct the war aims of the United States.

Berkman was no steelworker. He had no connection with Homestead nor its strikers; they had never heard of him. He had come alone from New York to commit this piece of exhibitionism. The confused public put him down as one of the "Homestead Rioters." His one contribution served to set the people against unionism in all its forms. It also helped the steelmasters to make up their minds to run their mines and mills as they damned well pleased.

Henry Frick didn't die from the bullets and knife wounds. He was too tough for that. With showmanship that matched his nerve, he remained in his office until quitting time that day. Doctors came. Frick would take no anesthetic. "I can help you probe better without it," he said.

Once bandaged, Frick was propped up in his chair with pillows, and there he stayed, dictating and signing letters until the day's work was done. The public cheered a brave man.

That night, from a bed in his Homestead mansion, Frick gave out a statement for the press. "I do not think I shall die," he said; "but whether I do or not, the Carnegie company will pursue the same policy and it will win."

Henry Frick was correct. Not for forty-five years would a steelworkers' union amount to anything. In the interval, many a blast-furnace and rolling-mill man cursed, not Frick, but Alex Berkman. They often said they wished Berkman had chewed down hard on that capsule before ever he got to Frick's office.

20 *The Cinder Shore*

CHICAGO had its labor troubles, too. They were sudden, numerous, and, quite typical of the place, reeking with wholesale murder and other violence. Mr. McCormick's Harvester Works, coupled with a small band of pure anarchists, had brewed a pot of violence that blew up in the terrible Haymarket affair, and Mr. Pullman, who was very set in his ways, had goaded his Palace Car makers into what became the Debs Rebellion, and required the attention of General Nelson A. Miles and thousands of Regulars to put down.

But Chicago's rising young steel industry never once got out of hand. It had started rolling Bessemer rails as early as 1865 in a plant erected by Captain Eber B. Ward, the first American rolled-steel rails ever made. Twenty-five years later, and in keeping with the trend of the times, steel mills in Chicago, Milwaukee, and Joliet merged to form the Illinois Steel Company, a lusty giant which boiled its ore in fifteen blast furnaces, stirred its iron in eighteen puddling furnaces, and blew its pig into steel in nine Bessemer converters. Here was a real threat to Pittsburgh's supremacy.

That shore of Lake Michigan south of Chicago was level as a prairie and handy to water and rail—grand country for a steel man, or for almost anybody who wanted to make something to sell to America. It was especially good for steel, even better than Pittsburgh. The soft-coal fields of Illinois were just next door, and they contained enough coal to please the Devil himself, who was said to favor Chicago from the first, anyway. The limestone quarries of Michigan were an easy day's haul. Lake Superior's iron mines were two days, often four days closer to Chicago than to Ashtabula and Conneaut, Pittsburgh's main ports.

As a user of steel Chicago had no peer. It was the great railroad center of the country. Pullman, McCormick, Swift, Armour, and a thousand others had come or were on their way to build plants and factories in Chicago, many of them along the south shore.

Every year or so a new steel plant raised its stacks along the waterfront. The Block brothers, L. E. and P. D., made enough money buying scrap iron and other old junk to found the Inland Steel Company. Soon or late others came to the south shore—Republic Iron & Steel, the vast American Iron Foundries, and Youngstown Sheet & Tube. The great Pullman Works, a city even when it was built, continued to expand until it sprawled over the state line into Hammond, Indiana.

That was the way the Cinder Shore came into being. Like Pittsburgh, Chicago's Cinder Shore lived its days in a murk that even the brisk winds off Lake Michigan could not dispel. Its nights were murky enough, too, but they were animated by the snorting fire of Bessemers and the sudden brilliance of blast furnaces being tapped. A man could ride the South Shore Railroad for miles and be entertained by pyrotechnics that were amazing and were interspersed with a seemingly endless procession of white-hot rails and beams and blooms, being moved through the dark by invisible forces.

For many years, and until incredible Gary was built on the sands, the dominating barony of the Cinder Shore was the South Works of Illinois Steel. South Works smoked and glittered all over six hundred acres, larger than many baronies. Here ten thousand men worked, and what little talk they made during working hours was carried on in twenty-seven languages.

Polyglot from the first, the Cinder Shore's proletariat held fiercely to their various national groups, living in Polish, Swedish, German, and Hungarian boarding houses; forming social, religious, and burial societies, and observing the feast days of the countries they hailed from.

Each race had a "big man," a natural leader to whom it turned for advice and help, and who was often given consideration by the steel companies. Alfred Hero was known as king of the Swedes, who made up the best men of the rigging crews at the ore docks. Hero planted his saloon at Buffalo Avenue and Eighty-eighth Street, handy to Linnaean Hall—an ironic name for anything in a place where not even thistles could grow.

Here all Scandinavians came to drink and talk, and often to see Hero about a small loan, for the "big men" were all bankers in a way. Battling Nelson, the champion boxer, often dropped in at Hero's, although the Bat never touched anything stronger than ginger ale.[1]

The many Irish of the Bessemer and blast-furnace departments liked to gang up at Mike Loftus' place on Baltimore Avenue, to watch dog fights or to fight among themselves, and of course to drink whisky. Or if they

---

[1] Almost forgotten by the sports world, Battling Nelson still lives in Hegewisch, Ill., where he owns property but reports that high taxes keep him poor.

wanted to gamble they could go over to Big Tom O'Don-
nel's at Ninety-second Street and Exchange Avenue.

Funerals and undertakers appear to have always
played a leading role in South Chicago. The Poles, Aus-
trians, and Hungarians loved funerals as much as they
did eating and dancing, and they considered no funeral
worth the name that could not boast two brass bands
and a mile-long procession, with the various societies
parading in full uniform. Funerals were usually followed by a big party, which often resulted in a stabbing
and another funeral. It all made entertainment for the
boys and business for the many undertakers.

Louis Krebs was an undertaker notable for the fine
job he did on one Jimmy Smith, a bum whom Krebs
fished out of the Lake and embalmed to such good effect
that the corpse was solid. This corpse was kept in Krebs'
place for years and was used for playing pranks. It was
also borrowed on occasion by the wives of drunkards.
They'd put it to bed with the old man where he would
find it when he roused from his stupor. It was reported
to have effected at least two permanent cures of inebri-
ate steelworkers.

South Works, like all other steel plants of the period,
was a fabulous place for undertakers. In those days almost no attention was paid to the safety of steel-plant
employees. Steel mills were veritable slaughterhouses,
and those along the Cinder Shore killed so many men
that they brought on the War of the Undertakers.

This sinister drama began when the City passed an
ordinance providing that the corpse of a man killed in
any factory accident should be taken to the nearest un-
dertaking parlor. Immediately Mr. Finerty, who had em-

balming offices at Ninety-second Street, moved down to Ninetieth, a position two blocks nearer the main gate of South Works. Mrs. Murphy moved her select parlors to a spot a few doors closer than Mr. Finerty, and Mr. Adams, who had been left far in the rear and probably found business very dull, picked up and moved his esoteric apparatus into a shop at the very corner of Eighty-ninth Street and Mackinaw Avenue, almost opposite the main gate.

It was well worth while to be near a main gate. Forty years ago pretty nearly everything in a steel plant was dangerous. Of all hazardous places a blast furnace stood high in the record of killing and maiming. This was the place where the raw material was reduced to pig iron.

Ore, coke, and limestone were piled in layers inside the tall brick-lined stack, which was enclosed in what was called a "well," filled with water. Heat was blown into the stack, fluxing the mass inside. The molten iron fell to the bottom and was drawn off through a tapping hole into gullies. Each gully was dammed at certain places to allow the metal to run into a long "sow," to which were attached the "pigs," as the pattern molds were called. Each sow "gave" from twenty-four to forty pigs, depending on the casting-house design and size. Each mold held from one to two hundred pounds of iron. The sow and pigs got their names from a fancied likeness to a female pig suckling her young. Hence, pig iron.

Making a cast was dangerous in the old days, for here was a shed filled with pools of molten metal, and a man often missed his step, especially if he had taken more than two puddlers' cocktails following every cast.[2] Another dangerous job around a blast furnace was that of top filler. He was the man who remained on top of the stack while the furnace was being charged. He had to hang to his high, narrow perch and see that the right quantities of ore and coke and limestone were dumped into the stack. Gases were prevalent around the top of a furnace. Many a top filler fell from his perch and was never seen again, any part of him.

Sometimes a hot furnace broke through and let the metal into the water well. When that happened, one could hear it in the Loop, ten miles away; and one day they did hear it in the Loop, and the few sorry remains of five men were taken to Mr. Adams' parlors in burlap.

Bessemer converters ranked along with the blast furnaces as dangerous places. A Bessemer in blow contains about twenty-five tons of metal, and one of them at South Works let go one day, scattering hot metal all over the shed but miraculously harming no one. The metal did, however, burn up a suit of clothes that hung in Ed Ring's locker.

Ed Ring was long king of the Bessemers at South Works. He had been among the sparkling volcanoes ever since the first converter was put into blow at South Works in 1882. He retired a few years ago, and he is probably the worst burned man ever to live it out.

It happened twenty-two years ago. Ed and his crew were pouring a heat of Bessemer steel into ingot molds.

---

[2] It was a custom at blast furnaces everywhere for the gang to go outside the plant for a drink following every cast. "When I came to South Works," says William R. Hanahan, for fifty-four years a blast-furnace man, "I was given a passbook and pencil. It was understood that a man had to go out for his beer after each cast." A cast, a drink—one followed the other as night the day, only more often.

Several had been filled. Everything was working fine. The next mold, Ed thinks today, must have been damp. In any case, Ed started to pour. That was the last he knew for many weeks.

Ed was standing right over the metal when it blew up with a roar of flame. Ed's clothes were burned from his body, and so was most of his skin. As a matter of course he was taken to the hospital, but physicians said there was no hope for him. He was a gone man. He lay there fourteen months, while skin was grafted here and there all over his body, including his face. The grafting process worked well, and when he could walk again, Ed went back to his Bessemers at South Works.[3]

Ed Ring recalls that insurance companies used to ask frightfully high premiums of a Bessemer man. One of Ed's helpers once applied for a policy. Asked his occupation, he said that he was a "supervisor of vessels," believing that the "supervisor" would indicate himself to be some sort of foreman who didn't work in dangerous places. It worked, and the lad got a lower premium rate. It still tickles Ed Ring to think about it.

They didn't have a Captain Bill Jones at South Works, but they had Billy Field, who was enough for any steel plant. The first shift young Field worked as a common laborer at South Works lasted twenty-four hours. When it was done his foreman told him to run along home, get a quick bite to eat, and to run right back to the plant as fast as he could. Billy Field did so, and they had him

---

[3] Now seventy-eight, Ed Ring is still a huge and husky man, but he says he is getting weak. He can no longer perform the feat that made him famous before the explosion brought him new fame as the most-burned-man alive. Ed's feat was to pick up eight building bricks between the fingers of one hand. One brick weighs 4½ pounds.

work another twelve hours. It set the pace for the rest of his life, and also for the men who were to work under him, as foreman, as superintendent, and finally as the big boss in the front office.

Field drove his men much as Captain Jones did at Braddock, a way that killed off the weaklings and left a crew of hellions who could stand anything short of being boiled in a Bessemer. Twelve hours was the usual shift, and once a fortnight they worked right around the clock. Once a fortnight, too, they got twenty-four hours off. In theory, this twenty-four hours off duty was supposed to let a man catch up with his rest. Instead, most of the younger men, and many of the older, used it for a good-sized drunk, from which they returned to the plant in a condition dangerous both to themselves and to other workmen.

But it was the way of life in a steel plant. Billy Field, the big boss, probably slept less during his hectic life than the men he drove. Even when he became general manager of the works it was nothing for him to do seventy-two hours without sleep, then put on a dress suit and attend the Chicago Opera. At times he was known to have been on the job for one hundred and sixty-eight hours at a stretch, with no sleep but brief catnaps he took in a hard chair in a shack on the plant. Once, when two steam pipes blew out and killed four of his workmen, Field stayed in the mill an entire week, living on sandwiches and catching a few winks now and then in his hard chair.

And men came to believe that Billy Field led a charmed life. He once was struck and knocked twenty feet by a stray beam of iron; again the top of his hat was neatly seared off by a white-hot rail. A blast furnace exploded in his face, killed five men and burned a small hole in Field's coat. "These goddam shoddy clothes they make nowadays," Field remarked, "just can't stand it."

One time it looked like a close shave for Field. A load of rails ran him down and pushed him off the dock into Lake Michigan. He sank out of sight at once. But John (the Buck) Buchanan, a South Works employee, was handy. He pulled Bill Field back onto the dock. Billy gave old Buck an autographed photograph which ever afterward occupied a prominent position in the Buchanan parlor. Men who had never heard of Andrew Carnegie, nor even of Captain Bill Jones, swore by Billy Field. They called him king steelmaker of the Cinder Shore, which in their opinion meant the greatest steelmaker on earth.

It was men like Billy Field who drove the American steel industry rough-shod into world's top position, and in a brief time. And the example of men like Field doubtless helped to give the steel industry the name of slaughterhouse. They took chances with death every day, these ruthless, hurrying demons like Field. They slept little, worked endlessly, and became big bosses.

The ordinary workman, endowed neither with Field's brains nor even with his stamina—he, too, risked his life every day, often needlessly; he worked furiously, he worked double shifts, all in emulation of his chief. But he didn't become superintendent. Quite often he turned out to be only a subject for the arts of Mr. Finerty or Mr. Adams or Mrs. Murphy. It cannot be proved, of course, but one may guess that Billy Field's careless, driving method of rising in the world played an unseen part in more than one horrible accident.

That one day off, every two weeks, loomed large in the

lives of steelworkers. When a young man was to be married, for instance, all plans for the event were made to fit the groom's twenty-four hours off shift. The Irish, the Swedes, and the Americans might get married any old day, regardless of the shift, but not so the Polish. It took a little time for two Poles to be properly wed.

A Polish wedding always called for a party and often for a ball. If a ball, the bride came prepared to dance the very soles off her shoes. Everybody, and there might be as many as eight hundred present, must take his turn throwing a piece of hard money in an attempt to break a plate set up on a table, an old custom dating from nobody knows when. When a man had thrown his money at the platter, he was entitled to dance with the bride.

There was no stated sum, simply an amount in keeping with the man's job at the steelworks. A foreman's dignity required that he heave a five-dollar gold piece, maybe a twenty-dollar coin. Laborers threw a cartwheel, a silver dollar. Fifty cents was proper for an aged man or a young boy. Often plates were broken to the tune of a thousand dollars, for the evening, and when a Polish bride was pretty and also the daughter of a minor boss at the works the amount ran to more than two thousand dollars.

Commonly, when the boys got their twenty-four off shift, they played hard. There was plenty of chance to play hard anywhere along the Cinder Shore. A street called the Strand was the main stem, lined with saloons and dance halls. The red light was one block over, on Harbor Avenue, where the Red Mill and Harry's place stayed open until morning. The girls of the red light liked to have the boys hire a boat, early Sunday morning, to take them out to Breakwater Pier, to get the slag and cinders blown out of their long hair. Rough lads from the ore carriers swarmed along the Strand and Harbor Avenue. There were often gang fights with the Polish and Hungarian steelworkers.

Crime ever flourished in South Chicago and near-by places. There was more crime here than Pittsburgh ever knew. Car-barn bandits grew to James Boys proportions and called for huge posses to chase them into the sand dunes and shoot it out. Bank stick-ups were common affairs. Trigger fingers were nervous, here in Chicago. Murders were so numerous on the Cinder Shore that Chicago papers gave up trying to list them. Thugs and easy-money men flocked into the city on the lake from everywhere.

A gang of counterfeiters cleaned up big at South Works one time. The boys at the plant still talk of it. Using checks printed from a perfect die, the counterfeiters flooded every saloon for blocks around with fake pay checks on Illinois Steel. The same counterfeit die turned up again, eleven years later, and before the gang was rounded up most saloons on the Strand had their walls papered with the false checks.

Local politics seemed to play a bigger part in the lives of Cinder Shore workers than they did in most steel towns. Poles and Irish were the leading politicians, and commonly there was less interest in a national election than in whether a Pole or an Irishman was to be elected dogcatcher in South Chicago. At such times racial lines were sharply drawn. The polling places resembled shambles before the day was over.

It really mattered little whether a Polack or a Harp was elected to a city office along the Cinder Shore. The regions around the various steelworks remained unchanged. The streets were heavy mud, almost clay, in winter; and in summer they were dust. Both the clay and the dust, of course, were well mixed with cinders from the mill stacks and from passing locomotives, which thundered by every few minutes, heading for the Loop and for every part of the Republic, too.

Vacant lots and alleys were often covered with piles of soft coal, and directly over these flapped the wash lines of steelworkers' families. Folks in the Bush—that part of South Chicago where the Hunkies lived—didn't go in much for white clothes, although the women tried to wear white petticoats. Not for long, though. The hottest water, the strongest soap could make black turn gray, but never to white—not near a steelworks. The undertakers alone simply had to have white shirts, or they would lose caste with their customers among the Poles and Hungarians who liked to see an undertaker dressed up nice in black and white.

Joliet Works of Illinois Steel wasn't on the Cinder Shore proper, but it made steel enough to lay a blanket of cinders and slag all around the city of Joliet. The works were noted for two things—the fastest rod-mill crew in the country, and an eight-hour day.

People came from miles around to see the famous Joliet Works rod-mill crew in action, and the boys loved it. They'd catch the spitting-hot rods in their tongs, toss them into the air like a juggler, and slap them into the next machine with a gaudy flourish. It made a showy sight and called for oohs and aahs from sight-seeing girls.

Rod mills were as hot as hell itself, and men soon learned not to have metal buttons on their pants; a hand that touched one came away with a big blister on it. A rod mill was particularly dangerous to the legs—any legs that got in the way of the millions of swiftly moving rods; and at one period each of six men in the Joliet rod-works possessed a leg that never pained him more, being of sound wood and replacing one of flesh lost when a hot rod struck it fair.

A noted rod catcher here was one Jerry McLaughlin. He could keep two sparkling rods in the air at a time, and his hands and arms were strong beyond belief. To please the boys when they wanted him to show off, Jerry would double up his naked fist and crash it clean through a sheet of corrugated iron. At Joliet they were always sorry that Jerry never got a chance to trade punches with John L. Sullivan.

Another Joliet boy of considerable fame in the industry was Amos Clinker. When Amos felt that he needed a little exercise he would tie a rope around three steel billets, weighing one hundred and fifty pounds each, take the other end of the rope in his mouth, and lift the four hundred and fifty pounds clear from the floor by his teeth.

Many a man who came to work at Joliet thought he had got into a three-ring circus by mistake. But Joliet Works was a forward-looking place. Twenty years before such a thing became common in the steel industry, the Joliet Steelworkers' Union put it up to the management to try out an eight-hour shift. The officials were at first properly horrified at a proposition little short of blasphemous. The union urged that it would undertake to show a greater profit for the plant on eight-hour shift than it was making on twelve hours. The management agreed to the experiment for six months.

Harry Hall, now of Gary, Indiana, but then a head

roller in Joliet Works, recalls what happened. "We watched production carefully," he says, "and we watched every man in the crew. We asked foremen to fire any employee we found lazy or incompetent. At the end of six months the management agreed that we had lowered costs and increased production, and that we had also reduced labor turnover. As for the crew, we made not quite so high wages working eight as we had done working twelve hours. But we were content.

"The eight-hour day was ever afterward in force at Joliet Works. I always understood that the Joliet management later urged other U.S. Steel plants to try the eight-hour shift; but they wouldn't and had to go through strike after strike before they gave in."

Although the workers at Joliet and South Works were unaware of it, and probably wouldn't have cared if they had known, their plants were soon to lose some of their wild individualism. In 1898 those steelworkers who could read at all saw in their papers that something called Federal Steel had come into being and had purchased the plants they worked in. Federal Steel also had bought the Minnesota Iron Company, the Minnesota Steamship Company, the Mount Pleasant Coke Company, and the Elgin, Joliet & Eastern Railway. It seemed that J. Pierpont Morgan of New York had put up the money and that a Chicago lawyer, Elbert H. Gary, was to be boss man.

All this gave the boys in the mills something to talk about between heats, but it seemed far away, in another world. They figured Federal Steel must be just about the biggest company of any kind in the world, and let it go at that. Its birth had made no visible change in their lives. It had cast no shadow across the Cinder Shore.

Things nearer home were more interesting to talk about, and the boys laughed uproariously at an incident at South Works that year. One of the several Polish undertakers got drunk during Christmas week of 1898. He had been brooding a good deal over poor business. Suddenly he heard that a new company had bought the steel plant. He dressed up in his best clothes and went right down to the plant office. "Wat's matter dis new Federal Steel don' send me no business?" he demanded. "I ain't had no customer from you all dis mont'."

Laugh? The boys at South Works like to have died.

21 *Colossus Takes a Stroll*

A MAJORITY of the men who worked in steel plants at the turn of the century could not read an American newspaper, and many of the forty races could not read their own language. Thus they missed the surface manifestations of a vast battle that was to affect them all, and their sons and grandsons.

Even the literate, who read the papers every day in the week, could see only the ripples of the struggle that began about 1898 and lasted more than three years. The real struggle was conducted submarine-style. Only when a torpedo went off did steelworkers—or, for that matter, the general public—know of a new move by the opposing forces. They saw the spume in newspaper headlines. Even today, forty years after, not all the varied forays and repulses are known.

The War of the Steelmasters and Bankers had its inception in the forming of Morgan's huge Federal Steel Company. This gave Andrew Carnegie something to think upon besides writing pieces for the magazines about the wonderful life led by American workingmen, especially those of steel mills. Federal Steel was the first threat to Carnegie supremacy since the first Bessemer rail was rolled in America.

For a year or so all had been well with the two companies. During the brief war with Spain both Federal and Carnegie had done a good business, observing a gentlemen's agreement about prices. When there came a lull after the war, Carnegie reverted to character—which, so far as business ethics were concerned, was usually likened to that of a hyena. He at once broke the steel-rail pool by underselling the market.

Judge Gary, head of Federal Steel, was greatly worried, as well he had reason to be. He urged his master, Pierpont Morgan, to buy out Carnegie. But the old Corsair wouldn't listen. "I don't like Carnegie," growled the elder Morgan, "and I won't give him the satisfaction of buying him out. That's what he wants."

Presently the newspapers announced an interesting and seemingly unrelated incident in the business world. What amounted to a wire and nail trust had been formed under the name of American Steel & Wire Company by John W. (Bet-a-Million) Gates. Gates had started his career as a swashbuckling salesman. He bragged that he had sold barbed wire to every farmer between Chicago and the Pacific Ocean. He peddled enough of it to set him up as one of the biggest stock gamblers in the country and by all odds the most unpredictable. This latest move of Gates had brought virtually all the nail-and-wire-making concerns into one group.

The various plants brought together in Gates's whopping concern had previously, as individual mills, purchased all their raw material, in the form of steel billets, from the Carnegie company. On formation of the trust, Gates notified Carnegie that American Steel & Wire wouldn't be needing any more of Carnegie's fine steel billets; they were going to make their own.

Now, the celebrated Moore brothers got into the financial pages again. William H. and James H. Moore had

already formed what amounted to a Match Trust in their
Diamond Match Company, and they had also organized
the huge National Biscuit Company. The Moores now
announced the merger of two hundred and sixty-five tin-
plate mills into a single corporation. They wrote Mr.
Carnegie to cancel any orders he might have of theirs for
steel billets; said they were going to make their own
steel.

At about this juncture J. P. Morgan & Company made
headlines by organizing the National Tube Company,
composed largely of mills making tube steel which had
always bought their billets from Carnegie. It was casually made known that National Tube was erecting its
own blast furnaces and rolling mills, which would of
course manufacture steel billets.

All this sounded mighty fine to the boys who worked
in steel mills. More mills, more jobs, they figured. It was
good news.

Meanwhile Carnegie and his great manager, Frick,
had a falling-out over the price of coke sold to Carnegie
Steel by Mr. Frick's smoky sideline, the H. C. Frick
Coke Company. The Carnegie concern was rocked almost to pieces by the resulting internecine battle. Carnegie started to oust Frick. Frick sued. Carnegie sued.
Frick prepared to present evidence in open court that
would show the *real* profits of the Carnegie company—
steel costing $12 a ton to make being sold at $23.75, with
a high tariff "to protect our industry and our workers
from cheap foreign steel."

The revelations Frick promised would have been too
much, even for the crude sensibilities of 1900. Frick and
Carnegie never spoke to each other again, but the quar-
rel was patched up. Frick resigned as manager and as a

director, although he retained his stock in the company.
Young Charlie Schwab was put in to head the Carnegie
forces after the shake-up.

Faced with this trouble within and with enemies on
all sides of the business front, still Carnegie made no
move to sell. That is, no apparent move. Everything he
did pointed to the contrary. One day in 1900 front pages
all over the country shouted that the Carnegie company
was due for a huge expansion. Little Andy announced
that he was going into the business of manufacturing
steel tubes in a big way.

Carnegie agents appeared at Conneaut, on Lake Erie,
and bought five thousand acres of waterfront property
for a site. Contracts were let, or were alleged to have
been let, to erect a tube plant costing $12,000,000.

The boys in steel plants everywhere were happy at
the news, and many of Carnegie's foremen had visions
of a new job as some sort of superintendent at the new
tube works. "Going to employ ten thousand men at Conneaut," was the word that went round.

A bit later newspapers carried another exciting item
in Column One on the front page: "Carnegie Interests
to Build Huge New Steel Rod Plant at Pittsburgh," ran
the banner headlines.

Nor was that all. Within a few weeks the world was
told that Andrew Carnegie had made arrangements with
George Gould to extend Carnegie's Bessemer Railroad
from Pittsburgh to a junction with the Western Mary-
land Railway; it would connect Carnegie mills with the
Atlantic Seaboard. . . . Let the damned Pennsylvania
line charge what freight rates it wanted to, Carnegie
steel should travel on a Carnegie road.

Merely as an afterthought, it seemed, the little Scot

said in print that his firm also planned to build a fleet of ore carriers for use on the Great Lakes. "Present rates for transporting ore are too high," he said. "By God, they can't stop Little Andy!" the men in the steel mills told one another between heats. But a few canny industrialists may have thought that Carnegie's threat of a fleet was something of a gesture against John D. Rockefeller, who had a Great Lakes navy of his own.

The steelworkers who read the newspapers were very happy at this expansion of their industry. But there was sheer panic among steelmasters and railroad men throughout the eastern states. Wars between nations often brought prosperous times to steel mills and railroads; but a war between steel and railroad men, that was something else.

The moneyed boys and speculators of all kinds ran to Morgan in droves and in distress, asking him to do something about this mad Scotsman. Morgan still wouldn't meet Carnegie in person, but he was prevailed upon to attend a banquet, ostensibly given in honor of Charlie Schwab, the smiling young president of Carnegie Steel. At the banquet Charlie gave them the works in a brilliant, good-natured, and highly optimistic talk on the future of steel, with special reference to the Carnegie kind of steel. He cited the stupendous profits being made by his concern and intimated that these were chicken feed compared to the "earnings" that would accrue as soon as his company had completed building its own rod, wire, tin-plate, and tube mills, and had its railroad and ore-carrying fleet ready.

Old steel men today like to romanticize this celebrated banquet, which was held on December 12, 1900, and to say that out of it alone came the Steel Trust. The banquet may have had something to do with the trust, but more likely it was the truly desperate circumstances of war among the Titans that brought about what followed.

In any case, Mr. Morgan listened silently at the dinner. Then he took Mr. Schwab aside and asked him a hundred questions, one after another. Later, there were other meetings between the two men.

While the Morgan-Schwab conversations were going forward, Morgan also was attempting to purchase Rockefeller's immense ore holdings on the Mesabi iron range. Mr. Rockefeller, through his son, said he was not at all interested in disposing of his ore.

Henry C. Frick was known to be greatly admired by the elder Rockefeller for the manner in which he had handled the bloody affair at Homestead; Frick, indeed, was a man after John D.'s heart. Mr. Morgan asked Mr. Frick to see Mr. Rockefeller. Frick did so and came away with the Lake Superior Consolidated Mines in his pocket. How much he paid was never known. Wall Street know-it-alls rated the amount all the way from $32,000,000 to $80,000,000, either sum a fairly good profit over what Rockefeller had paid the tragic Merritt brothers, who uncovered the ore and put their lives and their fortunes into its development.

Morgan was now ready to act. He acted quickly. With Schwab as intermediary—for he still wouldn't see Carnegie in person—Morgan purchased all the Carnegie company holdings for a sum usually reputed to have been $492,000,000.

Things now began to happen swiftly indeed. Morgan bought John W. Gates's American Steel & Wire. He took over the Tin Plate Trust by buying most of its stock. But these were not enough for Morgan. To make the deal worth his while, he acquired substantially all the stocks of the American Sheet Steel Company, the National Steel Company, American Steel Hoop, and American Bridge. On April 1, 1901, the birth of the United States Steel Corporation was officially announced. It was an infant for a Rabelais to describe.

The new giant, largest industrial group the world had known, was capitalized at $1,402,000,000—a set of figures to stagger anyone but an astronomer. It was a sum of money beyond comprehension. The magazine *Life*—in those days printed for literates—ran a cartoon of a schoolroom, in which well known men appeared as small boys. At the blackboard was a lad easily recognized as Pierpont Morgan. He had just written a string of figures that reached away across the board. A little boy with Andy Carnegie's face held up his hand. "Teacher," he protested, "there isn't a sum like that in my arithmetic." Said teacher: "But Pierpont has his own arithmetic."

Common steelworkers didn't know what to make of it. A joke went the rounds of the mills and became famous. It concerned a steelworker's wife who was teaching her son about Creation. "Now, Johnnie, who made the world?" Johnnie replied, "God made the world in 4004 B.C., and it was reorganized in 1901 by J. P. Morgan."

The stock market immediately went into one of those booms, being churned mightily by the unseen hand of James R. Keene, the freebooting manipulator whose talents Morgan hired for the occasion. And despite the fact that tangible assets—which is to say, property—of U.S. Steel were put at $682,000,000, which made the stock better than half purest water, the public ran crying to buy U.S. Steel Common.

There were reasons other than Keene's thimblerigging for running to buy. An important decision of the United States Supreme Court was handed down at this moment and doubtless had a fine effect on corporation stocks and bonds. It was a patent case and concerned the steel mixer invented many years before by the redoubtable Captain Bill Jones of Braddock. The Court held that U.S. Steel alone had a right to use the Jones Mixer, and it cracked down hard on Cambria Iron Works, no part of the Corporation, for using the device. Henceforth, the use of mixers of all sizes was subject to the rights of the Jones patents.

Another inducement to buy U.S. Steel Common was seen in the matter of prices. Heretofore steel rails had been selling at $23.75 a ton. The Corporation announced a raise in price of steel rails, "due to increased costs of operation," to $28 a ton. It is worthy of note that the price remained stationary thereafter for thirteen years.

At the time it was born the colossus known as U.S. Steel employed 168,000 workers. Whatever the cause of those "increased costs of operation," they were assuredly not due to increased wages. Wages stayed where they were. That is, for a time. A little later they were slashed unmercifully.

Wise old steelmasters like Henry Frick and Henry Phipps apparently did not like the look of the new monster. They sold all their stock in the Steel Trust, discreetly but quickly. "Mr. Frick," recounts his admiring biographer, George Harvey, "was unquiet. He appreciated the danger of the company's over-capitalization. . . .

Careful study . . . convinced him that declines in earnings were inevitable, and he began to liquidate his
holdings."

While Frick and Phipps and other wise men were unloading, U.S. Steel started a campaign to have its employees buy Corporation stock. Many of them did, but it
was the public outside the steel industry which purchased U.S. Steel Common as fast as engravers could
manufacture the pretty certificates.

Manipulators of stocks were in for a few years of
heavy, sweet clover. They'd hammer U.S. Steel up for a
few months; then they'd hammer it down, and start all
over again. It was a lot of fun, and it paid well. In 1904
they hammered it down so hard that Common sank to
$8\frac{3}{4}$. Thousands of small investors, including hired girls
and butlers in the mansions of steel barons, lost all their
savings.

Stock high, stock low—it never made any appreciable
difference to the boys in the blast furnaces and rolling
mills. "Wassa mat de wages?" one Tony Cicala, employee of Lorain Steel, part of the new Corporation,
wanted to know of his foreman one time in 1903. "De
Corp stock, she was go whoosh—way up—but de wage,
she was never go whoosh onless she whoosh down."

It was a question most steelworkers wondered about,
as they continued to work twelve hours a shift and to
earn just enough to keep South Chicago and certain
areas around Pittsburgh in a condition which the description of "slums" did not libel.

The workers groused a good deal, but they did their
grousing in carefully chosen society. Never did they do
more about a union than talk; it was understood by all

that the plants of U.S. Steel would not tolerate a union.[1] It was commonly known to employees that the Corporation maintained a large detective force in the plants. These plant dicks were called finks and could not be told from an honest workingman. Finks didn't wear uniforms or badges.

The Steel Trust was born. Now it must grow. A year after its incorporation U.S. Steel casually purchased the Union Steel Company at Donora, and the Sharon Steel Company at Sharon, both in Pennsylvania. This was two-bit shopping, but the properties were needed to give the Corporation sufficient blast-furnace capacity.

Certain individualistic concerns either were not asked or refused to join the new colossus. Jones & Laughlin, dating back to beyond Carnegie's beginnings, was one. Youngstown Sheet & Tube was another. Colorado Fuel & Iron, soon to be known as Rockefeller's Western Barony, remained intact and remote. Inland Steel continued to go it alone. Another big independent, Republic Iron & Steel, decided to keep its independence.

None of these firms was singly a menace to the corporation that now controlled half of the pig-iron output of the United States, two-thirds of the steel ingot production, and owned 58.3 per cent of the Lake Superior ore —plus a huge fleet to move the ore to the furnaces. But down in the Deep South was a potentially dangerous competitor. It was the Tennessee Coal & Iron Company.

Tennessee Coal & Iron had known a long and hectic life. Only after 1900 had it emerged as an up-and-coming concern. It was a paradox, combining the most advanced technology with a labor policy compared to

---

[1] Apparently Joliet Works was an exception. See Chapter 20.

which a U.S. Steel plant was Utopia. The company had
been founded on the discovery of coal in 1850 near
Nashville. For the next fifty years the original and sub-
sequent companies had their ups and downs, being
something of a football, kicked around a good deal by
speculators. In 1899 mergers with Henry F. DeBardele-
ben's iron interests at Birmingham, and with other
smaller concerns, brought about Tennessee Coal & Iron.

These mergers in themselves might not have given
U.S. Steel a second thought, had it not been for certain
gifts which God and the State of Alabama had conferred
on T.C.I., as the great iron company of the South was
known. These gifts were many and bounteous.

Nowhere on earth had the ingredients of steel been
found so closely packed together as at Birmingham.
They were, as some T.C.I. Negro employee remarked, all
as handy as a pantry. One wall of a narrow valley was
solid and excellent coal, the Warrior Field. The valley's
other wall, called Red Mountain, was well named, being
composed of iron ore for the most part and of limestone.
As if this were not enough for one small area, God
planted large deposits of dolomite on the valley floor.
Dolomite is a fine flux for use in blast furnaces.

Where God left off, the State of Alabama took a hand.
It always had a good many convicts on its hands, and
these it was happy to rent out to T.C.I. at an extremely
moderate hire. The convicts, coupled with plenty of
cheap "free" workers, both black and white, kept T.C.I.'s
labor costs well below those of U.S. Steel.

There had never been an ugly thing like a union at
Birmingham. When the white miners even talked about
an organization, Don H. Bacon, T.C.I.'s capable and
ruthless manager, locked them out and brought in

Hunkies by the trainload. His mine boss, the hell-yelling Captain John D. Hanby, knew how to handle the Negro help, according to the many tales about the Captain; he'd knock a nigger down one minute—the next, give the fallen man a box of snuff. Conditions at the Sloss mining camp, near T.C.I.'s mills at Bessemer, were pretty bad. An eyewitness said he could not think of anything quite to describe them. "A scene of unmitigated squalor and desolation," was the best he could do, and he apologized for an understatement.

Given all these happy conditions, Manager Bacon had built the T.C.I. company into a concern that was making fine steel and a lot of it. It could meet anybody's price, but it didn't have to: by 1900, or a little later, T.C.I.'s rails had a name for being the best made in the United States. The company had specialized in open-hearth manufacture of rails, a process that had lagged in many of the mills in the Steel Trust combination.

Perhaps not even all these advantages would have given U.S. Steel undue worry; but when they were coupled with a brand-new move by the irrepressible John W. Gates, why, Mr. Morgan's Corporation sought to widen its fences a bit.

It will be recalled that when U.S. Steel was forming, Gates had sold it his American Steel & Wire. Only Gates claimed that he had been forced to sell. Then, when the Corporation was formed, Gates had been wholly ousted from the new group. He swore by all the barbed-wire gods he could think of that he would get even with Pierpont Morgan and his crew.

What Gates did was to get control of T.C.I. stock. Then he laid plans to merge T.C.I. with the sizable Republic Iron & Steel Company of Youngstown, Ohio. It would be a combination to challenge even the monster of Steel. Everything toward the merger was going ahead in good order when 1907 rolled around. It was a very bad year for people without ready cash. Money flew into hiding. Mr. Morgan learned that the Trust Company of America, a large banking house, needed a considerable sum of cash, and at once. When he discovered that the Trust Company's security for a loan would be stocks in T.C.I.—which had proposed to set itself up as a second Steel Trust—Mr. Morgan said he would lend the money and take the stock.

Republic Iron & Steel was to be no part of a merger so long as J. P. Morgan & Company were interested in the United States Steel Corporation.

Next thing Mr. Morgan wanted to do, of course, was to put his T.C.I. into the Corporation. It called for delicate work. The press was already aroused at the ogre of Trusts. Muckrakers were loose and had been prying into the secrets of Big Business. A trust, any trust, was the bogeyman at large in the land. President Roosevelt and much of Congress were on a trust-busting spree to entertain the voters and to make sure of all happy returns for the Republican administration at the next election.

Roosevelt the First had no radio to carry his voice to the People. He didn't need one. He was the most startling chief executive the country had ever known, and when he shouted his voice could be heard in all corners of the Republic. Now he shouted. He shook his famed Big Stick, gritted his even more famed big teeth and yelled that there would be no more mergers in the land, of Steel or of anything else.

The Panic of 1907 was now in full swing. But Mr.

Morgan was not panicked in the least. He lurked in his cavern on Wall Street and sent Mr. Frick and Mr. Gary as emissaries to the man in the White House. They simply informed Mr. Roosevelt, very quietly, that Jupiter himself had said the great Trust Company of America might go down in a crash that would take thousands of companies with it. Chaos, in fact, yawned. The only manner Mr. Morgan could see to avert such a frightful calamity was to merge T.C.I. into U.S. Steel.

It was a tough spot for the man in the White House. He fumed awhile but quieted down. Tennessee Coal & Iron became an integral part of the ambulating colossus.

Part of the press damned Roosevelt as a truckler to Big Business, but the matter soon ceased to be a political menace. The memory of the Common Man of the United States is very brief.

A little later, during an idle moment, Congress looked into the matter of U.S. Steel, but decided there was nothing much to be done about it. In those days you just couldn't buck the hand of God and the House of Morgan at one and the same time.

Meanwhile, U.S. Steel had been largely responsible for a new term of speech in the American language. "He lives and acts like a Pittsburgh millionaire," was the phrase. It had a number of implications, not all of them happy.

22 *The Elegant Steel Barons*

IN THE summer of 1901 the dense smoke that enveloped Pittsburgh seemed to rise for an instant as the city paused briefly to note the effect of the new Steel Trust. This moment of clarity revealed that U.S. Steel had made thirty-odd millionaires, overnight, in the city of Pittsburgh alone. Then the smoke settled down again, thicker than ever, but lighted now by something other than the glare of Bessemers. The new raw steel barons had begun to glitter.

Even before the arrival of the Trust, Pittsburgh had a score of all-metal millionaires, most of them quite recent, and the additions to their ranks made a sizable Barony of Steel. All the barons set about immediately to make it the most elegant ever seen.

Between thirty and forty of the new rich were known as the Carnegie Partners, young and middle-aged men who had served their master well in the rolling mills and the blast furnaces. They still smelled pungently of burning coke. It is possibly apocryphal, but also indicative, that a Penn Avenue barber reported the first shampoo one of these new barons ever had resulted in two ounces of fine Mesabi ore and a scattering of slag and cinders.

Typical of that first summer of U.S. Steel was a scene in Pittsburgh's expensive but hardly exclusive Duquesne Club. Sprawled all over two chairs and a table was one

of the young new barons of Steel. He was as drunk as a
fairly well boiled owl and had covered page after page
of the club's embossed stationery with figures. "I am trying to find out," he told a steward who brought him another drink, "whether I am worth six million, or if it is
eight million." He never did learn.

Seven of the Carnegie Partners immediately set sail
for Europe, with their wives and families, and at least
one included a handsome mistress in his entourage. The
way these barbarians lived and traveled founded the
myth, in Europe, that all Americans possess more of
wealth than of any other one thing, except vulgarity.
One of the traveling Partners was reported to have
asked a secretary of the Archbishop of Paris for his
"lowest price on that church of Notre Dame, C.O.D.,
Sewickley Heights, Pennsylvania, good old U.S.A."

Another partner moved his ménage into a brownstone
in New York City. He quickly became homesick for the
inimitable air of the Monongahela, and moved right back
to his home town, selling his Fifth Avenue palace at a
heavy loss. But "losses" meant little to brand-new steel
barons. For a time money flowed in faster than they
could spend it.

They made heroic efforts to spend it, though. Most
of them seemed to consider the suburb of Sewickley
Heights to be the highest possible heaven; so onto the
Heights they moved. Architects shuddered at the desires
of the new barons, but obeyed. And presently there
arose on the high bluffs north of Pittsburgh some of the
gaudiest monstrosities ever beheld by startled eyes.

The architecture of Sewickley Heights was varied and
rather difficult to describe. One neat job, set in the center of forty acres, was patently founded on a reading of

Ivanhoe and carried the Baron Front-de-Bœuf motif right down to a moat with drawbridge, although the attached sun parlor seemed to stem from the New York Aquarium at the Battery. It will give an idea.

Another splendid tribute to U.S. Steel started out to be a simple Norman castle, with battlements, but wound up on one side and in the rear looking like something the Mikado might have ordered put up in a moment of sheer fancy. The owner of this place wanted comfort as well as beauty. When his architect asked him if he wanted a porte-cochere, he replied: "Hell, yes! Better put in five of them; and make sure the flush don't sound loud."

The sudden flood of gold swept good old Alex Peacock fairly off his feet. Alex had been general sales manager for Carnegie—a good-natured, generous, and loud Scotsman who had started life as a drygoods clerk. Alex didn't move to Sewickley with the main herd of steel barons. On Highland Avenue in Pittsburgh he built Rowanlea, a positively terrific country place encircled with a nine-foot fence that was entered through gates so massive they rolled on wheels. An iron figure of a *Felis leo* glared from the top of each gatepost. White marble columns stood about everywhere there was room for a white marble column. These were alternating round and square, Doric and Ionic, for Alex liked variety, and they were very pretty.

There was one thing about Alex Peacock. He never tried to go high-hat, and he never forgot his old friends. He hunted them up, and if they were not in a happy condition, he paid their debts, paid for their operations, their babies, their funerals. He threw parties at his

Rowanlea, and in Pittsburgh hotels which he took over entire for the occasion. He traveled around the United States a good deal. Once, in San Francisco, he had a sudden longing to return home. He hired a special train, stocked it with champagne for his many guests, and rolled nonstop across the mountains and prairies, while express trains were sidetracked and the U.S. Mail waited for U.S. Steel to pass.

Into their new mansions the steel barons heaved everything their womenfolk could think of. When a neighbor bought two gold-plated pianos, Alex Peacock installed four. He liked to sit in his sultan's parlor, take off his shoes, and put his feet up on one of the gorgeous instruments. Then he'd talk about the great days when he sold Bessemer rails to the Union Pacific, meanwhile snapping his galluses, which had solid gold buckles.

The new baronesses loved flowers, or said they did, and the growing of American Beauty roses became an important industry in Pittsburgh, even though most of the barons themselves preferred a good big posy to a mere rose. Calla lilies—there was a decoration for you, fit either for an afternoon tea or for a small evening party of eighty or a hundred of one's friends. Calla lilies had size to them.

On the heels of U.S. Steel's incorporation, the new barons and their wives high-tailed into New York, where they bought jewelry by the case and sculpture by the carload. These are no figures of speech; they actually bought tons of junk in lots. They didn't know a Rubens from a Renoir, but it mattered little; they got few of Rubens, anyway, and even fewer of Renoir, but they bulled the "art" market into a new high. In Europe, the manufacture of "Old Masters" especially for the steel-baron trade became a recognized and a flourishing business.

Portrait painters were never in such demand. One Carnegie Partner had his wife painted no fewer than fourteen times, by both American and English artists, each time by a different man. The prices paid for these jobs would have amazed the late John Singleton Copley. One baron, having heard somehow of a man named Copley, told his secretary to get in touch with that artist. "I want for him to paint the kids," he said.

It wasn't long before all sorts of artists moved to the Steel City in order to be close to the fountainhead. Two smart lads came and set up as experts in heraldry, and one of their first commissions was to compose a coat of arms which a Carnegie Partner had embossed on the bands of his one-dollar cigars. Heraldry bloomed as it never had before in America, even in Chicago's Packingtown families. The two experts had nice British accents and gave the impression they had some sort of connection with the Heralds' College in England. They traced the House of at least one Carnegie Partner direct to Geoffrey Plantagenet, which was very fine, and drew a quartered shield to dazzle a belted earl. In a little while the wives of the barons were speaking fairly casually of *gules* and *argent* and *ermine*. One cruel commentator of the period remarked that *sable* would make a better *field* for a steel baroness. But the remark was doubtless a bit too subtle to register.

Not only experts in heraldry were attracted to Pittsburgh. The place was a Klondike, all easy digging and with gold in every riffle. Mass biographers mushed in. They composed huge volumes—called mug books in the trade—that were printed on vellum and bound in leather and gold. In these the barons were pleased to have their steel-engraved portraits and a carefully edited biographical note.[1] They were sold "By Subscription Only" and cost all the way from two to five thousand dollars a copy.

Salesmen for nickel-plated bathrooms appeared. So did people who wanted to sell Ming porcelain of doubtful origin. Landscape artists showed up to tell the barons to throw those cast-iron deer out of their yards and put in fountains of Italian marble, preferably pink.

A rolling-mill foreman who is a cultured man recalls an evening he spent in the mansion of a steel baron in 1903. "It seemed to me," he relates, "that, although the rooms were huge, there was little space for moving about. Whichever way one turned, there was a big vase, half as large as an open-hearth ladle, standing on the floor. Either that, or a statue in bronze or marble. Paintings crowded each other on all the walls, in some cases almost touching. The place was more like a poorly arranged museum than a home."

The king of all steel barons never really lived in Pittsburgh. Andrew Carnegie's vast home in New York was his headquarters in the United States. Even before U.S. Steel arrived Andy had purchased seven-hundred-year-old Skibo Castle in Scotland and had a piper to play every morning, whether or not the Laird was present. With the birth of the Steel Trust, Carnegie devoted his attention to spending a part of his incredible fortune. He always made sure that his name was carved deep into the spending. If his memory survives another century, it

---

[1] The father of one baron had been a bricklayer. In the book, the old man became a "prominent building contractor."

will likely be due to the many libraries that have "Carnegie" over the door and are possibly the most civilizing gifts ever left behind by a wealthy barbarian.

Henry Frick, baron of Coke as well as of Steel, put several millions into Pittsburgh real estate, but for himself he had had enough of cinders. He moved to New York City and set up as a patron of the arts. Tom Morrison, who had worked long years in the hot mills, built a red sandstone palace in Pittsburgh but lived quietly. Tom Carnegie's widow took six million dollars out of U.S. Steel and immediately bought an estate in the Adirondacks, another in Florida.

In Pittsburgh the parties given by barons often became scandalous. The most celebrated of them began in a large downtown hotel, but the place wasn't anywhere near large enough. The host of the evening, a Carnegie Partner, noting the cramped quarters of six floors of the big hotel, hired the Pittsburgh Natatorium and moved the crowd there, en masse and at once, where, so a guest remembers, everybody got gloriously drunk. In itself this would have caused little comment, but the Partner himself and scores of his guests of both sexes disrobed and went in swimming *au naturel*. It took some doing to keep *that* party out of the newspapers. Graying men who were present at the Natatorium affair say it was something to have pleased Petronius. No woman seems to remember it.

Several of the steel barons, both Partners and others, were known to keep mistresses, and they were fairly discreet about it. One baron not only kept a mistress but made no bones over the matter. In the downtown building where he had his offices, this Roman fitted up a large suite in the taste of a late Victorian Messalina. Here at regular intervals, which surprisingly seemed not to lessen with the years, he was entertained by a woman of rather aristocratic bearing. Only one woman, always the same. That she was a wholly charming creature, there could be little doubt; but she was a constant irritation to the office employees of her master. The old baron had given orders that when his mistress came into the building she was to be whisked at once to the top floor, in regal aloneness. He was explicit in his order; no matter *who* might be waiting for an elevator, the charmer was to be taken up first, and alone. Vice presidents and general managers, as well as clerks and stenographers, fumed and waited in the lobby until the old man's darling had been delivered at the Harem Floor, as employees termed it.

When this old Roman died, at a great old age, the girl was sent a-packing, but not, it was said, until a cash settlement had been made which has permitted her to live quietly and happily ever since.

Within two or three years after the arrival of U.S. Steel the term "Pittsburgh millionaire" was coming into use. It denoted freehanded and ostentatious spending to a point well below any vulgarity that had been seen. Diamond Jim Brady gave the term wider circulation. Brady was no Pittsburgher, and he may not have been quite a millionaire; but he sold things made of steel, and he was usually identified with the Pittsburgh crowd. Brady dressed like a super three-card-monte man. He staged parties that were orgies of display. He gave gold-plated bicycles to actresses, ordered champagne in hundred-case lots, and lived in a suite of rooms that would have delighted the Sultan of Sulu.

On top of Jim Brady and the many steel barons came Harry K. Thaw, not a true baron but the son of a wealthy yet cultured Pittsburgh family whose money had been acquired in Steel, Coal, and Railroads. Young Thaw caused the term Pittsburgh millionaire to be known in every hamlet in the land.

At eleven o'clock on the night of June 25, 1906, Harry Thaw sat in evening clothes at a table on the roof of Madison Square Garden in New York. He was watching a first-night performance of *Mamzelle Champagne,* a comedy with music. Near the end of the show Thaw was seen to get up from his seat. He walked leisurely to the rear of the audience, pulled a revolver from his pocket and shot three bullets into a man who was sitting alone at a table. The man died instantly. He was Stanford White, aged fifty-three, and America's most famed architect.

The resultant trial of Thaw on a charge of murder was the most lurid in years, or since a man named Stokes had killed the celebrated Jim Fisk over a woman, back in the seventies. Newspapers reviewed the life and works of Harry Thaw from the time he made his first appearance on Broadway as a lush spender. Thaw's more printable escapades included riding a horse into the staid Union League club, playing cowboy with a cab horse on Broadway, lighting cigars with five-dollar bills, and giving lavish entertainments for chorus girls.

The Thaw case was of particular interest not only because it was as filled with leers as a satyr, but also because it gave a new term to American jurisprudence. Thaw said that he killed chiefly to save his young wife, Evelyn Nesbit, from the attentions of the allegedly voluptuous White. The killing, his counsel averred, happened during a "brain storm," or *dementia americana,* which had suddenly enveloped the mind of the defendant. "Brain storm" has since been used to excuse those charged with murder.

The original brain-storm plea worked like a charm. Thaw was incarcerated in an asylum—for a time. He strolled out through the gates one day and escaped into Canada. The startled Canucks drove him back across the Line. He gave himself up and was held for a time in hotels in Colebrook, then in Concord, New Hampshire. There were long-drawn-out extradition proceedings. For the next few years newspapers seldom came out without something new about Thaw. He had been committed again. He was in. He was out. There was another sanity trial. On May 20, 1924, he was adjudged sane once more and released.

Lads in the steel mills followed the case with unusual interest, and remarked, with many another, that you just couldn't convict a really rich man of murder. Socialists and other agitators were highly pleased at the Thaw doings and made capital out of them. They declared that such a farce was proof enough that Gold ruled the courts and that working stiffs need not look to the Law in their fight for better conditions.

Charles M. Schwab had been president of Carnegie Steel. He became the first president of the new Corporation. But heading a barony wasn't enough for Charlie. He wanted a barony all his own. Moreover, he didn't get along very well with Judge Gary, chairman of the Steel board, whose pious mouthings irritated him. So Schwab bought into the Bethlehem Steel Company, a giant that had grown up in eastern Pennsylvania [2] out of the brains of old John Fritz, late of Johnstown, and the money of Joseph Wharton, one of the biggest of the "independent" barons.

Schwab also organized something called the United States Shipbuilding Company which promptly went into the hands of a receiver, with a scandalous loss to stockholders. Out of the ruins of the "shipbuilding" company, plus the original Bethlehem Steel, Schwab built Bethlehem Steel Corporation which later became U.S. Steel's biggest competitor, as it is today.

A home on Sewickley Heights, even one with ten portes-cochere, would hardly do for such a steel baron as Schwab. He wasn't a mere baron, anyway; he ranked up there somewhere near Andy Carnegie. And in New York Charlie Schwab erected a castle that wasn't so old as Skibo but a damned sight more elegant. It cost five million dollars, without the fixin's, and was a House of the Ages. The large smoking room was fairly pure Flemish. There was a Louis XVI parlor, a Henri IV library—with books—and a Louis XIV dining salon. Any of its many marble bathrooms would have been large enough to house the family of a blast-furnace man at Bethlehem.

Following Schwab as head of U.S. Steel was William E. Corey, called the Iron Chancellor by some admiring newspaperman of Pittsburgh. Corey had come up through the ranks, working in the plant at Braddock be-

---

[2] Bethlehem, Pa., was named by a religious sect, the Moravians, who settled there in the eighteenth century. South Bethlehem is the steelmaking community.

fore he was put in charge at Homestead. Among his contributions was an improved method of hardening steel. This patent brought Corey a good deal of money besides his stock and salary. When he had made his pile he longed not so much for a new mansion as for a new wife. He got his first wife, a very fine woman, everyone said, to divorce him and went ahead with plans to marry Maybelle Gilman, an actress he had met when she was playing the Steel City with the *Mocking Bird* company.

Corey's move came as a genuine shock to his baron friends. They were crude men, and often they kept a mistress; but their homes remained intact. They pleaded with Corey not to go ahead with the wedding. It was 1907, and most steel barons had become touchy about the reputation they had achieved for unlimited vulgarity; adding divorces to the indictment would be too much. Barons, indeed, no longer were amused to hear "Pittsburgh millionaire." They hoped that at least the Corey wedding would be discreet.

The Corey-Gilman nuptials were discreet to the extent that they were not held in Madison Square Garden. They took place in Hotel Gotham, New York, and with the full benefit of both Church and Press. The supper, so Corey told newspapermen, cost $5,000, the flowers, $6,000. Corey's gift to the bride was a $200,000 château in France. He had set aside, he said, $200,000 for honeymoon expenses. Incidentals leading up to the marriage were put at a good round $500,000.

All that added up to something. So the steelworkers who read of it told one another. The Corey-Gilman wedding made a fine feature story for the radical as well as for the conventional press. It was known around Pittsburgh that Corey's first wedding had been accomplished for exactly five dollars, everything included. The boys told one another that there must indeed be a lot of money in Steel—somewhere. Thirty years afterward the costly didoes of the steel barons are cited by Communist Party organizers in Lackawanna, Braddock, Youngstown and Gary.

Because of his divorce and wedding Corey's relations with U.S. Steel, and especially with Judge Gary, seemed to suffer. He resigned his position and left the Corporation in 1911. Divorce came in 1923. Maybelle lived on in France. In 1929 she announced somewhat plaintively to a world that had largely forgotten her that she was thinking of marrying Don Luis de Bourbon, of Spain. It was the last time she appeared in the news.

As for the Iron Chancellor, he made business connections elsewhere and lived until 1934. The obituaries devoted as much space to Maybelle Gilman as they did to the Chancellor himself. Her name, indeed, will likely live longer than Corey's. Old-time steelworkers in Pittsburgh today always refer to the Homestead plant of U.S. Steel as the Maybelle Gilman Works and will tell you that Corey once attempted to have the plant so named, officially.

John Munro Longyear was no steel baron. His barony was iron. His uncanny sense of ore, as related earlier, led him to some of the greatest though not original discoveries on the Marquette, the Menominee, the Gogebic, and the Mesabi Range.

Well, with all the mines panning out so well, Longyear felt the need for a suitable home. This he built in the town that gave him his start, Marquette on Michigan's Upper Peninsula. It was a wonderful home, of sixty rooms, built of solid rock, and it would have been impressive even in far-away Sewickley Heights, at the other end of the iron-and-steel trail. It was in much better taste than most of Sewickley.

The Longyear mansion in Marquette was completed in 1900. A little later a railroad sought to run a branch line near the Longyear property. Mr. Longyear went to the courts to prevent it. A steel baron might thrive on smoke, but not so a baron of ore.

After a bitterly fought battle the railroad won. The road was built, and long trains rumbled past at all hours and spewed smoke and cinders through the Longyear windows.

John Longyear was no man to live astride a freight train. He first called in a photographer who took pictures of every room in the house and of every section of its exterior, including the porte-cochere without which no baron's home, either of Steel or of Iron, was complete. Then Longyear called in an army of masons.

The huge place was taken apart, stone by stone; every stone was wrapped in burlap and numbered, and the whole business piled aboard two long trains of box and flat cars. The leading locomotive gave a hoot of farewell, and John Longyear's mansion started on its way to the Atlantic shore.

At Brookline, Massachusetts, the stones were unloaded and taken to the top of elegant Fisher Hill, a wealthy part of the "Richest Village in the World." Here the masons went to work again, laying stone on stone until the sixty-room monster was complete once more, and except for the landscaping, which was even more baronial, was exactly as it had been when erected on the shore of Lake Superior.[3]

Marquette was shocked at the moving away, bag and baggage, bathrooms and all, of one of its leading citizens; and Marquette folk are huffy today when it is mentioned. But they ought not to care, and it is none of their business, anyway. Rather they should cheer that an Iron Baron showed so much imagination. It isn't everyone who will pick up and move a sixty-room stone castle halfway across the American continent.

One by one the steel barons aged, some of them very gracefully. A few of them learned to read books. Some even learned to use table forks and gave up, if somewhat sadly, their diamond-studded toothpicks and gold-plated cuspidors. They sent their sons to college and married off their daughters, when possible, into cultured families. For the most part the younger generation has lived quietly and seemly.

Charlie Schwab almost alone remains of the old originals, the true barons of the line who had served in the sweating ranks, who had chewed Battleaxe and spat fair into the blazing doors of open-hearth furnaces. One by one they died and were laid away, in stainless steel containers. In their way they were a magnificent show. America would hardly have been America without them.

---

[3] John M. Longyear died in 1922. On her death in 1931, Mrs. Longyear left the Brookline mansion to Zion Research Foundations, "a non-sectarian group for study of biblical lore."

23 *Pretty Cassie Chadwick*

THERE was one and only one woman who became famous among steelworkers the country over. It isn't of record that she was ever inside a steel plant. It is doubtful that a steelworker ever laid eyes on her; yet her fascinating doings were discussed between casts at Lackawanna, Braddock, South Chicago, Birmingham, and all way points. She even went into a song that is often sung today when old-timers get together over a puddler's cocktail.

Cassie Chadwick was to perform under a variety of names, but she was christened Elizabeth Bigley when she was born on an Ontario farm near Eastwood, in 1857. The first sign of budding genius came early. When she was twelve she had a hundred calling cards printed on which appeared "Elizabeth Bigley, Heiress to $15,-000." These she liked to give both to friends and to strangers, who thought the gesture merely the play-world efforts of a highly imaginative child. At eighteen, however, Elizabeth acted. She somehow got hold of a check that had been made out for fifteen dollars, to her father, in payment for some livestock. She altered the check to read "fifteen hundred dollars" and attempted to cash it. The girl already had ideas.

Father Bigley tried various ways of punishing his daughter, but he finally gave up hope of keeping her in bounds. He packed her off to Cleveland to live with her elder sister, the wife of a physician. Nothing much happened until 1882 when Elizabeth, who always had a liking for physicians, married a Dr. Blank, a highly reputable gentleman of Cleveland. In short order the doctor got a divorce. Elizabeth Bigley Blank disappeared.

She was busy, though. On her divorce she immediately became Madame La Rose, clairvoyant and hypnotist, and moved to Toledo. The trail grows dim for a time. In 1890 it becomes clear again. Madame La Rose no more than Elizabeth Bigley could help writing names on checks. She was convicted on a charge of forgery and sent to the Ohio pen for three years.

Madame La Rose emerged from the gray walls and started at once for Cleveland. When she got there she was calling herself Mrs. C. L. Hoover—a widow, she said. The widow Hoover remained in Cleveland and kept out of the newspapers. Four years later she was married to one of Cleveland's most eminent practitioners, Dr. Leroy S. Chadwick. That was in 1897, and the wedding was an event in the Euclid Avenue set, whose babies Dr. Chadwick brought into the world.

At this period of her life Cassie Chadwick, as she liked to be known, was a fascinating personality. Pretty, if not ravishingly beautiful, she had the face of a slightly sad angel. Hers was a trim, graceful figure, made for the hourglass lines of the nineties, and she wore clothes like a duchess. Her eyes were large, deep, and sincere. Her voice had something moving in it. And more than one ordinarily hardheaded and unromantic business man later swore that the woman possessed hypnotic power. In view of the record, she doubtless did.

One day not many months after her marriage, Mrs. Chadwick engaged a prominent attorney of Cleveland, a friend of her husband's, to go to New York City with her. It was to be a highly important and a strictly confidential trip, she warned.

The attorney was kept completely mystified until what seemed to be the climax of the strangest professional trip he had ever made. This climax occurred on Fifth Avenue near the Fifty-ninth Street intersection.

As soon as the two Clevelanders had arrived in New York, Mrs. Chadwick engaged a hansom cab. They drove uptown. On the way the woman remarked something to the effect that "you can spank a naughty child, but you simply can't paddle a big man of finance." This didn't make much sense to the lawyer, but before he could ask to know more, the woman stopped the cab. She told the cabbie to wait, that she would be gone only a few minutes. She asked the lawyer to remain in the cab.

The lawyer saw the trim figure of Mrs. Chadwick flit across the Fifth Avenue sidewalk. She went without hesitation to the front door of a castlelike mansion and disappeared inside the pretentious entrance. The lawyer was slightly dazed. He knew that the pile of stone and marble was the American castle of Andrew Carnegie. It made him chew on his cigar pretty hard.

Ten or fifteen minutes later the woman came tripping out the same entrance. She was carrying a bulky package, a large envelope, in her hand. She seemed to be calm and entirely possessed. She directed the cabman to drive them back to their hotel.

On the way downtown the attorney intimated that he should like to know—in fact that he ought to be told—what all this was about.

"You needn't worry," the woman said. "You will be paid your fee."

"I'm not worrying about my fee. What I want to know is, what business you have with Andrew Carnegie. And why am I here?"

"You are here because I wanted a competent attorney along—just in case the gentleman made my call difficult." She paused a moment, then went on, subdued, possibly embarrassed.

"As to the gentleman in question—well, perhaps the great man was indiscreet in his youth. Men sometimes are, as you know. And as a lawyer you understand that an innocent victim of such indiscretion must not be allowed to suffer in poverty."

"H'm-m," was all the attorney could think of.

"However"—the woman brightened perceptibly—"it was all settled very quickly, as you see." She tapped the large envelope in her hand.

"I see," said the lawyer. He asked no more.

He got his fee, a right good thumping one, on return to Cleveland with Mrs. Chadwick. The odd "business trip" on which he had done nothing never quite dimmed in his mind.

Not long after the trip to New York, the Chadwick home on Euclid Avenue in Cleveland took on new luster. Dr. Chadwick had a fair income but hardly enough to support three maids for whom Mrs. Chadwick presently bought sealskin coats, making them doubtless the only three maids in Cleveland thus attired. It was the only ostentation noted of the Chadwick ménage during that first year of the Chadwicks' married life.

At a date unknown, but at approximately this period, Mrs. Chadwick appeared at a large Cleveland bank. She would talk to no one but the chief official. To him in a private room she exhibited a package which caused the official to whistle happily under his breath. In the big fat envelope was what was obviously a trust fund amounting to an even two million dollars of principal, the various documents signed in the distinctive script of Andrew Carnegie and properly witnessed. All the papers seemed to be in good order.

It is possible that the lawyer who had accompanied Mrs. Chadwick to New York had whispered about the Fifth Avenue call to the Cleveland banker. It would have been a natural thing, seeing that the lawyer had close business connections with the bank. In any case the banker was very happy to handle a big trust fund with the Carnegie name on it—the name of a man then rated greater than John D. Rockefeller and next after J. Pierpont Morgan. Mrs. Chadwick demurely mentioned that she wished the fact of the trust fund kept secret. The banker assured her that such was common practice. He gave her a receipt for the papers she turned over.

Cassie Chadwick now stepped into a pace that amazed Cleveland. For the next five years she ran the new steel barons of Pittsburgh a close race in large and vulgar spending. Old-timers in Cleveland still talk of it. The staff of Chadwick servants grew. A footman in livery appeared. So did a butler. One time Cassie telephoned a Cleveland department store and asked them to remain open, for her privately, a short time after the usual closing hour; Mrs. Chadwick wanted to buy a few trifles undisturbed by *hoi polloi*. The store stayed open. Cassie showed up and purchased a thousand dollars' worth of hose and handkerchiefs.

She liked to play Lady Bountiful. In 1900 she selected twelve Cleveland high-school girls and took them on a three months' tour of England and the Continent. In 1902 she collected a group of kids from Cleveland slums and gave them an outing in the country. Cassie was kind to dumb animals, too. She had fresh green clover fetched from Ohio fields to feed the horses of the Chadwick stable.

She did a good deal of traveling, much of it alone. The good doctor, a kindly man, let her have her way. Whether or not she had told him of the "Carnegie private trust fund" is not certain, but it would seem likely that she had.

During the winter of 1903–1904 she staged what was to be one of the last of her grander gestures. She chartered a special train, filled it with Cleveland friends, and took them to New York for a single performance of Wagner's *Parsifal* at the Metropolitan Opera House.

It had long been apparent that Dr. Chadwick's income could not support the elegant carryings-on of Cassie. She had become a noted, almost a notorious, character in Cleveland. No scandal had attached itself to her; not that. She kept her skirts very clean. She had borne a son to the doctor and lived circumspectly. It was only her showy manner of living that caused talk.

Cassie had long fascinated two newspapermen. They were Charles Martin and Robert Larkin of the *Cleveland Press*. The boys figured it might be interesting to learn where the money came from that Cassie Chadwick spent so lavishly.

One thing led to another. Martin and Larkin soon discovered that Cassie was none other than "Madame La Rose," who had done time for forgery. Tracing back, they found she had once acquired money by mortgaging furniture that belonged to a sister and a brother-in-law.

She had spent the cash on herself. Getting back even further, the boys learned of the raised check back in Ontario.

Without more ado the *Cleveland Press* came out with a story that said Mrs. Leroy S. Chadwick was an ex-convict and probably an awful fraud to boot. Cassie had her attorneys bring a suit for libel. And then the Chadwick affair burst in style, blowing in all directions at once.

The Cleveland bank hurriedly took another look at those "Carnegie" documents. They still looked good but the bank thought Mr. Carnegie ought to see them. The Scot came to Cleveland. He told the bankers and the press, who told the nation, that he had never established a trust fund for any supposedly illegitimate daughter. Further, he had no illegitimate children of either sex. The woman, he said, was a complete hoax. He had never seen or heard of her. As for those papers in the bank, they were forgeries. He scrutinized the signature and pronounced it a very good imitation of his own.

Sensations followed. In Brookline, Massachusetts, a capitalist named H. D. Newton said he had loaned Cassie Chadwick sums totaling $198,000 on her personal notes, backed by a "trust fund" held by a Cleveland bank. Mr. Newton said he had understood that Mrs. Chadwick was a natural daughter of the King of Steel, Mr. Carnegie.

In Pittsburgh, a builder of railroad cars revealed that he had loaned Cassie Chadwick large but unnamed sums on similar notes. "They seemed to be backed by plenty of good collateral," he said.

But it was in small, quiet Oberlin, Ohio, that the Chadwick touch struck hardest: a solid, conservative bank there closed its doors.

A check-up showed that the Oberlin bank was holding Cassie's notes to an amount close to half a million dollars. One bank official later went to jail. Another died of what was said to have been shame and grief.

Cassie talked very haughty when she was arrested. But it soon appeared that she could not raise bail for the insignificant amount of five thousand dollars.

Cassie's trial, in the language of the day, was a lulu. It brought out the fact that a number of persons besides those already named had been duped in a similar manner. It had been Mrs. Chadwick's practice to get a loan from a bank or an individual, sometimes both. These she would repay by a loan from another source, and so on. The loans grew larger each time. How long she could have continued of course isn't known, but experts seemed to think she might have got along pretty well for several more years, had it not been for the Cleveland paper's exposé.

The Cleveland lawyer testified that he had accompanied her to New York and had seen her enter the door of the Carnegie mansion. Carnegie vowed again that he had never laid eyes on the woman.

Cassie's defense was that she herself was the result of a careless moment in the youth of the great steel baron; that the documents of the so-called trust fund were genuine in every respect, right down to the signature.

The jury did not believe Cassie. On March 27, 1905, she was sentenced to ten years in the Ohio penitentiary. There was no appeal to higher court. She went to prison, and there she died of a heart ailment on October 11 two years later.

Following the crash of the Oberlin bank, Andrew Carnegie was said to have paid many but not all of the de-

positors' claims in full. He still denied any connection
with the woman but said he felt very sorry that his name
had been used to break a bank.

A recurrently favorite song of the era was one named
"Tammany." It had a lively refrain in pseudo-Indian
tempo. Some parodist wrote a new version that took the
country, now conscious of the Cleveland adventuress
and rather pleased with her, by storm. Went the chorus:

> Carnegie, Carnegie;
> Cassie Chadwick on his knee;
> Girl of a long past mem-o-ree.
> Carnegie, Carnegie,
> Sandy Andy, you're a dandy,
> Car-ne-gie.

To fit the meter the accent on the steelmaster's name
had to be moved to the final syllable, which was no trouble at all. How the iron and steel boys sangs that parody!
You could hear it rendered with gusto by the crew of an
ore freighter heading down the Lakes for Conneaut on
a pleasant evening. You might hear a strophe of it between the thunders of a rolling mill. It was even hummed
discreetly by clerks and big officials in the offices of
U.S. Steel in Pittsburgh.

Popular songs are like that. You can never tell what
they will do, nor how far they will go. The Carnegie-
Chadwick song became the nearest thing to an official
Steel song that was ever written.

24 *Mr. Gary Gets a Monument*

LESS than five years from the day of its birth U.S. Steel had more money in its coffers than it knew what to do with. It attempted to rectify this condition in 1905 by setting aside $50,000,000 for construction of a new plant.

In announcing the intention to add still more production to the largest industrial group in the world, Judge Gary, its chief executive officer, tried to be casual. The new plant, he said, was simply to round out the Corporation. U.S. Steel, in the eyes of its competitors and of the general public, was already pretty well rounded out. Cartoonists drew the Corporation as a fatter and even more sinister ogre than Standard Oil. But there wasn't any law to prevent the Corporation from building one or ten new plants if it wanted to.

The Corporation went ahead, organizing the Indiana Steel Company to build and operate a plant which Gary said was to be the most efficient in the world.

Before any official announcement had been made about Indiana Steel, there was a leak somewhere. The leak was a mere drip from one or more of U.S. Steel's board of directors. It was to the effect that a huge steel plant was to be erected somewhere in the Chicago area, and that Hammond, Indiana, seemed to be a favorable site for such an enterprise.

Hammond was on the Illinois-Indiana line, just south of Chicago and on the Cinder Shore. It had once been a small meat-packing town, but it hadn't done very well. As soon as the leak occurred, Hammond real estate went into a boom. The dismal sand dunes along the lake shore had never been dignified by a price. You might have had them, if you were that crazy, for a few dollars an acre—virtually write your own ticket. In a few weeks they jumped to one hundred dollars an acre, to five hundred dollars, to a thousand dollars.

The same was true of near-by communities, for the leak had indicated only that lightning was going to strike somewhere in the general area. Property began changing hands, and its "value" increasing every day, in Indiana Harbor, East Chicago, Whiting. Rumors and counter rumors flew thick. Men reputed to be "insiders" were listened to with respect. Then the bubble burst. Judge Gary announced brightly one day that Indiana Steel had acquired a nice site on the lake shore in Indiana, just east of Hammond.

Hammond and the other towns wilted into a numb condition from which they were years in recovering. Many promoters were ruined, which pleased everyone else. Gary's announcement was an earthquake in Hammond, which talks about it thirty years after.

Once it had picked the site, the Corporation, under its harmless camouflage of "Indiana Steel" went ahead rapidly. It dredged a harbor into the sand dunes. Trees were planted, wide streets laid out. And an army went to work at putting up what was then and still is the biggest steelmaking plant in the world. The job required three years, and when it was done U.S. Steel's grateful directors showed their appreciation. They named the place

"Gary" in honor of the small-town lawyer who had been at the helm through the tempestuous early days of the Corporation and had brought it, safely if not quite untarnished, through the attacks of Government and competitors.

Gary, Indiana, could not have happened anywhere else on earth. In March of 1906 it was a dismal, uninhabited shore of sand on which grew a few struggling pines. Only gulls held commerce there, and when the gulls were not screaming, the silence was broken only by the sighing of Lake Michigan's endless winds in the pines and the whistle of distant locomotives.

In February of 1909, when the first steel was made, the Gary Works smoked in orderly array all along six miles of waterfront. It was the one hundred and forty-third plant built or bought by U.S. Steel.

The city of Gary, which soon had a population of fifty thousand, and today has more than double that number, was something new in steel towns. Instead of clustering around the works, the community was built up on the other side of the railroad tracks—one mile, two miles, five miles from the stacks. It is probably the quietest residence section of a steel town anywhere.

The city center also was a departure for steel towns. Lawns appeared in front of the fine library and city administration buildings. Some attention, but not too much, was paid to architecture and landscaping. Parking strips with trees lined the better residential streets. A gymnasium, a community club, even a country club followed. School buildings such as no steel town had seen were put up. The police station, down to its cells, was so elegant that a tough Hunky, put in one of them to sober up, awoke to believe he was in the Palmer House at Chicago.

All of Gary wasn't quite so nice. Out on the edge a packing-box town grew up, and later came a Negro quarter; still later, a Mexican quarter. But when it was built, Gary was almost unbelievable.

The city's great day arrived on July 23, 1908, when the harbor was officially opened to the first ore boat. It was proper that the vessel was the *Elbert H. Gary*, 549 feet long and carrying 10,500 tons of the Mesabi's best ore. She was also carrying five hundred business men and well-wishers, of whom, so one recalls, four hundred and ninety were roaring-drunk.

As the vessel nosed into the man-made harbor, Navy ships, acting as a convoy for U.S. Steel, boomed a twenty-one gun salute to Old Glory, raised by young Mary Louise Gleason, daughter of the first general superintendent of Gary Works.

Some of the local and imported *eminenti* attempted to make speeches from the bridge of the vessel, but nobody listened. Beer flowed freely. There was a parade with bands, a tour of the works, and Hunkies at the blast furnaces wondered at the doings. Workers for the plant had been brought in from other U.S. Steel operations in South Chicago, Joliet, and Pittsburgh. No works ever opened with a better crew.

Gary continued to thrive. So did United States Steel. The land at Gary was sold and administered by a sort of subsidiary, the Gary Land Company, and it is commonly believed in Gary today that sales by the land company brought in enough money to pay for the orig-

inal cost of the land and for building the steel plant to
boot. It is probably true. It is also true that in spite of
the slums of the Negro quarter, the city of Gary is one
of the best industrial communities in the United States.

Judge Gary was a pious man. He did not approve of
Sin in any of its pleasant and varied forms.[1] From the
first he did what he could to keep the new city what is
technically known as "clean." There were saloons, of
course, but no recognized red-light district. Gary has
always had two shortages—one of housing, the other of
amusement for strong men.

Chicago wasn't far off, and it was well stocked; but it
took the best part of an hour to get there. So, enterpris-
ing persons moved into Calumet City, a huddle of shacks
that grew with the years and came into fullest flower
with Prohibition.

Calumet City was the acknowledged hellhole of the
Cinder Shore. It is in Illinois, astride the Indiana line,
and is handy to Gary, to Indiana Harbor, East Chicago,
and Pullman, all steel towns. Steelworkers flocked to
Calumet in droves. You'd find it busy any night in the
week and on many days. The eight-hour shift was a fine
thing for Sin.

Here in Calumet, Al Capone had his central distribut-
ing point for his fine liquors, wines, and beers. John
Dillinger often holed up in Calumet after a bank job.
The Barker gang liked Calumet and stayed around a
good deal. This was the place where the locally celebrated Willie Harrison lived—and died.

---

[1] Directors of U.S. Steel always received a twenty-dollar gold piece
for attending board meetings. In pre-Gary days it had been their custom
to match the coins until one director had them all. Gary put a stop to
the practice. "It is gambling," he said, "and undignified."

Steelworkers of the district talk more of Willie Harrison than they ever did of the great Dillinger. Willie was a smooth gangster who kept his name out of the papers and his body out of jail, most of the time. He had a big hand in all the rackets. But Willie knew too much. One night some of the mob called and asked him to go motoring. It was said that they took Willie to a Calumet barn, struck him quite hard, shot him full of holes, then fired the barn.

But Willie Harrison lives on in the manner of John Wilkes Booth. Many steelworkers who knew Willie say that he somehow escaped the guns and the fire and will one day show up. A few claim to have seen him. He is one of the big legends of the Cinder Shore.

As for the Gary Works, their size passes all belief. Stretching for six miles along the shore of Lake Michigan, their countless stacks and hulking sheds present a feudal scene that is heightened by a moat in the form of the Calumet River. It is perhaps the best fortified of all Steel baronies. It is surely one of the most efficient.

For size, it is enough to know that Gary is the largest steel plant on earth. In their first thirty years of operation the Gary blast furnaces spewed forth forty-five million tons of pig iron, which was made into steel and "tin" on the spot. Gary Works coke is baked in one thousand ovens, and the gas from the ovens is not wasted; it lights the city of Gary. Slag (waste) from Gary's pig iron is not dumped to make ghastly piles. It is washed and treated and comes out looking like huge popped corn. Then it is sent to a near-by factory for use in the making of cement. Thus, "waste" from the Gary Works lights the mills and the town and paves the

streets. The boys in the mills have a little joke; they tell
that U.S. Steel technicians are now at work on a problem: how to catch the flying sparks from the hot-rail
saws and make them into Fourth of July sparklers.

When the Gary plant was being built, Bessemer was
on the wane. The open-hearth process of making steel
was coming in. At Gary the open hearth came into its
own.

Nowhere near so spectacular as a Bessemer converter,
the open hearth had been developed in England and
France by Sir William Siemens and Emile and Pierre
Martin, back in the sixties. Its adoption in the United
States was slow, but soon after 1900, as related, Tennessee Coal & Iron had become noted for the high quality
of its steel rails, which were made in open hearths. The
Bessemer process calls for very high-grade ore, while
open hearth will make steel out of any old ore, and will
use junk and scrap, too. On the completion of Gary's
open-hearth department, the annual tonnage of open
hearth in the United States for the first time passed
Bessemer.

At the Gary Works, in a seemingly endless shed, the
doors of the open hearths glitter at you through the
gloom. You can't see the confines of the shed, it is so
murky, but you feel its vastness; and it is filled with
swirling cinders and gases and noise.

For a quarter of a mile a track runs past the furnaces.
On this travels the mighty charging machine, a machine
you have to see to believe at all. It stops in front of a
door. The door is opened wide, and out belches red and
white flame as though the doors to hell had been kicked
open. The man on the charging machine moves a lever,

and a gigantic arm, a sort of ramroad, snaps out to shove
a car loaded with pig and scrap metal into the maw,
dumps it, then returns the empty car to its carriage.
It is a trite thought, no doubt, but you think for a moment that you have stepped out of life and into a nether
world where imps are making hell blaze with a forced
draft. . . . When that car of scrap is dumped into the
hearth, the furnace roars louder than ever, and a man
slams shut the door. You can still see the flame through
the open slot.

Furnace Number Eighty-three is ready for tapping,
says Richard Ferguson, master melter. He gives you a
pair of plain goggles and lets you stand close to the furnace slot. You peer through it, and you look on something that defies description. You might as well say that
what you see is an intense boiling, bubbling mass of a
color and appearance you never saw before—and let it
go at that. And you may, if you are given to reflection
and poetic thoughts, well think you will never be closer
to an Old Testament hell than now. Here is Gehenna,
Sheol, Tartarus.

Meanwhile the great shed around you is filled with a
constant roaring that is punctuated by sullen booms. A
siren blows. It is merely the telephone. A screaming
siren, loud enough to wake a city, in place of a bell's
tinkle. . . . It gives an idea of the tools they work with
in Steel.

Ferguson talks at the phone a moment. The man at
the other end is in the plant laboratory. He has tested a
sample of the brew in this furnace, and he says that the
puddle of hell in Number Eighty-three is ripe for tapping.

They lead you around to the back of the furnace. A

man in an asbestos suit is crawling toward the furnace wall, a steel rod in his hands. Back of him, in a long pit, is the biggest ladle you will ever see; it will hold one hundred and fifty tons of molten steel.

The man in the asbestos suit seems to be fumbling around, but he knows what he's doing. He is knocking out the fire clay of the tapping hole. In a moment there is a burst of bright light, of fire, and the man in the gray-white covering leaps away. The fire seems to leap, too, until it is a cloud of flame—or is it flame?—that blots out everything beyond. Your face glows hot.

One of Ferguson's helpers proffers you a pair of deep blue goggles. You'll have to wear them if you want to see the flow of the actual steel. This stuff is too hot to be seen with the naked eye; only the light, not the steel, can be seen without cobalt goggles. So you put them on.

Even a Dante would be struck at the sight revealed by the colored glasses when they are turned toward flowing steel. It is a beautiful and a terrifying spectacle—the flames, the smoke, and God knows what else, leaping and eddying around like a whirlwind—a wind that now seems wholly wild, now formed of countless symmetrical patterns. It is as if some magic were allowing you as a special privilege to *see* the substance and body of a hurricane being born. You don't think of it as merely hot metal being poured.

To call it a "wind" that you see through the goggles is lame talk, but it must suffice. There it is, billowing, swirling up and around, first blue, then purple, then magenta, then violet. Look, and name it if you can. And through it all, through this nightmare of dizzy patterns, you can see the Niagara of molten steel flowing into the big ladle. This is the birth of steel.

When you take off the goggles, it all looks different, but no less hypnotic. Perhaps you wonder aloud how hot that flow of metal is. "It is twenty-nine hundred and ninety-three degrees," says Ferguson. It comes as a sort of shock that anyone should pretend to know how hot that stuff is. Ferguson shows you a gadget that looks for all the world like one of those stereoscopes which used to stand on parlor tables, and through which you looked at pairs of photographs. It's an optical pyrometer. A man who knows how can look through it at that seething mass and tell to a degree its temperature.

Now, you note that one of the helpers is up to something. He picks up a large paper bag full of some substance, walks a few steps nearer the big ladle, and heaves in the bag. There is a dull boom like far-off cannon; flames and smoke reach for the high roof of the big shed, and a flash of heat drives you back. Again and again the man heaves a bag, each time answered by a roar and a boom. It is one or more of several substances —carbon, perhaps, or manganese—that they are adding to the brew, to make it exactly right for a special order; and it suddenly dawns on you that steel is much like soup, mixed and seasoned to the appetite of the consumer.

The ladle fills rapidly with its one hundred and fifty tons. From a lip at the top it is overflowing. This is the slag, the waste. It flows into a receptacle big enough but much smaller than the ladle. In the manner of steelworkers in dealing with anything of or near normal size, this vessel is called a thimble.

As far as you can see up and down the pits is a row of molds, all stacked in place and awaiting filling. They won't wait long. A traveling crane rumbles along the

track near the roof, and two big hooks are lowered
through the murk. They fit the handles of the ladle,
and up it goes, as if it were a bag of feathers and not
one hundred and fifty tons of steel.

The crane moves the ladle over the first mold. Men
cluster around. The ladle is lowered to the top of the
mold. There is a burst of sparks that fly everywhere.
The ladle lifts, moves on, and the process is repeated.
Sparks fly and molds are filled until the last drop is
drained. This is pouring a heat.

The things in the molds are now ingots. They weigh
some five tons each. They are two feet square and seven
and one-half feet long. They will be made into rails.

When the steel has been in the molds long enough to
solidify, but is still red-hot, the molds are stripped off
and the upright ingots are hauled to the soaking pits
at the head of the rolling mill. Soaking pits aren't what
they sound like. They are really a furnace, heated by
gas, into which the cooling ingots are put. Here they
are kept until their temperature is even throughout.
Two thousand three-hundred and fifty degrees is considered about right.

Here in the rolling mill the drama goes on. From the
soaking pit comes a cherry-red ingot, the ikon of Steel,
on a small car. The operator dumps the car, the ingot
strikes the first rolls in a thundering crash of sparks and
noise. On it goes, through roll after roll, each time becoming thinner and longer. The noise exceeds all continuous noise you ever have heard.

You will have to look sharp to see a man anywhere.
The place seems all but deserted, but you'll find a couple
of lads standing in the rollers' pulpit, high above the
floor. The pulpit is a hot place, summer or winter, and

two men always are there. Sometimes the heat gets a man, and he flops. That is why they work in pairs.

The ingots continue rolling on and on, but you would never recognize them. Now they look like monstrously long tongues, coming swiftly and as if wilting through the rolls. It is red-hot steel, still, two hundred and fifty feet of it, and as it passes near where you stand a sudden flash of intense heat envelops you, then dies as quickly. The long tongues begin to take shape, a shape you recognize as the conventional rail of American commerce.

These limp blistering tongues, longer than any serpent in the Bottomless Pit, give you an idea of what could happen in a rail mill if one of them broke loose, got off the rolls, and went on a rampage. Sometimes they do, and men who have seen them thus tell of dreadful things.

When the rails are shaped they go to the saw, where a whirling blade cuts them to 39 feet 8 inches in such a rain of fire that you wonder how men survive it. When a perfectly sawed rail has cooled it is exactly 39 feet long.

Everywhere you are struck by the fact that you see few men on the job. Men are there, of course, but in modern mills like Gary Works they lurk in corners and pulpits and press buttons and move levers. It is the same in the sheet and the tin mills. Here are Gargantuan rolls and presses that make sheet steel out of ingots and press it thin into metal for tin cans, automobile bodies, refrigerators, freight cars; into wheels and axles and plates; into pipes and tubes and window frames; into beams and metal ties and table tops and stairs and even shingles. Here are being rolled and pressed the material backbone and ribs of America. Seeing such plants in full swing, one might think that a hundred men, no more, were on the job; it is uncanny. Yet, somewhere in Gary Works, ten thousand men labor on weekdays, a few hundred on Sundays. (Both blast furnaces and open hearths must operate seven days a week.)

Throughout the plant no man works at a place where a machine can do the job. Steelmakers today are mostly machine tenders. Machines are as safe as experience can make them, yet the best of steel mills is no haven of safety. One factor that cannot be removed is the diabolical, almost hypnotic influence doubtless cast over steelworkers by the overwhelming majesty of the materials and the instruments they work with. If you doubt this hypnotic influence, go visit a blast furnace, an open hearth, a rolling mill. The sights to be seen all day and all night—the belching Bessemers, the sinister flow of hot pig down the seething gullies of a blast furnace, the terrible beauty of tapping an open hearth, and that endless procession of long red tongues, crashing and roaring through the rolling mills—these are hasheesh enough to make a man dream strange dreams at a moment when he should be tending strictly to the business in hand.

Outside, in the yards, it is little better: nine-hundred-odd coke ovens smoking and blinking; high stacks that spout fire one moment, black smoke the next; car upon car of red ingots moving through the night; the whistles, the sirens, the roars and booms that come from the depths of the plant. It all makes a drama of epic size, a drama to move the imagination of the dullest-witted proletarian. Men get used to it. They never become immune.

It was an understanding of the dangers inherent in making steel that caused Judge Gary, as head of U.S. Steel, to issue an order that should have made his memory secure without naming a city for him. In 1906, or two years before there had been much talk of safety in a steel mill, Gary gave a general order to all plants in the Corporation. "The United States Steel Corporation," it read, "expects its subsidiary companies to make every effort practicable to prevent injury to its employes. Expenditures necessary for such purposes will be authorized. Nothing which will add to the protection of the workmen should be neglected."

This was quite revolutionary. Steel plants of the period were thought of as slaughterhouses, both by the public and by the industry itself. Steelmaking and accidents went hand in hand. There was little or nothing to be done about them. More than one big boss, some within U.S. Steel, said aloud that the Judge was crazy.

Gary backed up his order. He made a new job, that of safety engineer, and put one of his young executives into the position. He was William H. Cameron. It was up to Cameron to find out what caused accidents in a subsidiary plant, no easy job. Steelworkers believed much as their bosses did—that accidents just happened. Cameron found opposition on both sides. In a short time, though, he learned some of the most prolific causes of mishaps. He recommended changes here and there. Gary backed Cameron to the limit. Within a year's time the Corporation could look back on its record and see what had been accomplished. In five years the record was startling. It got better every year.

Steel has often been a pig-headed industry in the

United States. It lagged in adopting the use of coke in place of charcoal. It lagged in adopting the Bessemer, and then the open-hearth process. But when Steel finds a thing good, it goes whole-hog for it. It was so with organized safety. In 1906 Steel was as dangerous an industry to work in as you could find. Thirty years later Steel's accident severity rate had dropped to less than one-third of the 1906 figure; its accident frequency rate was one of the lowest in any industry, heavy or light.

Judge Gary's order alone did not make steel mills safer. The coming of workmen's compensation laws probably had the greatest effect of all. These laws put a cash penalty on accidents, to be paid chiefly by employers. Cash penalties did a lot for safety.

But this should not detract from Gary's pioneer move. It was a brave as well as a wise thing to do. If the Judge, as head of the biggest steel concern in the world, had only been a little wiser or, it may be, a little braver, he could have gone a step further and saved all of Steel— its workers, its bosses, its profits—from the black cloud of trouble that had been forming ever since the war at Homestead, Pennsylvania, in 1892. If Gary had taken that one step, which might have been called a concession, it would have made a far greater monument for him than a mere city, which by 1919 was getting pretty grimy, anyway.

25 *Struggle in the Smoke*

IN HIS most Christian moment Judge Gary could never have dreamed of taking a step toward recognition of a union. There was no perceptible reason for his doing so, plenty of reason why he shouldn't. Had he mentioned such a thing aloud, the building at 71 Broadway in New York City would have quaked with the sudden horror of U.S. Steel's board of directors. It would have been a case of mass apoplexy.

The time for a steel union hadn't come. Homestead was a quarter of a century in the past, and steel barons still regarded Homestead as Englishmen did Waterloo. It was a Sunken Road into which the steelworkers' union had fallen, and had been covered deep. The combination of Frick and Pinkerton, plus the idiotic contribution of Alexander Berkman and the public's reaction to it, had pounded all life out of the handful of members who remained of the Amalgamated Association of Iron, Steel and Tin Workers.

In the meantime there had been a few futile stirrings in the smoke. When U.S. Steel was formed in 1901, a feeble attempt had been made by the Amalgamated. It was scarcely a gesture. In 1909 a flare-up of unorganized workers at the plant of the Pressed Steel Car Company in McKees Rocks, Pennsylvania, had been taken in hand by the I.W.W.—not the Amalgamated—and whipped into a fiercely fought strike. Two strikers were shot down by the Pennsylvania State Constabulary. The strikers retaliated by killing five of the troopers. At the same time the Amalgamated made a motion toward a general strike. It was pitiful and was put down without a shot. A year later, in Bethlehem, the workers stirred briefly, but to no purpose.

All these affairs had been local incidents. It could hardly be said that a union was involved. Quiet had reigned in Steel's "union" life so long that only the old-timers could remember battle. The somnolent Amalgamated drowsed on, its officials apparently content to sit in their offices and receive such union dues as old die-hards sent in voluntarily. Steel barons had no objection whatsoever to the kind of union the Amalgamated was, after the Homestead smoke had blown away.

It isn't to be thought that the long peace was due to contented labor. Steelworkers still had the twelve-hour day, with its twenty-four-hour shift every two weeks. Except for the highly skilled, wages were low. The casualty rate, in accidents, was still high, though improving. The casualty rate in occupational diseases was high and growing higher. The men lived in the most horrible parts of the most depressing towns in America.

But for one thing, Steel would never have known its quiet quarter-century. That thing was fear. It was the fear in steelworkers of company finks—detectives— with which every steel plant was infested after the Homestead riots. Henceforth, the steel bosses made sure they should know what the serfs were thinking and saying.

To call a steelworker of the period a "serf" was no great exaggeration. The whole policy of Steel was feudal

—an unconscious policy, perhaps, but that is the way it worked out. Company houses, company water and light, company stores, company unions, company mayors, company sheriffs, company police, company newspapers, company schools, even company priests and pastors. And of course the company finks—those employees, both paid and voluntary, who kept foremen and superintendents informed of the private talk and actions of employees. A mumbled protest about low wages might bring immediate discharge. Two such protests surely would. Fear, suspicion, ruled every man.

So life continued in the steel towns for more than twenty-five years. Not even politics was overlooked. Local elections were a foregone conclusion, for only company men were allowed to run for office, whether mayor or dogcatcher. But in state and national elections the hand of Steel often took a part: Just before polling time notices in six or eight languages appeared on plant bulletin boards. They informed the proud electorate, for instance, that unless the admirable Senator Boies Penrose were returned to Congress the steel mills of Pennsylvania would be closed down tight, and God alone knew when they would reopen. It had an effect.

During this long period of seeming peace and contentment, the forces of unrest were wholly suppressed. The first warning of what was ahead in the steel industry came in January of 1916. In East Youngstown, Ohio, unorganized workers asked for an increase in wages. Business was good. The companies met part but not all of the demands. Employees struck. The mills shut down. Word went around that two trainloads of strikebreakers were being brought into town.

In a flash East Youngstown blew up in such a riot as

it had never known. Mobs of strikers stormed the mills.
Armed guards shot them down. Three strikers were
killed, many wounded. And now the mob turned on the
city itself. Strikers, broken into gangs of howling der-
vishes, raided stores and saloons. They rolled barrels of
whisky into the street and drank it out of tin cans, out
of the bungholes. Crazed men ran through the shacks
and tenements scattering bundles of flaming waste. In
half an hour every piece of apparatus in Youngstown
and East Youngstown was fighting a score of fires. Six
city blocks were laid flat.

Hurry calls brought militia. It was all over as quickly
as it had begun. But for a few hours East Youngstown
had been given a taste of real revolution.

The affair at East Youngstown did two things. It
caused the steel bosses to double the vigilance in their
mills. It told the American Federation of Labor, or at
least some part of that aristocratic organization, that the
Hunkies in the steel mills might be ripe for a union.

The Federation always has worked slowly. A good
deal of talk about Steel went on in its rarefied chambers
for the next two years. Then, in the summer of 1918,
with the United States at war, the barons of the Federation grudgingly agreed to lock horns with the barons of
Steel. They came to their decision not from choice but
because of pressure from the ranks. In August the Federation formed the National Committee for Organizing
Iron and Steel Workers. The title sounds strangely like
that of the group which twenty years later was to fight
not only Steel but the Federation itself.

The plan was to stage a hurricane drive simultaneously in all steelmaking districts from Buffalo, New

York, to Pueblo, Colorado, taking in the ore carriers on
the Lakes and the miners of iron. The National Committee was to organize all the various trades found in Steel
into a group that would present a united front to Steel.
It was the next thing to an industrial union. Cash and
organizers for the drive were to be furnished by a number of international unions.

The plan had its inception in the mind of William Z.
Foster, an old-stock American who had been a Socialist,
an I.W.W., and finally an organizer in the A.F. of L.
Foster had just completed a spectacular job by organizing the packing-house workers in Chicago, something
that old union heads had said was impossible.

Foster realized the task ahead of him. It called for
courage, of which he had plenty. It must be done speed-
ily, if at all, and it would take a lot of money. Foster
was a brilliant and a fast organizer. The Federation
promised him sufficient funds.

The drive got off to a poor start. Instead of the simul-
taneous attack that had been planned, with organizers
in all important steel centers, the cautious moguls of
the A.F. of L. provided only enough cash and men to
begin the campaign in one district, the Chicago-Gary-
Joliet area. Foster was disappointed. He felt that such a
tin-pot attack on a nation-wide industry would be a mistake; that it would give Judge Gary, the acknowledged
generalissimo of all steel, opportunity to defend the one
affected area successfully and meanwhile to marshal his
forces for defense elsewhere. Foster was correct.

Monster meetings held in South Chicago, Gary, Indiana Harbor, and Joliet proved at once that steelworkers
wanted a union. They not only attended the meetings

by the thousand but signed union cards and paid their dues in advance. Inside a week more than three thousand had joined. A week later it was a stampede.

Demands were formulated at the meetings. They included the eight-hour day; the right to join a union; one day's rest in seven, and higher wages. The more important demands were for the shorter workday and the right of collective bargaining.

Judge Gary displayed his generalship. Although a few months previously he had stated that, come what might, U.S. Steel would adhere to the twelve-hour day, he now came out with an order that amounted to granting the eight-hour day, with time and one-half for overtime. The order was effective in all plants of the Corporation.

It took a good deal of strength from the budding union. Steelworkers in the Chicago area might think that their threat of a union had had something to do with the Judge's order, but not so in other districts. Outside Chicago, steelworkers everywhere thought that the eight-hour day and time and one-half had been granted them by the free and good will of the Corporation. It was going to make union organizing a whole lot harder.

Foster was now sure that unless quick and wide action were taken, his committee would be discredited before it really got to work. He moved his office and most of his organizers into the Pittsburgh area and sent a flying squadron of fearless men into the steel towns.

They had to be fearless. We were still at war with Germany. A trade-union organizer had about the same status as a "German spy," who seemed to lurk everywhere. Most steel towns were company towns, and when an "agitator" entered one he laid himself open to the quick-trigger violence of company police.

Foster was in command but he did not remain in his office. He moved with the flying squadrons much of the time, and they got some warm receptions. In Monessen, a Monongahela town, the burgess (mayor) refused to permit a meeting and had the organizers run out of town. From near-by Charleroi the boys went ahead by sending loads of sept-lingual propaganda into Monessen and finally calling for a mass meeting. Ten thousand miners from the surrounding hills marched into town and the meeting was held.

It wasn't quite so easy in Donora. No halls could be hired. Organizers were jailed on sight as idle persons. The local Lithuanian Society suddenly expelled its president, who was thought to be too friendly with the steel company, and opened its hall for meetings.

At McKeesport, the union hall was constantly picketed by steel-company officials and detectives who took down the names of any employees who entered. The men were promptly discharged. This went on for weeks, with every discharged man adding to the strength of the organizers.

The older towns of Braddock and Rankin, which had a dim recollection of unionism, presented no great difficulties. Men joined by the hundred every day. Organizers were not molested. In North Clairton, Foster and his squadron were arrested and fined for holding an "illegal" meeting. But public opinion was with them. Old Mother Jones showed up, fire still in her voice, and helped put the town into the union ranks. Homestead no longer had a Fort Frick. Its town-company officials resisted by arresting Foster and several others, and no halls could be hired. Street meetings, in defiance of the burgess, turned the trick.

Duquesne, up-river from Homestead-Munhall, had a "fighting mayor," James Crawford, who swore loudly that Jesus Christ himself would not be allowed to speak in Duquesne for the A.F. of L. The boys tried it, though. Crawford's police arrested forty-four speakers, including Foster and Mother Jones, and threw them into the tiny Duquesne jail. All were fined, and Duquesne held out until the strike actually started.

Johnstown presented a tough problem. Long notorious for its low wages, it was ruled like a medieval state; and weeks of hard work, and some violence, were necessary before union meetings could be held. Wheeling, down in West Virginia, was easier. Cleveland workers joined up rapidly until the local had 17,000 members. Youngstown signed up more than 19,000. By August it was roughly estimated that 200,000 steelworkers had joined the new union.

Now Mr. Gompers, head of the A.F. of L., sought a conference with Judge Gary. The Judge did not reply to Gompers' letter. Foster's committee decided to take a strike ballot. The result showed approximately 98 per cent in favor of striking. Another attempt to meet Judge Gary was made. This time he replied, stating that although the Corporation and its subsidiaries "do not combat labor unions as such, we decline to discuss business with them."

Foster's committee now wired President Woodrow Wilson, just then on a western tour in favor of his League of Nations, asking him to use his offices to call a conference at which the head men of Steel and the union leaders could discuss matters. A reply from Secretary Tumulty held out no hope for such a conference.

While this attempt at dickering was going on, steel-

workers who had joined the union were being fired by
the hundred. In a short time, it appeared, there would
be few men to call out on strike. The Committee met
and voted to send out a strike call, effective September 22.

Next morning Foster's committee was alarmed. From
President Wilson came a request that the strike be post-
poned until after an Industrial Conference, set for October 6, could be held. The request came too late. The
strike order had been voted; and anyway thousands of
young steelworkers were spoiling for a showdown. To
their number were added the several thousand who had
been discharged for union membership. They had nothing to lose.

The strike call went out. It requested all iron and
steel workers who were not working under union agreements to remain away from work on the morning of
September 22. It went on to say that the Committee had
attempted to meet the heads of the steel companies and
present demands, but had not been successful. It asked
that no violence be committed. It closed with a warning
that "if we falter and fail to act, this great effort will be
lost, and we will sink back into miserable and hopeless
serfdom. The welfare of our wives and children is at
stake. Now is the time to insist upon our rights as human
beings."

Both Big and Little Steel—terms that had not then
come into use—were ready. There can be no doubt that
they welcomed the first show of strength since 1892.
And they didn't even need State or Federal troops. Not
in Pennsylvania, anyway. Allegheny County alone immediately mustered and armed five thousand deputy
sheriffs. It was much the same in the smaller towns,

where local governmental agencies were little more than public service departments of the steel companies.

Then there were the private armies of Steel—the Coal and Iron Police; the armed guards, the detectives, foremen, and company "home-guards"—employees who would not join a union.

On top of these, in Pennsylvania, were the hard-riding troopers of the State Constabulary, a group of tough fellows.who had been organized at the behest of the coal and steel companies after the great coal strike of 1902. These men, all able and fearless to a point beyond recklessness, were known to the workers as Pennsylvania Cossacks.

By September 30, a week after the strike call, approximately 365,000 men were out of the mills and blast furnaces. The shutdown was almost complete. Even faraway Colorado heard the call; the big plant at Pueblo went down. Only Birmingham, in the Deep South, continued to operate full blast.

Anyone could have told what would happen next. Three hundred thousand men actually on strike. Another hundred thousand either attempting to work or in enforced idleness. Perhaps seventy-five or a hundred thousand men, more or less armed, on the side of what is often called "law and order." The blood soon was flowing.

Gunfire rattled all along the Steel belt. Two strikers were shot and killed at the Lackawanna Works near Buffalo. Two more fell at Youngstown, and two at New Castle. At West Natrona, Pennsylvania, Mrs. Fannie Sellins, a mine workers' organizer, was shot and beaten to death in a clash between guards and strikers in which a striker was killed.

The battle was very bitter in Farrell, Pennsylvania; a guard and three strikers were killed. In Hammond, Indiana, four strikers were shot or clubbed to death; and one striker each was killed in Chicago, Cleveland, and Wheeling.

The score: strikers killed, 18; others killed, 2. The wonder of it was that the dead did not run into the hundreds. Hospitals of steel towns were filled to overflowing with wounded guards, deputies, "Cossacks," and strikers.

The Pennsylvania Constabulary were by far the most feared and hated of the suppressive agencies. They'd go anywhere on their horses. In Homestead they liked to ride their well trained animals up onto sidewalks and club half a dozen strikers who were talking; three persons constituted a mob in any steel town. The troopers rode into stores, into homes even, trampling and beating. They bragged, with reason, that two of the horsemen could break up a street meeting of two hundred unarmed strikers.

There was sabotage in the steel plants. Most of them were well guarded; but here and there, especially in the Pittsburgh district, the fires of blast furnaces that had continued operating were mysteriously turned off. Gas mains had sudden leaks. Parts of machines were broken or lugged off. The switches of steel-plant railroads were opened or jammed. Pot shots were taken at guards, police, troopers. Workers were beaten up.

Judge Gary, spokesman for all Steel, pretty much held his peace and let things go their way. It was wise generalship. He knew that the Amalgamated had no treasury. He knew that the A.F. of L. international

unions were doing nothing to help the strike, once it got
under way.

But a few steps were necessary, just to make sure. Up
out of the South rolled train after train of coaches.
They were loaded to the doors with Negroes, some few
of them experienced steelworkers and all of them promised a free ride and four dollars a day to work in the
steel mills up North. Strikers soon learned of this move
but could do little about it. In Gary, where one of the
first trains of Negroes was brought, the strikers attempted to prevent the importation. But the colored
men were landed and went to work under guard. So did
a number of white strikebreakers.

Clashes broke out on Gary streets and grew into rioting. The militia were brought in. Later they were moved
to Indiana Harbor, where similar trouble had broken
out, and Federal troops under General Leonard Wood
came to put Gary under martial law.

Gary was the first spot to weaken. Said John Fitz-
patrick, one of Foster's lieutenants, of Gary: "A mill
foreman would take a squad of Federal soldiers and go
to the home of a striker. The foreman would enter the
house and tell John that he had come to give him his
last chance to return to work, saying that if he refused
to work he would be deported. Then he would take John
to the window and show him the line of soldiers waiting
outside. John would take a look at his wife and kids.
Then he would put on his coat and go back to the mills.
The foreman and his soldiers would then go on to the
next house and repeat the process."

By December some 40,000 Negroes, together with
many strikebreakers of varied races and colors, were
trying to man steel plants in Gary, Chicago, Youngs-

town, Pittsburgh, Wheeling, and Lackawanna. The families of strikers were getting hungry. There were no strike benefits, although forty-five large commissaries had been set up by Foster's committee and were feeding at least a hundred thousand families. In spite of these there was much suffering as winter came on.

Strikes can peter out as fast as they can spread. That first faltering in Gary soon became a rush to get back to work. The movement spread like the flu. In Indiana Harbor, Hammond, East Chicago, and South Chicago the boys told each other it was no use, the massed defenses of the steel industry were impossible to take. They went back to work.

Resistance was stronger in Cleveland and in the Pittsburgh area. But the ranks were crumbling here and there. Late in October full-page advertisements appeared simultaneously in newspapers of Pittsburgh and other steel centers. These showed a benign Uncle Sam, benign but vast and authoritative, who had one hand cupped to his mouth. He was shouting. You could tell what he was saying by the inscriptions in eight different "balloons" that were issuing from Uncle's stentorian throat: "Grizkite Prie Darbo!" said one balloon. "Menjenek Visszaa Munkaba" said another, and "Chodte Nazad Do Roboty." There were five other versions, not all of them in American type. What they meant was "Go Back to Work." Above the picture of Uncle Sam was a big banner. It said "The Strike Has Failed."

So it had. Except for Cleveland and a few scattered mills, the strike had indeed failed. The return to work was becoming a rout. Hungry men were pounding for admission to the steel mills. On January 7, 1920, the Committee for Organizing Iron and Steel Workers voted to call off the strike. The last sentence of the Committee's general order said that "all strikers are now at liberty to return to work pending preparations for the next big organization effort." Judge Gary and his able men had won, hands down, and no one would again challenge Steel, either Big or Little, until the Government itself became the challenger.

There were some quite awful accidents in the steel plants, before they were running normally again. The green help, both black and white, were not fit to handle hundred-ton ladles of molten steel, nor to manage the speeding, bounding, slithering hot beams and rails as they slid through the rolls.

More tragedy followed in the wake of the strike. The steel companies would not take back many of the men who had struck. This was of course their privilege, but they may have been shortsighted to use the privilege. Many a good steelworker, who wanted a union and was no more a Bolshevik than Elbert H. Gary, was forced out of the industry for good and all. Not only Steel but America lost something in the process.

The 1919 steel strike was the biggest industrial upheaval the country had ever known. The *New York Herald* estimated that it had cost $85,000,000 in wages alone, a most conservative guess. No one ever attempted to estimate the cost in suffering. As for the steel barons, they never said what it had cost them, but they probably figured it was cheap enough. They were due for a dozen more years of comparative calm, so far as Labor was concerned.

26 *The Steel Union Arrives*

The lads in the steel mills had some rather pleasant years between 1922 and 1929. Wages were good. Most of the time there was plenty of work. In fact, there was so much work to be done that in 1923 one of two things happened: Either the wages of common labor got too high to suit the steel companies, or there was actually a shortage of this kind of help. It is possible that both conditions were present.

In any case, Steel began importing Mexicans. It was a weird "immigration," and the latter part of it arrived just in time for the Crash of '29. It affected mostly the midwestern and the southern empires of Steel. Mexicans were brought into Colorado, where many of their race had been at work for years. They were brought into Birmingham, where they were new, and into the Chicago area, where none had ever been seen. How many they numbered is not known, but at one time Indiana Harbor alone had a Mexican population of ten thousand.

Indiana Harbor means Inland Steel. Mexican labor meant cheap labor. At least, the wages of Mexicans were lower. Many of the dark small men did not remain long on the Cinder Shore south of Chicago, but enough stayed on to become a problem after 1929. It has been a pitiful story.

The Mex were herded into colonies by themselves, virtually segregated. Either that, or they took to shacks and horrible tenements within the Negro districts. Often the Mexicans lived in quarters that were worse than the Black Belts.

On the whole they were easy to manage, and that is exactly why they were brought in. Of unions, no savvy. They committed no violence except among themselves, and their numerous stabbings were seldom heard of. Few of them ever got into trouble over white women, and almost none of them were taken for larceny.

When hard times came after 1929 the Mex were the first to be laid off at the mills. They had no vote, hence politicians paid them no heed. The Negroes were treated badly enough, but they did have spokesmen, both black and white; and there were race-conscious men to stand up big and strong for the various European populations of the steel towns. The Mexicans had nobody.

Mexicans are a proud people. They found it difficult to understand the "relief" business. They starved very quietly. Social workers relate that they actually had to take Mexicans by the hand and lead them to relief depots where they were given free groceries. They would get along with anything rather than go to the depots. A few beans, a loaf of bread—it was all right, señor.

As many as could rent or squat on land moved out of the steel towns. They got along, too, for no northern people, not even the Finns, can do as much with a few square yards of ground as a Mexican. As for the Mex who remained in the steel towns, they found life pretty hard. Their children died from lack of milk and other proper food. Light fare and chill winds brought illness even to tough adults. There was no work for months on end, in many cases for years. If the steel companies that had brought them to the cold smoky towns did anything much about the problem they had created, it is not of record.

The situation became so acute that relief agencies along the Cinder Shore urged the Mex to return to their old homes in the Southwest and in Mexico. County and city agencies would purchase railroad-coach tickets for a family, give them a basket of groceries, and see them aboard the train. Hundreds of them were thus shipped out of a country that a few years previously had thought it needed more laborers. That is, the steel companies had thought so.

Today, in 1939, there are some four thousand Mexicans in Indiana Harbor, perhaps a thousand in South Chicago, a few hundred around Gary. In the worst possible areas of these districts, one will see a tumble-down shack, its one window dolled up with highly colored placards, lettered in Spanish, and over the door a hand-painted sign, "Sociedad Pro-México." This is social headquarters, the club of the now unwanted dark-skinned men.

Strolling past near-by hovels, one is sure to see a woman at work with a packing box for a table, on its top a row of tamales in the making. Either morning or night there will be guitars and singing. So long as there is one tamale, one bowl of chile, there will be a guitar and a song. The well known cheerfulness of the Negro under the worst of conditions is matched if not exceeded by the Mexican's.

For those Mex who remained, things still aren't very good; but they are better. They now have a vote. They are childishly appreciative of the attention given them just before election. They haven't learned yet, any more than most Americans, the meaning of a gringo politician's politeness.

On their patches of ground the dark little men and women have demonstrated what can be done with a handful of seeds and a love of the earth. They are largely self-supporting, although many have broken down and accepted relief as a part of life in a queer land. If he can get even so much as one day's work a week in the mills, a Mexican does not worry overmuch. He's got his beans right on the old plantation. His wife makes the tamales at home. A guitar string lasts a long time.

Mexicans were the last wave of immigration to man the steel mills of the country, and the smallest. For many years the primitive forges and bloomeries were manned by Scotch, Welsh, English, and Irish immigrants. Then came the Scandinavians and Poles, to be followed by almost every race except Orientals and Icelanders.

Today, the movements of many people can be traced in the steel towns. In the large Pittsburgh area, skilled jobs are largely held by first- and second-generation Americans of Scotch, English, and Welsh parents and grandparents. These, with the Irish, also have most of the best jobs on the Cinder Shore of Illinois and Indiana. In all districts a sizable number of Poles and Hungarians hold good jobs, especially around the blast and open-hearth furnaces.

So far as numbers are concerned, Hungarians predominate at South Bethlehem. Poles are most numerous in the plants at Gary, South Chicago, Cleveland, and Lackawanna. In Allegheny County, which includes

Pittsburgh, Italians form the largest group of foreign-born.

One finds Czechoslovaks in all steel towns, and they are perhaps most numerous in Johnstown, Lorain, and Middletown. Aliquippa has a foreign-born population larger than its native-born. In all steel towns the German and Scandinavian population is far less than it was fifty years ago. But any old steel town today will present at least twenty nationalities, no matter whether Europe's prewar or its postwar boundaries are considered.

It is scarcely to be wondered at that forming a strong union in Steel was a job long in the doing. The 1919 affair was the greatest of the many efforts. When that strike was broken, Steel's labor remained pretty quiet until John Lewis and company formed the C.I.O. Even then the officials of the sleeping Amalgamated Association of Iron, Steel and Tin Workers did not stir.

Under Philip Murray the Steel Workers Organizing Committee of the C.I.O. started to function in the summer of 1936. They had a big war chest furnished by the Mine Workers, and they put hundreds of organizers into the field. Steel fought back with widespread newspaper and radio publicity, using the old cry of "Bolshevism" now modernized to "Communism." The C.I.O. and the Wagner Act were called more and worse names than were ever applied by Steel to William Foster, Bill Haywood, and the I.W.W.

Company unions were formed, along the lines of the plans long in use at Bethlehem Steel and Colorado Fuel & Iron. Steel plants were stocked with ordnance of all kinds, including tommy guns and tear-gas bombs. It was to be another of those wars to the finish, bigger and

worse than ever. By the first of January, 1937, all lines
were well marked; the trenches were dug for defense.
The new steel union had grown to one hundred and fifty
lodges with more than one hundred and twenty-five
thousand paid-up members.

Then one of those impossible things, one of those incidents that stagger the imagination of men, happened.
Out of a cloudless sky in March the United States Steel
Corporation announced that it had recognized and was
ready to deal with the C.I.O. To half a million men and
their families it was the biggest news story of the year,
perhaps of their lives.

Unless you had worked in Steel or lived in a steel
town, you could not know how incredible was the announcement. Here was the big barony of Steel, repre-
senting approximately half the total capacity of the
industry, recognizing a union—and without a struggle.
The kingdom of Carnegie, Frick, and Gary giving in
without a single discharge of musketry. No bombs, no
barbed-wire fences, no Cossacks. The sense of unreality
was heightened two weeks later when U.S. Steel raised
wages 10 per cent, established a genuine eight-hour shift
with a forty-hour week, and time and one-half for overtime.

Since that date steelworkers and others have talked
endlessly about the earthquake that must have shaken
U.S. Steel from within. There are a hundred versions of
what happened to secure that which to the workers
seemed a splendid and bloodless victory. The newspapers, of course, with their yearning for the dramatic,
printed all sorts of stories: secret meetings between
Myron C. Taylor of the Corporation and John Lewis of
the C.I.O.; the influence of this and that woman; the

dinners in a swell hotel in Washington, with Taylor and Lewis, their heads close together. The whole business was romanticized, just as the founding of the Corporation had been years before when it was said that Charlie Schwab talked to the elder Morgan and out of the talk came U.S. Steel.

The reasons for union recognition by the biggest employer in America would seem to be less romantic and to be founded on an acceptance of hard facts. The New Deal, the Wagner Act, the surge of unionism into even such notoriously nonunion industries as Motors, Rubber, and Lumber, must have shown Big Steel where the trend was. Still, it did no harm for the newspapers to dramatize what was doubtless the biggest industrial event of the period.

Closely after the Corporation, the big independent Jones & Laughlin recognized the union. So did many other firms not affiliated with Big Steel. A year later the C.I.O. had signed agreements with four hundred and fifty companies. Its membership totaled four hundred and fifty thousand.

What has come to be known as Little Steel chose to fight it out. Eugene Grace of Bethlehem Steel and Tom Girdler of Republic were picked as generals. They displayed forceful generalship. Attempts of organizers to get a foothold were put down quickly and fiercely in Youngstown, Niles, Canton, Massillon, and Indiana Harbor. In Weirton, too. In a gun battle at Republic's plant in East Chicago, ten persons were killed and forty-odd wounded.

Little Steel easily won its first campaign. And with the hindsight now possible, it is not difficult to see why. The union organizers were so completely upset by Big Steel's capitulation that they lost their sense of reality. Big Steel had been such a push-over that they thought Little Steel would be soft. Little Steel was anything but soft. It not only defended its trenches, it carried the war into the union camp.

Then, too, organizers had overestimated the desire of steelworkers for a union. They called a strike long before members were disciplined for such action. Moreover, it seems likely that a large infiltration of downright Communists into the steel union had taken place. The Reds wanted a strike at any cost, for political organizing purposes; what happened to the steel union was of minor importance to the Party Line. Today, most steelworkers believe it was Communist influence that started a strike which was lost before it got under way.

So, Little Steel largely remains open-shop, which is another name for a strictly nonunion shop. How long it can hold the line is problematical. The tide, these last few years, has been toward unionism. In spite of legal and political setbacks, it would appear that collective bargaining is still—in the summer of 1939—in full flood, not ebb.

Since about 1930 the biggest problem faced by Steel, both Little and Big, has not been Labor. The prevailing headache of the industry has been caused by the loss of old markets and a changing technology to meet the demands for new products.

For fifty years and more, rails were the backbone of the iron and steel trade. Close after rails came structural steel. The big plants in the Pittsburgh and Chicago areas were built on the idea that rails and beams always would be the dominant items of Steel. Along about 1920 the railroads began pulling up more steel every year than they laid. In 1930 the general construction business took a nose dive from which it has not fully recovered. Steel rails and structural forms piled up at the mills.

Only a few of the big men of Steel seemed to realize what was happening to their industry. Many of the so-called big men of Steel weren't steel men, anyway. The old-line barons were hardboiled; they didn't give a damn for much of anything or anybody, but they did know Steel. Many of the moguls of recent years have had no, such knowledge. They are primarily bankers, lawyers. They like to be known as "Statesmen of Steel" and "Steel Diplomats." Their understanding of the making of steel and of Steel's markets has been nil. Some of them got into their top places in a manner not wholly unlike that of the superintendent of a certain small steel company in the South. It is worth relating.

Through a family and banking connection this man, whose name might have been Smith but wasn't, got a job as superintendent of the company's plant. He knew absolutely nothing about the job, but he was a good guy and treated the boys in the mill right. They liked him.

Smith's chief reason for living was to get fairly drunk in the morning, every morning, and to remain that way throughout the day and evening. This he managed to do quietly, and he never got in the way of workmen.

Once a year it was the custom of the ranking officials and the board of directors to visit the plant. When that day rolled around, Superintendent Smith turned up even more potted than usual. This wouldn't do. The boys in the mill didn't want to see a good friend fired. They lugged him into a dark corner of the casting shed and covered him up with a tarpaulin.

The official party walked through the mill gates and were greeted with the usual blast of whistles and the ringing of bells. They asked for Superintendent Smith, to show them around in the customary manner. The boys reported that Smith had been sent home under a doctor's care. Smith had been working day and night, they told, at fixing a leaky gas main. He had been overcome by fumes and had to be removed in an ambulance.

A foreman did the honors of showing the directors over the plant. When questioned he related that Smith never seemed to sleep, that he was killing himself by working long hours on the plant, that he had to oversee everything. The directors were impressed. "We hope," went on the foreman, who was an excellent liar, "that Smith will be recovered from the gas sufficiently to attend your meeting tonight. But he had a close call."

Meanwhile, the boys in the casting shed had managed to get Smith sobered up. He appeared at the directors' banquet and meeting that night to hear his president speak of "our tireless Superintendent Smith, who never sleeps." Smith was glorified in speech after speech by the appreciative directors. As a climax they voted him a big raise in pay and gave him the title of Vice President and General Manager.

That incident, which is well authenticated, throws a strong light on many of today's barons of Steel. Knowing nothing of the industry they "managed" so gracefully, they did not see their markets slipping away.

Not all of them were that way. Ernest T. Weir, who had learned Steel from the furnace up, in the hardboiled schools of Braddock and Monessen, saw what was coming. In 1929 he founded the National Steel Corporation with George R. Fink, another practical steel man who had read the writing on the wall and had defied all Steel convention by building a plant at Ecorse, Michigan, handy to the folks who were taking the railroads' place as the largest consumers of steel—the men of motors.

In a shameless manner, National Steel slashed prices as they hadn't been slashed since the Federal-Carnegie price wars of 1899–1900. Further, National's plant had been built not for the manufacture of rails and structural steels, but for sheets, which was exactly what the motor industry needed. At the same time, National cut wages even more than it did prices. But there was no labor trouble: 1930 was hardly a time to pull a strike.

U.S. Steel after experimenting with the continuous rolling mill—an arrangement of machinery that passed sheet steel through a series of mills in a tandem train at a high speed, and replaced the old and much slower method of passing the sheets back and forth by hand at each mill—had rejected it; said it was impractical.

American Rolling Mills Company took the mill and perfected it. National Steel soon demonstrated what it could do. Then, U.S. Steel built its first continuous mill at Gary.

In the van making stainless steel was small but up-and-coming Allegheny Steel Company. The product took the country by storm. All of a sudden America decided that everything must be built of stainless steel, of chromium steel, of this or that alloy. Railroad trains, furniture, interior trim, mirrors—all began to shine and glisten with a product that looked utterly unlike the steels of yore. Even the fine old oak and mahogany of

high-toned barrooms were torn out, and replaced by the
new silverlike product. Aluminum also cut into what
had been Steel's markets.

The plants of the older companies had been built to
make "heavy" steels. The minds of the officials—many
of them the minds of lawyers and bankers—of the older
companies were geared to heavy steels. It is more difficult
to change a manner of thinking than to change a machine. But one had to follow the other. So, for half a
dozen years U.S. Steel and the more ancient of the independents reported annual deficits.

But it had to come. In 1936 U.S. Steel started a "$600,-
000,000 modernization program" that is still under way.
Early in 1938 it began operation of a new continuous
strip and tin-plate mill near Birmingham; and on December 16 of that year an even larger plant of similar
design went into production at Clairton, Pennsylvania,
under the Carnegie-Illinois flag of the Corporation.

The so-called "quality steels" came in with a bang,
the way most things happen in America, where the mass
becomes more herdlike year by year. Steel soon caught
up with the herd in the matter of steel that looks like
silver.

One may look at the new steels, the chromium-nickel
alloys which are said to be rustless, with mixed opinions.
Some say, Lo and behold, Steel finds new markets; while
others point out that stainless, rustless steel wears much
longer than simple steel, hence less will be needed for
replacements.

In either case the quality steels are being made by
processes which add to the already large numbers of the
industry's unemployed. The modern continuous mills,
as well as other recent machines, all but run themselves.

Many thousands of old but far from superannuated steel-workers will never work in their industry again. There isn't a place for them.

Despite considerable ranting to the contrary, Steel has not gone modern only in technology; it is also a more socially responsible industry than it has ever been. The critic will say that isn't much to brag about, when the record is considered. Well, let the critic name an industry that does please him. There simply isn't such a thing.

Even though in nearly every instance Steel, like other industries, has been forced into its new responsibilities, that fact does not detract from the gains made.

The company doctors of several large concerns have been doing a great deal of research in the disease known variously as conjunctivitis, inflammation of the eye, and cataracts. This infection has long been very common in the industry. It is caused by heat, sand, and fine particles of steel, plus the very glare of the furnaces. Some progress, but nowhere nearly enough, has been made toward its elimination. The thing that counts is that Steel is trying to do something about it. Pneumonia still has a fearfully high rate in all steel towns, though it is lower than formerly.

One of the worst abuses in Steel was the petty graft of foremen who collected money for giving a man a job and for letting him hang on to it. This practice grew into a scandal in a number of communities and resulted on one occasion in murder. It is a rarity today.

U.S. Steel has a successful group insurance in force for its employees. So have many of the independents. U.S. Steel's pension plan has been in operation for many years. It is based on age, length of service, and pay while working. In 1937 the Corporation retired 839 employees on pension. Their average age was not quite sixty-three years, their average monthly pension was $60.20. The total number of U.S. Steel pensioners as of January 1, 1938, was 11,615. Jones & Laughlin and other independents have inaugurated similar pension plans.

A little more than half of the entire industry is working under some form of collective bargaining with a bona-fide union. Ten years ago the total union membership in all steel mills was approximately nine thousand. Its influence on Steel was about the same as that of the Loyal Order of Moose. Today, union meetings are held openly in even such tough old nonunion strongholds as Aliquippa and McKeesport.

The steel towns themselves are no more beautiful than ever they were. Perhaps, as apologists say, a steel town simply has to look that way. But today's steel towns are better places to live. At least most old-timers think so. For one thing, espionage plays little part in union mills. True, there may still be a few spies; but they are not important.

It is a poor steelworker indeed who doesn't own the twin badges that America considers the marks of Success and Happiness, if not even of Civilization—a motor car and a radio. The house the steelworker lives in isn't much better than it was in the old days; but he can get away from it in his car, while the radio entertains him when he must be at home.

The problem of the unassimilated foreigners hasn't been solved. Whole masses of them still live by themselves in the grimy towns, reading their foreign-language newspapers, attending the meetings of the Croatian, the

Lithuanian, the Polish, and the Italian societies; listening to their own priests and pastors; holding their own feast days. It will likely take at least one full generation to do away with these foreign quarters, these Hunky towns and wop towns.

There can be no doubt that these seemingly indigestible parts of America will dissolve. They are in process of assimilation right now. The flow of new blood that kept them alien was dammed up long ago. When the next football season rolls around, cast an eye over the line-ups of the varsity teams of the University of Pittsburgh, the University of Pennsylvania, the University of Chicago, and Northwestern. Or, better still, take a look at the line-ups of the high-school teams in South Chicago, in Gary, in Johnstown, in Bethlehem.

Those hard-to-spell names, so numerous that even the All-American Team is joked about, tell what is going on. Nobody who plays American football can possibly be a "foreigner," no matter what his name. That guy is an American.

The Melting Pot of forty years ago turned out to be no quick brewer of Americans. Natives of old stock were surprised and alarmed that it had failed. As always, we were in too much of a hurry. We expected Americans to be made quickly and artificially, by night schools, Americanization classes and such things, all good things, too, but still short of miracle workers.

Only time can make real Americans—time and a clearer conception of what an American really is. For two centuries there was a never-ending flow of immigrants. That ceased long ago. It will take another century perhaps to blend the Old and the New Americans into something that will be neither Yankee nor southerner nor hunky nor wop. The process of blending is even now further along than many people think.

In the past, steel towns drew the sharpest social lines. There was a caste of company officials, another caste of highly skilled and well paid workers who were mostly English-speaking natives or immigrants, and lastly the great herd of common and semiskilled labor of all races. These last always lived by the railroad tracks.

Slowly but surely the second generation of those who lived by the tracks have been moving into better jobs, marrying the daughters of native Americans, living in the American manner. These new Americans cannot often read the language of their fathers. The Polish and Lithuanian and Croatian societies are filled with old, not young, folk. In another generation the new Americans will have forgotten how to speak their grandfathers' language.

Self-appointed patriots still rise on occasion in the steel towns, as elsewhere, to shout about the menace of "aliens in our midst" and what they term "isms." They are talking through their hats. It takes only twenty minutes to make Bessemer steel out of pig iron. The open-hearth process requires about seven hours. If one or even two generations will make good Americans out of transplanted Europeans, then the process is good enough and ought to be as rapid as we have a right to expect.

As for those isms about which the professional patriots shout so much, there is no greater danger to a country's liberty than enforced patriotism (i.e., nationalism). We have many examples of what happens to countries who are fed on that diet. The ism most needed by America—which includes the steel industry—is a lot of healthy self-criticism. The United States ought to be such a fine place to live in that all aliens here will *want* to be Americans.

If there are no more waves of immigrants, the alien quarters of the many steel towns ought to dissolve within two decades. As for Steel itself, what lies ahead is now less in the hands of the steel barons than in the hands of the technicians and the labor unions. The technicians have plenty to think about to keep up with the rapidly changing demands for new kinds and shapes of their product. The unions in Steel have hardly got their feet solidly on the ground. In Little Steel, in fact, they still have to fight for recognition.

When and if the industry is thoroughly unionized, it is possible that Labor will do much to improve a business that has been both the glory and the shame of industrial America. That is, if Labor doesn't lose its head completely, as it has done recently on too many occasions, and go hog-wild.

ACKNOWLEDGMENTS

A great deal of this book came out of the memories of veteran iron miners and steelworkers, many of them dating from the time of Captain Tom Walters and even Captain Bill Jones, both celebrated men in their respective lines. It had to come from the veterans or not at all, for there are few books about the common men of the mines and mills. I talked to these old-timers in deep holes, in mine dryhouses, in front of open-hearth furnaces and Bessemer converters, on Great Lakes boats and ore docks, and in the homes of many who had been retired by age.

Some more of the book came out of the yellowing files of newspapers which tell dimly yet surely of both great and dismal times in the steel cities and iron towns. Then came the books. For the most part these have dealt with the incredible Iron and Steel Barons, in whom I had a lesser interest than in figures nearer earth and slag—the men who made the Barons possible.

From first to last I met with the aid that authors take too much for granted from the most courteous people on earth—the men and women of the libraries and historical associations. Without their help in locating old files and obscure books, I should have been lost for much documentary evidence. I feel deep gratitude for the generous aid extended me by Harvard University Library, Boston Public Library, Boston Athenaeum, New York Public Library; Carnegie Library, Pittsburgh;

Chicago Public Library, John Crerar Library, Chicago; Ishpeming Public Library; Peter White Memorial Library, Marquette; Ironwood Public Library; St. Louis County Historical Society, Duluth; Duluth Public Library, Virginia (Minn.) Public Library, Hibbing Public Library, Gary Public Library.

BOOKS

BALDWIN, LELAND D., *Pittsburgh: The Story of a City*, Pittsburgh, 1937.

BOUCHER, JOHN NEWTON, *William Kelly: A True History of the So-Called Bessemer Process*, Greensburg, Pa., 1924.

BRIDGE, J. H., *The Inside Story of the Carnegie Steel Company*, New York, 1903.

BURGOYNE, ARTHUR G., *Homestead*, Pittsburgh, 1893.

BUTLER, JOSEPH G., JR., *Fifty Years of Iron and Steel*, New York, 1923.

CASSON, HERBERT N., *The Romance of Steel*, New York, 1907.

CASTLE, HENRY A., *Minnesota, Its Story and Biography*, Chicago and New York, 1915.

CHURCH, SAMUEL HARDEN, *A Short History of Pittsburgh*, New York, 1908.

COTTER, ARUNDEL, *The Story of Bethlehem Steel*, New York, 1916.

CURWOOD, JAMES OLIVER, *The Great Lakes*, New York, 1909.

DAVIS, HORACE B., *Labor and Steel*, New York, 1933.

DAVIS, JAMES J., *The Iron Puddler*, Indianapolis, 1922.

DE KRUIF, PAUL, *Seven Iron Men*, New York, 1929.

Dictionary of American Biography.

FITCH, JOHN A., *The Steel Workers*, New York, 1911.

FOSTER, WILLIAM Z., *The Great Steel Strike*, New York, 1920.

FRITZ, JOHN, *Autobiography*, Boston, 1912.

GOODALE, STEPHEN L., *Chronology of Iron and Steel*, Cleveland, 1931.

HARVEY, G. B. McC., *Henry Clay Frick, the Man,* New York, 1928.

HENDRICK, B. J., *Life of Andrew Carnegie,* New York, 1932.

History of the Upper Peninsula of Michigan, 1883.

INGALLS, E. S., *Centennial History of Menominee County, Michigan,* Menominee, 1876.

MITCHELL & COMPANY, *Marine Directory of the Great Lakes,* 1914.

MYERS, GUSTAVUS, *History of the Great American Fortunes,* New York, edition of 1936.

OSBORN, CHASE SALMON, *The Iron Hunter,* New York, 1919.

SAWYER, ALVAH L., *A History of the Northern Peninsula of Michigan,* Chicago, 1911.

STOWELL, MYRON B., *Fort Frick, or The Siege of Homestead,* Pittsburgh, 1893.

SWANK, JAMES M., *A Collection of Statistics Relating to the Iron and Steel Industries of the United States,* Phila., 1888.

TARBELL, IDA M., *The Life of Elbert H. Gary: The Story of Steel,* New York, 1925.

VAN BRUNT, WALTER, *Duluth and St. Louis County, Minnesota,* Chicago and New York, 1921.

WALKER, CHARLES R., *Steel, the Diary of a Furnace Worker,* Boston, 1922.

WALKER, J. BERNARD, *The Story of Steel,* New York, 1926.

WILLIAMS, RALPH D., *The Honorable Peter White,* Cleveland, 1905.

WIRTH, FREMONT P., *The Discovery and Exploitation of the Minnesota Iron Lands,* Cedar Rapids, 1937.

PAMPHLETS AND MONOGRAPHS

HARRINGTON, D., *Some of the Results of Recent Research on the Control of Silicosis,* Washington, Bureau of Mines, 1938.

Historical Souvenir of the Virginia Enterprise, Virginia, Minn., 1909.

Iron Port of the World, Escanaba, Mich., 189?.

Landis, Paul Henry, *Cultural Change in the Mining Town,* University of Minnesota, 1933.

Whitaker, Joe Russell, *Negaunee, Michigan,* University of Chicago, 1931.

NEWSPAPERS AND PERIODICALS

Files of the *Pittsburgh Press,* the *Pittsburgh Post-Gazette,* Pittsburgh, Pa.; *Cleveland Press; Daily News,* Chicago; *Solidarity,* Cleveland and Chicago; *Gary Post; Daily Press,* Escanaba, Mich.; *Agitator, Iron Home,* and *Iron Ore,* all of Ishpeming, Mich.; *Mining Journal,* Marquette; *News-Tribune,* Duluth; *Virginia Enterprise,* Virginia, Minn.; *Daily Tribune,* Hibbing; *Pioneer Press,* St. Paul, Minn.; *Michigan History Magazine; The Iron Age; Steel; U. S. Steel News; Harper's Monthly Magazine.*

INDEX